Union Pacific #101, City of San Francisco, climbing Sherman Hill, Wyoming, hauled by EMC Diesels 931–905–906 with fifteen cars. Engine 821, 4–8–4 type is returning light to Cheyenne after helping #103 up the 1.8 grade. Photo by R. H. Kindig.

RAILROADS OF TODAY

Books by S. Kip Farrington, Jr.

FISHING THE ATLANTIC OFFSHORE AND ON

PACIFIC GAME FISHING

SPORT FISHING BOATS

A BOOK OF FISHES

ATLANTIC GAME FISHING

THE DUCKS CAME BACK

SHIPS OF THE U. S. MERCHANT MARINE

INTERESTING BIRDS OF OUR COUNTRY

GIANTS OF THE RAILS

RAILROADING FROM THE HEAD END

RAILROADING FROM THE REAR END

RAILROADS AT WAR

RAILROADS OF TODAY

Juvenile

BILL THE BROADBILL SWORDFISH

C & O extra #2705 South, 2—8—4 type, running over the Logan Sub-Div. hauling the
coal direct from the mines to the yard at
Russell, Kentucky. Courtesy C & O RR.

RAILROADS OF TODAY

S. KIP FARRINGTON, Jr.

Coward-McCann, Inc.   New York

Dedicated to the American railroaders who served in the U.S. Armed Forces and the Railroad Operating Battalions in World War II

CONTENTS

FOREWORD   xi

I   THIS IS YOUR MODERN TRAIN   1

II   ELECTRO-MOTIVE   13
     Pioneer in Diesel Progress—Builds Diesels Exclusively

III THE NEW "CENTURY"   21
     *A Great Train of America—Cars of the Century—
     Motive Power—Names for Century Cars—Cen-
     tury Personnel—Building the Century—Dicta-
     phone Service*

IV   BRAKE DEVELOPMENT   36
     *"HSC" Electro-Pneumatic Brake—"AP" Decelostat
     Equipment—"AB" Freight Brake Equipment—
     24-RL Locomotive Brake Equipment—Hot Bear-
     ing Detector*

V   THE SANTA FE TRAIL   46
     Famous Trains and Hotels—Mail Trains

VI   THE NEW POWHATAN ARROW   55
     *Norfolk & Western's Crack Speedliner—Cars of the
     New Powhatan Arrow*

VII UNION PACIFIC LOOKS AHEAD   61
     *Western Development: Retarder Yards—Modern
     Yard at Pocatello—North Platte Yard—Aspen
     Tunnel*

VIII WESTERN MARYLAND   78
     *Railroad of Today—Motive Power—Mountain Rail-
     roading—Pilots for Pushing Rocks—Port Coving-
     ton Terminal*

ix

IX   THE POSTWAR EMPIRE BUILDER   86

*First of the New Streamliners — The Oriental
Limited*

X   THE ROCK ISLAND STORY   93

*"Planned Progress"—Track and Bridge Projects—Sig-
naling—Centralized Traffic Control—Shops and
Engine Houses: Laboratory—John D. Farrington*

XI   UNION SWITCH & SIGNAL COMPANY   103

*Coded Track Circuits Developed—C.T.C. and Coded
Carrier Control—Unusual Installation*

XII SANTA FE C.T.C.   114

*Plains Division Installation Speeds Freight—When
Booming Trains Are on the Move—C.T.C. Rail-
road Watchman—C.T.C. Motor Car Indicators—
C.T.C. Machine Combinations—Fewer Break-In-
Two's*

XIII THE CINCINNATIAN OF THE B.&O.   123

"Armchair on Wheels"

XIV THE C.&O.'S "500"   130

*Steam Turbine-Electric Locomotive—How the "500"
Operates*

XV   THE EAGLES   136

*New Equipment on Missouri Pacific: Texas & Pacific
—Factors in Faster Schedules—New Coach and
Front-End Cars—New Sleepers for the "Eagles"
—General Features of New Equipment*

XVI THE NICKEL PLATE   147

*Road of Fast Freight—Motive Power—The Progres-
sive Nickel Plate*

XVII NASHVILLE, CHATTANOOGA & ST.
LOUIS   155

*The Progressive "Dixie Line"—Bridge Improvements
and Replacements—Plant and Rolling Stock Improvements—A Streamliner Is Created—Industrial
Development—Nine More Diesels*

XVIII THE SOUTHERN PACIFIC   168
       *Diesels — Improved Freight Handling — Peacetime
       High for Freight*

 XIX   NORFOLK AND WESTERN   174
       *Portsmouth-Cincinnati C.T.C.—Operation Mt. Zion
       —Special Aspect at Water Stops—Approach-Me-
       dium Aspect—Passenger Trains Take Sidings*

  XX   ATLANTIC COAST LINE   183
       *Recorder Aids Diesel Performance—The Story the
       Tapes Told—Marked Dial Helpful—Conclusions*

 XXI   SANTA FE DIESEL OPERATION   190
       *Transcontinental Service: Diesel Instruction—Diesel
       Instruction Car*

XXII   THE CENTRAL'S POSTWAR PROGRAM   196
       *$233 Million Spent—River Takes Siding on the Cen-
       tral—Service with a Smile*

XXIII JOURNAL BEARINGS FOR HIGH SPEED
       FREIGHT SERVICE   210
       *Roller Bearings—Roller Bearing Application—Servic-
       ing Roller Bearings—Roller Bearings Are Quality
       Bearings—Roller Bearings Reduce Lading Dam-
       age—Friction Bearings 100 Years Old*

XXIV   THE NEW U.P. TRAIL   224
       *C.T.C.: Roller Bearing Stock Train—Motor Car Sig-
       nal Men—Inspection Cars—Sun Valley—Building
       the West It Helped to Pioneer—Roller Bearing
       Stock Train*

 XXV   THE GREAT NORTHERN   236
       *Old Bill Rides the Diesels—New Equipment—Facts
       and Finances*

XXVI   ROCK ISLAND ROCKETS   244
       *Coach Yard: Rocket Freight—New Equipment—Car
       Service and Repair—Rocket Freight*

xi

xxvii BALTIMORE & OHIO 251

"Sentinel Service" Speeds the Freight Car—Traffic "Blue Book"—Automatic Records—Plant Improvement—Communications: Car Retarders

xxviii CHESAPEAKE & OHIO 263

"Show Window" of the C.&O.: Ticket Reservations —The "Pere Marquettes"—Central Ticket Reservation Bureau

xxix MISSOURI PACIFIC 270

Green Fruit Movement: Instruction Car—"Classroom on Wheels"—Impact Recorders

xxx THE SANTA FE TODAY 276

Canyon Diablo Bridge: Argentine Yard—New Argentine Hump Yard—Canyon Diablo Bridge

xxxi LOOKING AT TOMORROW 288

Improvements on Norfolk and Western—A Great New Pier: Pier "N"—"Land of Plenty": Industrial Development

FOREWORD

The railroads of America are more than 400,000 miles of track; nearly 50,000 locomotives; approximately 1,800,000 freight and passenger cars; shops; stations; office buildings; warehouses; grain elevators; and pier facilities.

The railroads are a lot of people: Around 1,400,000 engineers, firemen, conductors, shopmen; office workers; technicians; scientists; traffic, fuel, agricultural, industrial, and financial experts.

The railroads are a lot of people; more than a million stockholders. Who are they? Where do they live? They are people you meet everyday—your neighbors and friends—two-thirds of them are men and one-third are women. They live on farms, in villages, towns and cities of America from coast to coast.

The railroads are a lot of people: Altogether more than half of all railway bonds outstanding in the hands of the public are held by life insurance companies, banks, educational institutions, and foundations.

There are hundreds of thousands of bond holders . . . many million of bank depositors, life insurance policyholders, young men and women in educational institutions—so, all have a tangible stake in the railroads.

The next time you have a trip to take . . . the next time you have freight to ship . . . the next time you hear the railroads mentioned in conversation . . . when you think of the railroads . . . remember . . . the railroads are a lot of people—and you are one of them.

Three facts stand out in the 1948 record of the railroads.

The first is that the railroads moved, with an all-time record efficiency, a freight traffic well above any prewar year and only slightly below the record peacetime year of 1947. Measured in tons of freight hauled one mile, this traffic approximated 640 billion ton-miles, only 2.3 per cent below 1947, but 43 per cent above 1929, the prewar record year.

The second fact is that increases in cost since 1939 have been so much greater than the increases in rates that even while handling this tremendous traffic with record efficiency, the railroads were able to earn a return on the net amount invested in them which averaged barely 4¼ per cent. And out of this return, of course, the railroads must pay interest, rentals and other fixed charges, while out of what is left for the owners, a considerable part of the cost of providing necessary improvements must be met.

The third outstanding fact in the record for 1948 is that the railroads, not taxpayers, spent one and one-quarter billion dollars on improvements to their plant and additions to their equipment. When final figures are in, it may well be that this, too, is an all-time record for such expenditures made to increase the capacity and improve the service of the railroads to the public.

A major element in this program was the installation during the year of more than 100,000 new freight cars, as compared with 63,000 in 1947. Even with this increase in the supply of equipment, however, there is continuing need for still more new cars, and the railroads now have orders in for more than 100,000 additional.

These additional freight cars are but part of the improvements programmed by the officials for the year 1949 and 1950. Preliminary reports indicate that in that year, again, railroad investment in improved plant and equipment will exceed a billion dollars. It is difficult to continue such investment, however, if railroads are able to earn on the money invested in them, and subject to all the risks of business, only a little more than is earned on United States bonds, the most nearly riskless investment on earth.

The future of the railroads depends upon having an opportunity to earn a return which will average, over the whole industry, and taking bad years as well as good, not less than 6 per cent on investment which is commonly considered to be the minimum on which business can be successfully conducted.

The increases since 1939 in major items of cost of railroad operation—wages and payroll taxes and the prices of materials, supplies and fuel—has averaged 101 per cent. In other words, they have doubled. On the other hand, the increase in the average level of freight rates has been only slightly more that two-fifths as much, and the average revenue received for hauling a ton of freight one mile has gone up only 28 per cent.

The railroads have met this disparity, in part, by increased volume of business and increased efficiency in handling it. The ton-miles of freight traffic in 1948 were 92 per cent above 1939 and passenger traffic in 1948 amounted to 40.4 billion passenger miles, 12 per cent less than in 1947, but 78 per cent more than in 1939.

One important measure of the increasing efficiency of railroad operation is the fact that in 1948 they carried an average of 1,175 tons per freight train, the greatest on record. At the same time, there was a slight increase in the average speed as compared with the two preceding years, so that the net output of transportation per hour by the average freight train was greater than ever before. The 1948 average of 18,658 ton-miles of freight per hour compares with 10,580 ton-miles in 1929. This performance was made possible by improved operating methods, more powerful and efficient locomotives, better freight cars, improved signaling and other devices, as well as heavier loading.

So let's make it our motto "To travel and ship on the railroads of the United States and Canada."

My only regret in writing this book is that it is not possible to include all of the American railroads in it. The great majority of them are definitely "Railroads of Today."

I am particularly indebted to the publishers of "The Railway Age" magazine for their many courtesies in helping me prepare this book. I am indeed grateful to Olive B. Flannery, Herbert Worthington and Charles Tyler for their work on the manuscript. For the use of their wonderful pictures, my most sincere appreciation is again due H. W. Pontin of the Rail Photo Service, Preston George, Richard H. Kindig, Otto C. Perry and Bruce D. Fales, the last name a newcomer whose skill in photography is a real addition to a book that contains many excellent railroad photographs that have been taken by these leading railroad photographers who have given a great deal of their time and effort for the railroad industry. I cannot thank them enough for the use of their many fine pictures.

S. KIP FARRINGTON, JR.

East Hampton, New York
February 1, 1949

RAILROADS OF TODAY

CHAPTER I

THIS IS YOUR MODERN TRAIN

This time you are going by train. Your previous trips have been by automobile, by bus and by plane. Somehow, you have come to regard train travel as outmoded, in spite of a change in appearance of the cars and motive power that has now and then caught your attention. You remember the cumbersome Pullmans of the past, the chair cars, the open-end observation with no particular desire to renew their acquaintance. Possibly, within your time, you have ridden in cars with Pintschburner lamps, with open platforms, untidy toilets and water coolers that were out of ice. You arrived at your destination hot and grimy from coal smoke and wearied from noise and vibration and buckling stops and jerking starts.

The railroad of yesterday has left you with memories only of discomforts and wearying miles in which open windows and cinders had a distasteful part. And then, gradually, you become aware of a change, emphasized, perhaps, by the advertisements you have noticed, by the fact that the snorting steam locomotive is giving way to a new sleek machine called a Diesel, ablaze with bright paint. Autumn colors have been introduced into the railroad picture, and stainless steel outside sheathing and an unbroken continuity of line that makes it difficult to find where one car ends and the next begins.

To know better just what the train of today offers the traveler you have decided to make this business trip on one of these new Diesel-powered streamliners, operating between two large metropolitan centers. The distance is approximately 500 miles and the time required is eleven hours, for an average of about 45 miles per hour, which includes ten scheduled stops. The route is partly mountainous and exceptionally scenic, and for this reason you choose a much-advertised day train called the *Mountaineer*.

You make your reservation, and on the morning of your departure you arrive at the station with a certain sense of relief that you are not driving your car over the heavily-traveled highway. You remember, not so long ago, seeing a billboard beside the highway over which you were driving with a picture of a new streamliner and the words: NEXT TIME TAKE THE TRAIN. This had planted the thought in your mind that it might be interesting to renew your acquaintance with rail travel as an escape from those burdensome hours at the wheel.

You notice that the *Mountaineer* has some cars with glass-enclosed cupolas or domes, and you are intrigued by the promise of the view from these panoramic observation roofs. Your grip goes aboard the coach in which you have a reservation through a separate opening adjoining the vestibule and you walk along the platform toward the head end of the train for a look at the motive power. The competent-looking Diesel is as sleek and clean as the cars behind it. You hear the throaty murmur of powerful motors, indicative of unleashed power. Over the cab is mounted a two-way horn, each half similar to the horn of your car. The windshield, like the windshield of your car, has two windshield wipers. You notice that the journals of the cars carry the word "Timken," and this is the first time you learn that the same type of roller bearings used on your automobile had been engineered into the modern train.

Boarding your coach you are immediately impressed by the spotless interior, the broad windows, the restful color tones. You find your seat and sink into a foam rubber reclining chair. Its comfort is comparable to your favorite living room chair by the radio. There is a folder in the seat entitled "Sightseeing Along the Route of the Mountaineer." It contains a map of your route and information about the country and the communities through which your train will pass. There is historical and geographical information and the time at which the *Mountaineer* will pass points of particular interest is indicated.

You think back to the days when the timetable and the unin-

2

telligible bawling of a station name by a brakeman were the only means of orienting yourself. The train begins to move, smoothly and effortlessly and silently. A voice comes over a loudspeaker in a bulkhead, welcoming the passengers aboard the *Mountaineer* and expressing the wish that they enjoy a pleasant journey.

A short time later a uniformed attendant enters the car. He pauses at your seat, checks your seat number and addresses you by name, much to your surprise.

"You are Mr. John Smith?"

"Yes."

"I am the train passenger agent, John Jones. If I can be of service to you at any time during your trip, please feel free to call on me."

You are happy to know Mr. Jones, as are many other passengers, for he renders service that lends to the full enjoyment of your trip. He explains that your fare includes full privileges in the observation car, the buffet-lounge and the Sky-Dome. This, then, is your introduction to a modern de luxe coach train.

From time to time, you call on Mr. Jones for information concerning the train equipment and accessories and discover that he is a veritable railway encyclopedia. Most coach trains, as well as all overnight and transcontinental trains, include a stewardess in the crew, you are told. The stewardess, on the longer runs, is of particular aid to women traveling with children and the railroads of today leave no stone unturned in their efforts to provide every comfort and convenience for mothers and youngsters, a feature that makes train travel a pleasure rather than a trial, even for the mother with a baby.

You glance at the fleeting landscape, realizing for the first time the high speed of the train. There is no lurch and sway, no clatter of noisy trucks; you almost seem to be floating. This, you learn, has been accomplished through technical advances in car and truck design, through the employment of a new type of rubber draft gears, springs and vertical and lateral shock absorbers, tightlock couplers and those roller bearings.

Outside temperatures are high, but air-conditioning keeps the cars of the *Mountaineer* cool and comfortable. You relax in your seat, listening to the music now coming over the loudspeaker. This is interrupted after a time, and a voice comes in to announce that "Midland is the next stop. We will arrive there in about three minutes." As the train slows, Mr. Jones comes through the car, pausing to explain that modern braking, or retardation, is accomplished by electrically operated brakes, which apply simultaneously on all cars, thus eliminating the backward surge and jolt of the older pneumatic brakes, which applied first on cars nearest the locomotive.

Following the velvet-smooth stop and a brief pause at Midland, the *Mountaineer* accelerates quickly to arrow-swift and silent flight. You leave your seat and walk through the coach, pausing for a drink at the electric water cooler, a look at the sparkling cleanliness of the rest room and its facilities, which include smoking and lavatory sections, a plug-in socket for your electric razor and even a slot for the disposal of the used blade.

The buffet-lounge car and its rich appointments provide a surprise and something of a shock, for you were not prepared for this sort of luxury on a coach train. There are soft-toned drapes, Venetian blinds, attractive murals, comfortable chairs, convenient ash trays and stands and small tables. Food and beverages are served at all hours to any location in the car. The floor is covered with Linotyle in a striking block pattern. The buffet with its stainless steel trim and fixtures, is spotless. Everything is in perfect taste and on a level with what you would expect in a fashionable resort.

As a newcomer to modern train travel, you feel that this is a pleasant adventure rather than a boring train ride, and you resolve to explore every nook and corner of the *Mountaineer*, as a prospector would examine a promising pocket or a gravel streambed that showed "color." Entering the buffet-lounge, you pass the "conductor's office" and your memory takes you back to the time when the train conductor hunted out a vacant seat and performed his clerical work under the most trying of conditions.

On the *Mountaineer*, the conductor's office is walled off at the front with a waist-high partition at the side. His accommodations include a desk, a chair, shelf space and a locker. He has access to both telephone and public-address equipment. The train telephone system has stations located at five points, including the extreme rear of the train, the crew's quarters in a section of the baggage car, and at the side of the engineer in the cab of the Diesel.

You have learned of the crew's quarters from Mr. Jones and notice that you never knew the train crew had any quarters. They include, you are told, a toilet, wash basins and lockers. On trains making longer overnight runs, the quarters include berths and showers. These so-called dormitory coaches, says Jones, point up the trend toward longer runs for dining car crews.

You enjoy a snack in the buffet-lounge; then make your way to the Sky-Dome car, having a keen anticipation of the treat you know is in store for you. This Sky-Dome car has three passenger rooms, two at the usual floor level and the third in the dome over the middle portion of the car body. The car has a vestibule only at one end. The longer room below seats 28 and the one at the opposite end 18. Looking toward the dome section from the vestibule there are eight double seats on the right and six on the left. Space is thus allowed for entrance to the corridor on the left and the stairway to the dome. The corridor extends along the low floor under the dome and from it open the men and women's lounges and toilet facilities.

At the opposite end of the car are five double seats on the right, and four on the left where the under-dome corridor enters the smaller passenger room. The floor level under the dome is dropped below that of the normal elevation of the end passenger rooms. Ramps at the end of the corridor connect the two floor levels.

The overall height of the dome, you learn, is 15 feet and 10 inches above the rail, and two feet four inches higher than the remainder of the normal-height car roof. The seats in the lower passenger compartments are rotating reversing, with individual reclining backs. Those in the dome are rotating reversing, but nonreclining.

Mounting the steps to the Sky-Dome, you have the feeling of turning a corner on a panoramic mountain trail, when seeing

5

before you a breath-taking sweep of horizon. You have left the flatlands and are now entering the mountains, with their deep-slashed canyons and towering peaks. You lean back and look up through the curved glass at the sky-hung scenery, allowing a sigh of complete contentment to escape your lips.

This is the thrill of your life. You are riding a sightseeing bus, an airplane, a train—all at the same time. You feel that this is the first time you ever had a real looks at outdoors.

The glass which surrounds you is double-laminated safety glass, the outer pane having heat-and-sunray-resisting properties. Positive air-conditioning of the Sky-Dome is assured, you have been told by Mr. Jones, in spite of the increased air-conditioning load resulting from the glass dome, and the dome compartment, during tests, was kept at 78 degrees with a maximum outside temperature of 103 degrees. Car heating is arranged to provide amply for the additional dome space in the coldest weather. Effective electric light fixtures are installed. The Sky-Dome section of the car seats 24.

Time passes quickly in the Sky-Dome as eye-filling scenery occupies your attention and noon arrives before you know it. Your trip is nearly half over when you leave the dome section and make your way to the dining car.

Remember, this *Mountaineer* is a coach train of a type in operation on railroads all over the country, and not to be confused with extra-fare trains; yet it provides all of the comfort and luxury you would expect only through payment of a higher tariff. If, until now, the *Mountaineer* has been a source of surprise and wonderment because of its rich appointments your entrance into the dining car continues to sustain the sensation of traveling in the most aristocratic circles.

An attractive decorative treatment has been applied to the dining car. The color scheme is particularly attractive, with Persian red walls, black trim, and white ceiling. Spotless linens and full silver and china service, accented with a rose on each table, provide the atmosphere of an exclusive dining room. The long, narrow effect of the car has been reduced by a central break in the wall treatment and paneling offsets. Tempting menus are

6

offered at moderate prices. The food and service are the sort you would expect in the more expensive restaurants.

It is in the dining car that you fully appreciate the smooth riding qualities of the train. The *Mountaineer* takes the mountain curves with astonishing ease and grace. On a long straight-away on a valley floor the speed reaches nearly ninety miles an hour without disturbing the flat calm of the water in your glass. You are amazed that such riding qualities could be built into a train.

Leaving the dining car, you walk back to the observation-lounge. Here you find comfortable chairs and davenports. There are wide side windows and curving rear-end windows with a minimum of framework employed, allowing for a wide range of vision. The floor is carpeted with a deep-pile rug in a colorful pattern. There are magazines in leather bindings, end tables and a writing table. Adequate ash trays and a table large enough for a bridge game are included in the elaborate furnishings. Here, as on the walls of other cars of the *Mountaineer*, are murals which depict the historical background of the country through which you are traveling.

As the mountains close in again, a voice you recognize as that of Mr. Jones comes over the loudspeaker. "Attention, please. The Mountaineer is now approaching the famous Turnback Curve at the entrance to the Big Blue country."

In a few moments you see your Diesel turning a sharp hairpin curve and you have a view of the rainbow-hued locomotive and the foremost cars of the train, passing briefly in review, and you more fully appreciate the striking beauty of this modern stream-liner through seeing it in a moving perspective.

With the coming of darkness, you are introduced to the fluorescent lighting system which adds so much to the general interior attractiveness of the train, as well as passenger enjoyment. In addition to fluorescent lighting the cars have 25-watt incandescent lamps located in the fluorescent troughs for night and emergency lighting. The individual seat lights have both a 15-watt incandescent bulb for night lighting and a 25-watt light bulb for the purpose of reading.

7

You complete your 500-mile, 11-hour coach trip without the usual train fatigue. Many factors have contributed to this—the air-conditioning, the restful "Sleepy Hollow" car seats, the riding qualities of the cars and, above all, your freedom of movement back and forth through the train as you have taken advantage of the various lounges, observation and dining facilities. This is a welcome change, particularly on long trips, to the coach traveler who was previously restricted to his or her coach seat, as if on a plane, bus, or automobile.

Your trip on the *Mountaineer* has convinced you that the railroads are well on their way to taking their rightful place far in the forefront of land or air transport. Any passenger-carrying road that does not quickly bring some trains to the standard of the *Mountaineer* certainly seems doomed.

Inquiry reveals that over 90 separate manufacturing concerns have contributed materials and equipment to the makeup of the *Mountaineer*, from aluminum, stainless steel, and steel alloys to chair and drapery fabrics, and from translucent window glass to sound-deadening materials and radio antenna.

As a train acquaintance remarked, "It is like putting your favorite hotel on wheels."

Having completed your business, you reserve a roomette aboard the *Plainsman* for your return trip. Here, as on the coach train, you find comfort and conveniences that far surpass the overnight train of yesterday. Your recollection of overnight travel brings to mind curtain-shrouded aisles, open sections, berths in the process of being made up, stepladders and undesirable upper berths, a swaying journey to a distant toilet, disheveled ladies, complaints of crowded dressing rooms, and contortionist efforts to disrobe or dress in a tumbled cubicle.

You envied the occupant of a drawing room, or even a compartment, as a luxury you could not afford. Modern overnight trains include roomettes, available at but slightly higher cost than standard Pullman berths. These roomettes are arranged to provide quiet and privacy for both sleeping and daytime occupancy.

You find greater elaboration of effect incorporated in the appointments of the *Plainsman* than in your coach train. The car designer has clearly been given a free hand to produce the ultimate in styling and comfort. You see the results in the dining car and throughout the train.

A fellow traveler compares the *Plainsman* to the "Century," of the New York Central, Santa Fe Chiefs, or A.P. Streamliners which set the railroad style and are in the extra-fare bracket. However, the *Plainsman* is not an extra-fare train and consequently is without certain features of the Twentieth Century Limited and the Chiefs.

The dining car of the *Plainsman* has a seating arrangement that is entirely new to you but familiar to a large number of train travelers. This is a continuous serpentine seating arrangement in the car's center section, which places the diner facing toward the center aisle. Beyond the center section at either end are two conventional tables seating four each. Two tables at the extreme ends near the foyer bulkheads have fixed seats and folding aluminum tables with Formica tops. The serpentine seats are built in place with hair-filled backs and hair and spring seats upholstered in gray mohair.

Each table grouping is separated from the others by partitions. Those at the end of the serpentine seats are the same height as the seat backs, while the partitions which segregate the tables at each end are solid to chairback height, with edgelight plexiglas from the top of the partition to six feet above the floor. Mirrors at each end of the dining room accentuate the effect of space. At the larger tables mulberry drapes frame yellow venetian blinds. All trim is satin-finish aluminum.

The consist of the *Plainsman* includes a club car in the center of the train and an observation lounge at the rear. Train service includes a stewardess, a barber and valet shop, and a train secretary. Like the *Mountaineer*, the *Plainsman* has a public address system and radio.

Other of the road's overnight trains, the stewardess informs you, carry coaches with the reclining type "Sleepy Hollow" chairs. These cars provide comfortable and economical transportation. In combination cars of these trains there is space set aside for women traveling with small children, a feature that has found great favor with mothers.

The all-room sleeping cars of the *Plainsman* have circulating ice water in every room and each of the double bedrooms has an adjoining private toilet and washroom. The occupants may control the air-conditioning and heating to their individual tastes.

The *Plainsman,* you learn, is a typical overnight train in operation on railroads all over the country on transcontinental, north-and-south and intercity runs. Postwar shortages delayed the construction of modern cars and equipment, but the traveler of today is assured of this new "Speedliner Service" to almost any destination he desires. Like yourself, there are thousands who have been weaned away from rail travel by the family automobile and by the discomforts of yesterday's rail service. However, the traveler of today is rediscovering the railroad.

Discourtesy on the part of railroad employees has been a source of complaint, but your railroad of today, leaving no stone unturned in its selling technique, demands politeness of its personnel and every contribution possible to passenger comfort. This has been reflected on both the *Mountaineer* and the *Plainsman.* You find this courtesy in the willingness of members of the crew to explain painstakingly various features of the train about which you inquire.

You learn that mechanical maintenance of the track has much to do with the conditioning of the right-of-way for the modern high-speed streamliner, that signaling has been improved vastly and that train dispatching has become literally a "push-button" affair.

You are told that the *Plainsman* is equipped with "hot bearing detectors," and you are shown a panel which flashes a warning red light when a journal starts to overheat. You learn of a device which prevents sliding wheels and resulting flat spots, and also that the Diesel locomotive, in addition to pulling your train at high speed, can help to brake it on long descending grades with the dynamic brake, something after the fashion of using compression on your automobile to check its speed without too frequent brake applications.

Your sleeper on the *Plainsman* has 14 roomettes, two bedrooms and a drawing room. The roomettes face each other at the forward end of the car, seven on each side. The drawing room and bedrooms adjoin, and the passageway is on the side. At the rear of the car is a porter's section and a small general washroom. Two-tone carpeting is used in roomettes, bedrooms, drawing room, and passageway.

Your evening aboard the *Plainsman* includes a pleasant hour in the observation-lounge and a visit to the club car. A group here is discussing the modern train in connection with the advancement of communications, and you learn that the first commercial radio-telephone call ever made from a train was from the *Royal Blue*, of the Baltimore and Ohio, on August 15, 1947.

The man who had recently ridden the new Century, of the New York Central, states that the fall of 1948 saw the world's longest stretch of train-radio-telephone in operation over the 436 miles between New York and Buffalo on the Central, with passengers able to telephone any place in the world through links with "land" radio stations.

The train conductor has joined the group, and he smiles tolerantly. "The train-radio-telephone that makes it possible for a passenger, speeding between New York and Buffalo, to talk to London and Paris is merely an expansion of train-telephone service with which the railroad man on many modern roads is already familiar."

This is something that surprises you, as it apparently does others in the group. "I didn't know that," says a passenger.

"Do you mean that a crew member can talk directly to someone not on the train?"

The conductor nods. "Not only can a crew member on a fast-moving train talk with an operator in a station, but he can talk with crewmen aboard another train. Radio-telephones link the conductor on the 100-car freight train and the engineer in the cab, the crews on both freight and passenger trains. In many of

11

the big classification yards switch movements are directed over the radio-telephone by the yardmaster."

This seems incredible to you, and you realize how far you, as well as millions of other Americans, have grown away from your railroad, your modern train.

The talk turns to *centralized traffic control*, to "C.T.C." and you are amazed to discover that on the railroads of today the train dispatcher, with centralized traffic control at his fingertips, can operate switches and signals one hundred, and two hundred, and more miles away without the employment of hands other than his own. Through the manipulation of small levers and buttons on a panel before him, he can open or close a switch at a lonely desert siding beyond a mountain range.

The conductor of the *Plainsman* prepares to move on. "Yes," he concludes, "and there are C.T.C. installations where the train dispatcher's office is one hundred miles or more away from the nearest point on the centralized traffic control installation which he is operating."

"Do you mean," asks the man who had ridden the *Century*, "that sometimes the train dispatcher is one hundred miles away from the division over which trains in his charge are rushing at speeds up to one hundred miles an hour?"

"Yes," said the conductor.

"I don't believe I would care to be on a train on that particular division,"said the passenger.

"You are on that kind of a division now," said the *Plainsman's* conductor. "This is your modern train on a railroad of today."

CHAPTER II

ELECTRO-MOTIVE

Pioneer in Diesel Progress

On August 31, 1922, the Electro-Motive Engineering Corporation was incorporated at Cleveland, Ohio. The company was then under the direction of H. L. Hamilton and associates. A little over a year later the construction of the first rail motor car was begun. The years fled. The young concern became the Electro-Motive Company. Then, in 1930, it was the Electro-Motive Division of General Motors.

On October 25, 1947, Electro-Motive celebrated its twenty-fifth anniversary. It had attained then a production rate of five units per day, with a total employment of 12,000. A few men of vision and courage have built a mighty industry from small and humble beginnings.

H. L. Hamilton headed the first successful campaign to put an internal combustion engine on the front end of a train. The culmination of it all was a gleaming Electro-Motive engine pulling the General Motors "Train of Tomorrow" across America.

It is a great compliment to American industry to watch the leaders who pioneered the Diesel road and switch locomotives on the railroads of the country continue to forge ahead in the manufacture of the present-day Diesel. In fact, it is my opinion that there would be few other Diesels ordered than those produced by Electro-Motive if this concern could turn them out fast enough.

I have the good fortune to have been in on the birth of the Diesel, and I have watched it grow. I have been on many of the test runs, first runs, with dynamometer cars coupled in behind them. I have read and watched the tests of many others, and I

13

have seen them break in on different roads. The reactions of various motive power officials, road foremen of engines and engine crews, have been both revealing and a little startling as they observed the Diesels and realized what they could do. The dynamic brake alone is worth its weight in gold as a money-saver.

The behavior of General Motors' Diesels, their performance under all conditions, is something that I constantly marvel at. Years make little difference to these locomotives. Electro-Motive power on the Union Pacific over a period of 12 years, from an average of 7,000 miles per month the first year to almost 10,000 miles per month in 1947, has set an availability record of close to 90 per cent. These locomotives almost seem to improve with age.

G-M Diesels are always easy riding and they are always easy on the track. In comparison with other Diesels their builders have accomplished wonders in this respect. Another feature—a very important feature for my book—is the cleanliness in the engine rooms, and also the roominess; the crews can move around. There is no such thing as oil leaks, and these can be a sin and a delusion.

Very important, too, in Diesel operation on passenger trains in the winter months are the best possible type of steam boilers for train heating. The General Motors Diesel locomotives have the proven ability to render top performance under the coldest weather conditions.

There are no better traction motors, in my opinion, than those on the Electro-Motive job. Their four-wheel trucks prevent slipping. There is no idler wheel.

There is less exhaust and no such thing as gas or fumes in the cabs, a thing which crews appreciate. All parts of the engines and motors were designed with an eye to making easy their inspection and maintenance. If a motor goes down it can soon be placed in running order again because it is much less complicated in design than most others.

There is one important, not-to-be-overlooked feature about a Diesel locomotive. If one or two motors fail there is still enough power to keep the train moving.

As much as I have railroaded, I have never had a bigger thrill than to take 15 heavy-weight cars—a 1,300-ton passenger train—over New Mexico's famous Raton Pass, up that 3.5 per cent grade between Morley, Colorado, and Lynn, New Mexico, or up the 3.3 per cent grade on the westward slope and never see the speed drop below 20 miles an hour with no helpers. That's a Diesel for you.

The Sante Fe runs these magnificent 6,000-horsepower Electro-Motive F-3's and the 5,400-horsepower Diesels with 100-mile-an-hour gearing through from Los Angeles, California, to Chicago and back to Barstow, California, where they are cut out; then the engine that came in the preceding date goes into Los Angeles and then back to Chicago. There is an eight to ten-hour layover at Barstow which is consumed with a thorough inspection and the replacement of any part that may be needed.

The Diesel shops maintained at Barstow by the Santa Fe are some of the finest in the country—none more modern. There was never a piece of machinery made that did not require care and maintenance. Carelessness and neglect can ruin the finest automobile manufactured. On the other hand, regular inspection and proper servicing will be rewarded by peak performance, day in and day out. This applies to a Diesel as much as it does to your family car.

The Diesel shop at Barstow, staffed by experts, gives these splendid locomotives the finest service possible, with the result that the Santa Fe Diesels are piling up mileage and at the same time getting the highest on-time performance in the history of the road. And it must be remembered that this performance is over Raton Pass, Glorietta, across the rugged Arizona Divide, over El Cajon Pass—up and down heavy mountain grades all the way from Trinidad, Colorado, to and across the San Bernardino Mountains and the famous Tehachapis in California. Temperatures run from zero in Kansas and Colorado to oven heat of Needles, California, and the Mojave Desert.

The finest recommendation a General Motors Diesel can have is the fact that their 6,000-horsepower F-3 locomotives are used exclusively on the four crack trains of the Sante Fe Railroad

15

between Chicago and Los Angeles, namely the *Super Chief*, the *Chief*, the *El Capitan* and the all-important *Fast Mail*. The *Fast Mail* is the only solid mail train operating over one railroad west of the Mississippi River. The Sante Fe overlooks no bets in keeping these trains moving—and on time.

These F-3s sold themselves. They never would have been assigned to these tough runs if they didn't have what it takes. Usually, if an F-3 is not available, the Santa Fe uses the General Motors converted freight Diesel, which proved up from the beginning. These Electro-Motive locomotives were the first 5,400-horsepower Diesels used on the Sante Fe.

The General Motors Company always has maintained the finest possible instruction system. Their instruction books have been out a long time; they are complete and comprehensive to a degree seldom attained in this type of book. Another great help to the railroads and the men who maintain and operate the Diesels has been the General Motors public relations system.

One of the reasons—one of the big reasons—for the leadership of General Motors Diesels is a man named Cy Osborn, vice president of General Motors. He is a born engineer, an experienced railroader and a Diesel expert. He travels thousands of miles up and down and across the nation, riding dynamometer cars, checking Diesel tests, riding the big motors. It is not the end of the story when Diesels from Electro-Motive are turned over to the railroad, far from it. Cy Osborn goes along to check their performance. He personally keeps an eye on them for many days after they are delivered, observing them closely.

Cy Osborn is a go-getter all of the way. His enthusiasm for these G-M locomotives is understandable. His switch engines are equally fine engines as the road Diesels. In 1948 more than 1,200 General Motors Diesels of 600- to 200-horsepower were in yard switching and transfer service, with over 46 million service hours. The national average of availability was 94 per cent.

Cy Osborn was the first man to conceive the idea of the vista dome car. In 1944, Osborn was studying wartime freight movements through the Colorado Rockies. Riding the fireman's seat of a Denver and Rio Grande Western Diesel freight locomotive, he gazed through the wide, slanting windshield at the magnificent mountain scenery. His view was unhindered, from canyon floor to mountain peak. Gazing through the side windows, he could follow the mountains as they fell away behind the train. "Man, oh, man!" exclaimed Osborn. "If people knew what they could see from here!"

Osborn took the idea back to the engineering department of the Electro-Motive Company at La Grange, Illinois. The answer was the vista dome car, first used on the Burlington Railroad, the tracks of which pass the Electro-Motive plant. These vista dome cars are now used on the Chesapeake & Ohio, the Denver and Rio Grande, the Western Pacific, the Missouri Pacific, and B. & O. More are scheduled for other roads. These new cars have a definite part in the "Railroads of Today." The vista dome car, you will remember, was a part of the *Mountaineer* in the opening chapter, providing a new thrill for the train's passengers.

The vista dome cars, undoubtedly, will be used by more and more railroads with scenery to sell. They will not be used where there are overhead wires or no proper clearances, or on long stretches of hot desert country.

Cy Osborn and his business associates at Electro-Motive had an active part in designing the "Train of Tomorrow" which has done much to popularize the railroads. Millions of people were given an opportunity to see it while it was on tour. Millions of words were written, glorifying this new glamour train.

Next to the Electro-Motive Diesel, in my opinion, comes the Fairbanks-Morse. This locomotive is giving a good account of itself on American railroads. They are a fine product. The Fairbanks-Morse switching locomotive, I would say, is also next to General Motors.

The products of the American Locomotive are far behind these two. The Baldwin road Diesel has not been too successful, according to reports, and from my observations.

I only wish the readers of this book, around the United States, could have the opportunity to see what the Diesels will do in all kinds of fast running—on red ball trains, crack passenger runs, on heavy drags on heavy grades. It is something to drop down that 148 miles from Seligman, Arizona, to Needles, California, on the First District of the Arizona Division of the Santa Fe with a 3500-ton train, observing carefully all speed limits, and making the run in around four hours, with never a hot wheel or a smoking brake on the entire train, or to ride the Chief and never see the air set from yard limit to yard limit board.

With the exception of 12 miles, this is all down grade—dropping at 1.42 per cent for 126 miles, some places a trifle steeper— the longest sustained grade in the United States. It is a tough piece of railroad, particularly going up, and was the longest steam helper district in the country before the coming of the Diesels. The elevation at Needles is 476 feet above sea level, while Seligman is 5,234 feet in the sky. Diesels take 3,500 tons over this climb in around five and one-half to six and one-half hours—never at any time dropping below a minimum speed of 20 miles an hour.

Thanks to H. L. Hamilton, to Cy Osborn and the Electro-Motive Company, the Diesel has been developed to its present high degree. The Diesel-electric locomotive is here to stay. It has proved a godsend to many an American railroad. We see higher speed schedules for passenger trains; we see freight trains moving faster than ever before. Steam, of course, will be the power on some roads for a long time, especially those roads in the great coal-producing districts, as they should be.

No one pretends that the Diesel locomotive is the final word in railroad motive power. In their new Locomotive Development Center, opened in June, 1947, Electro-Motive engineers and designers are already studying the locomotive of tomorrow. More power to them. However, the Diesels will be hard to beat.

Builds Diesels Exclusively

On March 27, 1935, ground was broken for the 6 million dollar Electro-Motive shop at La Grange, Illinois. Since its completion this plant has turned out General Motors locomotives exclusively. Here was pioneered the mass production of standardized locomotives and up to the last quarter of 1948 it had built more than six million Diesel locomotive horsepower for railroad use.

At the beginning of 1949 the facilities at La Grange covered more than three million square feet, and it is constantly being expanded to meet the railroads' growing demand for this modern type of motive power. Everything that goes into a G-M Diesel, including all mechanical and electrical components, are designed and manufactured by a single organization. This undivided manufacturing and service responsibility assures the purchaser that every locomotive delivered will have that high performance quality which has made Electro-Motive Diesels pace-setters.

Since these Diesels made their bow in high-speed passenger service, 180 covered more than one million miles, in the last quarter of 1947; 24 had covered two million miles, and five had covered more than three million miles.

The priceless ingredient for the locomotive of both today and tomorrow can be summed up in one word—*experience*. This experience began when H. L. Hamilton and a little group of earnest souls began experimenting with a gas-powered, electric-driver motor car way back in 1922, and before that. In July, 1924, M-300, the first rail motor car, was completed.

Today that experience is paying off, as we find four out of five crack passenger trains, and nine out of ten of the modern fast freights pulled by General Motors Diesels.

Earlier in this chapter we mentioned the F-3 Diesel on the Santa Fe. In the F-3 locomotive, the railroads have what has proved to be the most versatile power unit on the rails. It incorporates the latest and most advanced improvements in Diesel locomotives, in their design, construction and performance. These engines are powered by the time-proved 2-cycle General Motors Diesel engine. They operate as a 1500, 3000, 4500 or 6000-horsepower locomotive. They are equipped with DC-AC generators, providing alternating current for auxiliaries for the first time in any Diesel locomotive.

By a simple, relatively inexpensive change of gear ratios, the F-3 locomotive can be equipped to give full-rated performance over a range that includes the heaviest freight drag, to combination freight and passenger work, and to 100-mile-an-hour heavy-duty passenger work.

The General Motors F-3 is a great piece of motive power, as operating men anywhere will tell you.

The Illinois Central's modern all-coach luxury train, *City of New Orleans,* grossed more than four million in its first year of operation. Earnings increased from $2.61 a mile in April 1947 to an average of $6.12 a mile for the full 12 months. Powered by a 6000-horsepower General Motors Diesel locomotive, this speed-liner makes the 921-mile run from Chicago to New Orleans in 15 hours and 55 minutes, with 19 intermediate stops—the fastest scheduled land transportation in history between the Great Lakes and the Gulf.

I cannot emphasize too strongly the part that "service" plays in creating good will and in furthering the expansion of any sound concern. Today General Motors renders two major services. One is to teach Diesel art to railroad men; the other is to give prompt parts and maintenance service.

In 1934, when the very first Diesel-powered trains were touring the country, the company's service manager organized a Diesel school for railroad men. The first experimental school, with 20 EMC district service men as students, met on October 15, 1934. In 1935, railroads had generated enough interest so that the Electro-Motive service manager was able to hold a special one-week school in which the students were all railroad vice-presidents.

When Electro-Motive came on the scene that last day of August in 1922, it was "on time" as it brought together the technical arts of the day and welded them into something new for the transportation system of the nation.

CHAPTER III

THE NEW "CENTURY"

A Great Train of America

The Twentieth Century Limited was the fulfillment of the dream of a man who had a flair for showmanship—George Henry Daniels, general passenger agent of the New York Central from 1889 to 1907. The first "Century" introduced to the traveling public such unheard of innovations as a barber shop, valet and maid service, and a train secretary. It established a standard of train travel years ahead of its time.

The five extra dollars you pay for the privilege of riding the Century buys not only the last word in train luxury, but gives you practically the same prestige as stopping at the Waldorf-Astoria. The New York Central is probably the only railroad in the world that rolls out a carpet for anyone less than a king or a rajah, but it is a daily ritual in the Grand Central Station preliminary to the departure of the Twentieth Century Limited.

This 260-foot maroon carpet is almost as famous as the Century. It repeats at intervals the train's name and is one of the spectacular features of the road. Except for the World War II years, it has been rolled out since 1922, a welcome mat for anyone with a ticket and sleeper reservations aboard this fabulous train.

The Century, the glamour train of the Central, just about heads the railroad fashion parade in the richness of its appointments. It has everything, including an original oil painting from the Grand Central Galleries. Like rolling out the carpet, there are many traditions in connection with the Century, including its reputation for "on time" performance, its luxury and the courtesy of its personnel.

Before it began operation the Century was advertised as the first train in regular service to make the run between New York and Chicago, a distance of 961 miles, in 20 hours. This seemingly brash promise of overnight service over a distance of approximately one thousand miles promptly brought a hoot of derision from our British cousins, and an English newspaper expressed the doubt that the high speed demanded could be maintained without injury to the engine, rails, and coaches. It further ventured the prediction that the project would quickly be abandoned by these money-loving Yankees.

What the British writer did not know was that his Yankee relatives had not only been toying with the idea for some time, but had actually operated a train between New York and Chicago on a 20-hour schedule during the summer and fall of 1893 to accommodate visitors to the Chicago World's Fair. Thus, the inauguration of the Twentieth Century Limited on June 15, 1902, was far from being an experiment, but was rather the resumption of the schedule of the famous Exposition Flyer.

The first Century was made up of a ten-wheel locomotive, No. 604, pulling five cars, which included three Pullman sleepers, over the rails of the Lake Shore and Michigan Southern. The train carried 27 revenue passengers. One of these passengers was John W. "Bet-a-Million" Gates. When interviewed at the end of the run in Chicago, Mr. Gates beamed at the reporters over his cigar and said: "The Twentieth Century Limited makes New York a suburb of Chicago."

The Century of Today operates with about 16 cars, carrying approximately 160 passengers. The record number of passengers carried on any one trip was on January 7, 1929, when the eastbound train, running in seven sections, carried 894 passengers.

In its first year of operation the Century carried some 29,000 passengers for a gross revenue of $442,000. In 1947 almost 130,-000 passengers rode the twin Centuries, with a total gross revenue of nearly $4,000,000. In 46 years of operation the gross yearly passenger revenue of the Century has averaged approximately $3,650,000, with a yearly average of close to 100,000 passengers. The total mileage involved was around 52,000,000.

In 1928 the Century set an all-time record for a single train by carrying more than 225,000 passengers, with a record gross revenue of more than $11,000,000. This represented more passengers riding the Century than all the first class passengers carried on all trans-ocean steamships between New York and Europe in both directions.

It was in 1905 that the 20-hour schedule between New York and Chicago was reduced to 18 hours. In 1912 the 20-hour schedule was returned and it held this time for 20 years. The present schedule, New York to Chicago, is 16 hours, and eastbound to New York, it is 15½ hours. The Century's early wood and steel cars, except the diner, were replaced by all-steel cars in 1910.

The first ten-wheel type engine was replaced by the faster Pacific type in 1907. This type of locomotive passed through many improved classifications in the next 20 years, to be replaced finally by the heavier and faster Hudson 4-6-4 type, which also saw various improved classifications, including a streamlined version, then came the Mohawk 4-8-2 type and Niagara 4-8-4 type before they bowed out to the present Diesel locomotive.

The cost of the entire first Century was about $115,000—approximately the cost of one sleeping car in the new Twentieth Century Limited. Production of the Century, which made its inaugural run on September 17, 1948, set the Central back a cool two million dollars. When we speak of the Century we are really referring to *two* streamlined, all-room trains, operating each way, overnight, every night, between New York and Chicago, which makes a four-million-dollar total for this part of top American trains.

This $4,000,000 is but a drop in the bucket, compared to the $86,000,000 spent on new postwar passenger equipment—the largest sum spent by any railroad on new passenger cars and new passenger locomotives. $65 million went into 720 new passenger cars and $21 million went for the last word in Diesel-electric locomotives.

Twenty-eight New York Central trains received all-new equipment. These represented twin trains which operate under 14 famous names.

The all-room sleeping cars of the average Century contain 137 units which provide 253 beds. In the train consist behind the double-unit, 4000-horsepower Diesel-electric locomotive there is the new-type railway post office car, cars with 22 roomettes, cars with ten roomettes and six double bedrooms, cars with 12 double bedrooms, a new full-length dining car of original design, a kitchen and crew dormitory car, the Twentieth Century Club car and the bedroom-observation car with a "lookout-lounge."

Before examining the appointments and decorations of these ultra-modern cars of the Century, we will highlight a few of the general features of what has quite correctly been termed one of the most luxurious trains in all railroad history.

The new Century, as we revealed in the opening chapter, placed in operation between New York and Buffalo what was at that time the world's longest train-radio-telephone service, over a distance of 436 miles. This service is being expanded at this writing, as more radio-telephone relay stations are built. Through this service the passenger can enter into voice communication with any part of the world.

All lighting on the Century is fluorescent, including the brilliant rear-end sign that blazes the words, *Twentieth Century*. Both direct and indirect lighting is used, separately and in combination, in the train. The rooms have fluorescent ceiling lights, and reading and mirror lights are provided.

The Lookout Lounge and the Twentieth Century Club cars have radio receiving sets. All cars are linked by an inter-car dial telephone circuit, making it possible for passengers to phone for service from other parts of the train.

A feature of particular interest to women passengers and elderly people is the pneumatically-operated vestibule doors, which swing open at the mere touch of a hand-bar and close automatically, eliminating the struggle with hard-opening doors when passing from one car to another.

Passengers sleep on luxurious and restful foam rubber mattresses. Add to this the vastly improved riding qualities of the new Century, and the traveler can enjoy deep and untroubled sleep. The tight-lock couplings and cushioned draft gears eliminate virtually all play in couplings, making for smooth train starts and stops. Electric-pneumatic brakes and an automatic correlation between train speed and brake application further add to the ease of deceleration.

The Century, of course, is completely air-conditioned. The cars ride on roller bearings. An important safety feature is the employment of an alarm system that automatically warns of rising temperatures in the journal and the consequent threat of an overheated bearing.

The Century always is protected by complete automatic control, which immediately brings the train to a stop if the engineer should fail to properly observe a restrictive signal.

Cars of the Century

Each of the all-room sleeping cars has circulating ice water, electrical appliance outlet and lavatory (washing) facilities. The bedrooms, in addition, have separate toilet-lavatory rooms. Each car provides sleeping accommodations for the porter.

The full-length diner seats 64 persons and is divided into five separate sections. In the center dining space is provided for 24 passengers on continuous leather serpentine sofas along the walls. Separated by winged partitions at either end of the main dining section are four dining tables. Additional space is arranged at one end of the car and at the other end there are built-in settees where passengers may enjoy cocktails before meals.

In the center section the angle of tables and seats is such that passengers do not look directly at those dining opposite. Both side walls here are completely mirrored, which gives an effect of space. The direct-indirect lighting is patterned to repeat in the mirrors.

The wing partitions are bright rust leather, tooled with silver lines. The chairs of the intermediate sections are covered in blue-green leather. The walls and ceilings are light gray-brown. A partition forms an intimate end section with tables for four on either side. The walls and ceiling, a slightly darker gray brown than the adjacent areas, are offset by the leather upholstering which matches the rust of the leather fins in the center section. Windows in the end and intermediate sections are framed in gray and silver drapes. The carpet is soft brown loop.

The car called the Twentieth Century Club has a barber-valet shop with shower, a train secretary's office with radio telephone booth, and a snack bar. One entire wall of the car is mirrored, which reflects the bleached walnut paneling of the other side of the car, creating the effect of a car twice normal width.

In the center are two six-foot rust leather sofas facing each other, with a low black Formica-topped coffee table between. Opposite the sofas is a large bleached-walnut magazine cabinet. Twelve extra-large lounge chairs, upholstered in soft gray-beige fabric, and two bleached-walnut tables with lamps, complete the furnishings of the center section of the lounge. Framing the mirrors of this section are two large gun-metal leather wing partitions, adjacent to which are built-in blue-green upholstered seats with black Formica-top cocktail tables. There are also two Formica-topped card tables, each with four bright rust-colored leather chairs. The floor has a soft brown loop carpet.

An unusual continuous fluorescent lighting fixture on the ceiling runs down one side, turning to the mirrored wall to give the effect, through its reflection, of a round-cornered square fixture.

The train secretary's office has full office facilities, including a dictaphone. The secretarial service is offered free of charge. The radio-telephone charges range from thirty cents for local-area calls upward, according to distance. Beyond the secretary's office is the service bar.

We turn now to the Lookout Lounge Observation Car, which is unique in its arrangements and design. We will start at the observation end. This is 12 inches above the normal floor level and seats 14 passengers. Extra-high windows provide wide visibility. The spacious effect of this area is increased by the light-blue ceiling. We find the same charm and luxury here that was

G.N. #2, the new streamlined Empire Builder, eastbound below Glacier Park on the Second Subdivision of the Kalispell Division. Courtesy G. N. RR.

Train secretary on the new Twentieth Century shows use of new Dictaphone Time Master, which is an important addition to the railroads of today. Courtesy N.Y.C. RR.

Beautiful new lounge car in the center of the new Twentieth Century Limited complete with secretary, train telephone, and barber. Courtesy N.Y.C. RR.

A distinctive railroad station that services the famous Greenbrier Hotel at White Sulphur Springs, West Virginia, on the Allegheny Sub-division of the Clifton Forge Division, C & O. Courtesy C & O RR.

New vista dome car on the C & O's new Pere Marquette operating between Chicago and Grand Rapids, Michigan, east of St. Joseph, Michigan. Courtesy C & O RR.

Interior of the new tavern lounge lunch counter cars in service on the C & O with the much-talked-of goldfish bowl in the foreground. Courtesy C & O RR.

Day-Nite chair cars providing the last word in comfort and luxury. Note how the footrests drop down from the back of the chairs in front of the passenger using it. Courtesy Rock Island Lines.

Santa Fe El Capitan #22 coming down the North slope of Raton Pass above Morley, Colo., with diesel #21, EMC F3 the General Motors test car, and fourteen coaches. Test car is cut in between third and fourth units. First District of New Mexico Division. Photo by Preston George.

Interior view of new lounge car, 1340 class, in use on the Santa Fe El Capitan — the only extra-fare coach train in the U.S. Courtesy Santa Fe RR.

A great train of the railroads of today. SP. #98 — the Morning Daylight with eighteen cars running eastbound over the Coast Division between Surf and Honda, California. Courtesy Southern Pacific RR.

Rock Island #7—the Rocky Mt. Rocket—leaving the La Salle St. Station in Chicago on the Chicago Division. Courtesy Rock Island Lines.

Rock Island Time Freight hauled by 3-unit EMC diesel #99 westbound at Romero, Texas, with eighty-one cars on Panhandle Division. Photo by R. H. Kindig.

Children's theater in family coach—new C & O passenger equipment. Copyright by Walt Disney. Courtesy C & O RR.

N. C. & St. L. Manifest Freight ASC—2 with diesel 806 entering CTC territory at the Hills Park Yard, Atlanta, Ga., Atlanta Division. Photo courtesy N. C. & St. L. RR.

designed into the dining car and the Twentieth Century Club cars.

At the very end, facing the rear, there is a sofa for two. This is upholstered in bright rust leather. This rust tone predominates in many of the new luxury-liners of the railroads of today. Just forward of this sofa are four gun-metal leather chairs; also, face-to-face sofas, upholstered in soft gray-beige fabric, seating three passengers at a low coffee table.

The two steps leading to the lower level are flanked by solid metal hand rails, designed as part of the glass partitions separating the two areas. Framed by the railings are two built-in bright rust leather seats. This lounge section has a large three-seat sofa, a card table with four chairs, and a cocktail table for two. The sofa is upholstered in gray-beige, the card chairs in rust leather, and the cocktail chairs in gun-metal leather. Wood on chairs and walls is bleached walnut. The floor is carpeted. Table tops and window sills are Formica.

In the partition at the forward end of the lounge, which separates it from the five double bedrooms at the forward end of the car, blue-green leather is inserted in the wood veneer to form a background for the spot-lighted original modern oil painting, loaned by the Grand Central Galleries of New York. The painting is changed periodically.

The Central has 400 reproductions of masterpieces hanging in the cars of its various famous trains, but here aboard the new Century we find for the first time on any train an original oil painting.

The new Century provides a fine example of how cleverly a man like Henry Dreyfuss, noted industrial designer, can overcome the problem of decorating a train so as to relieve the long corridor effect of the cars. Mr. Dreyfuss has done this through the use of winged partitions, intimate groupings of furniture, generous use of mirrors, colors, and fabrics, thus creating an effect of spaciousness and the air of a luxurious private club, at the same time giving freedom from enforced association with fellow travelers.

The train is tied together as a unit by the uniform color

scheme, by the upholstering, paneling and the general styling. The result reflects the hand of a master artist, supplemented by the manufacturing genius of the builders, the Pullman-Standard Manufacturing Company.

The cars of the new Century are in every detail de luxe editions of modern passenger equipment, fashioned and tailored to meet the demands of aristocratic speed queens of the railroads of today.

Motive Power

Four thousand horses, harnessed to the driving axles, haul the new Century down the water-level race track of the New York Central between Harmon, New York, and Chicago, on Lake Michigan. Fast-stroking pistons in four big Diesel motors spin the generators that supply the electric current for the eight traction motors, which in turn deliver their surging power to the wheels of the locomotive.

As in the days when steam engines pulled the Century, big electric locomotives haul the train from Grand Central Station to Harmon. Here the Diesel-electric job backs on, and it stays on right through to Chicago, eliminating the former locomotive changes necessary with steam.

Certain characteristics of these 4,000-horsepower streamlined speedsters, which have been proved in actual operation on the Century since their introduction, contribute to the train's riding qualities as well as its enviable reputation for on-time service. Among the comfort and luxury features made possible by the Diesels are stability and absence of smoke and steam.

Some may wonder how the Diesel can contribute to the riding qualities of the train. This is accomplished by the reduction of steam locomotive sway, a motion that is often communicated to the cars. On a steam locomotive the connecting rods and the driving mechanism are located outside of the wheels. On a Diesel the drive is *inside* of the wheels, allowing the use of an ingenious device known as "outside swing hanger suspension."

In other words, the weight of the locomotive reaches the axles outside of the wheels. This has the same steadying effect in reducing side-to-side sway as standing with your feet wide apart. Also, the electric drive is compact and smooth in operation as compared to the massive siderods.

The Diesels on the new Century were built by the Electro-Motive Division of General Motors Corporation. The design of these fine locomotives adds materially to the reliability of the motive power while on a run. If it should happen that one of the four engines fails, or that trouble develops in generator or traction motors, the train could still proceed with the remaining power.

A further advantage of the Diesel is its ability to overcome adverse snow and ice conditions. This is due to the fact that the driving axles are distributed over 120 feet of track. With snow or ice on the track the four driving wheels on the front truck may slip but they clear the rail for the twelve remaining driving wheels behind them. This gives the Diesel locomotive something of the ground-gripping attributes of a centipede.

The Diesel-electric locomotive has been developed into a magnificent piece of motive power and is perfectly fitted to the needs of the new Century.

Names for Century Cars

The names selected for railroad cars are not chosen at random but have a definite purpose in the railroad's scheme of things. Each name supplies pertinent information to the railroader concerning that particular car. It indicates not only the type of car but also its accommodations. Names are chosen in a meeting of railroad personnel whose business it is to select them. The names then are checked for duplication everywhere in the country with the Pullman Company's master list.

The first name is the specific name of the car, and the second is the "family" name. The Twentieth Century Club cars are the *Lake Shore* and the *Atlantic Shore*. The "Shore" indicates that it is a unique Century club car. A "River" car contains ten roomettes and six double bedrooms; a "Port" car contains 12 double bedrooms, and a "Creek" car designates one of the special Lookout Lounge cars of the new Century.

"The Water Level Route" is a famous New York Central slogan and so the names of the cars of the new Century were taken from the names of rivers, shores, bays, ports, and creeks along the route of the Central. Consequently, such names as *Peekskill Bay, Sandusky Bay* and *Peconic Bay* appeared on the sleek sides of the newest Twentieth Century Limited. These "Bay" family names tell you that a car so inscribed is a 22-roomette sleeper.

Names have always played an important part on the railroad, beginning in the days when engines were named. Modern train names, aside from their advertising value, lend glamour to the country's speedliners. And car names, with their lilt and charm, give color to the train, as they tell a story to those who know the code.

Century Personnel

At your service on board the new Century during its 961-mile run are 44 railroad and Pullman employees. They are listed as follows:

2 stewards	11 Pullman porters
5 cooks	2 Pullman attendants
12 waiters	2 Pullman conductors
1 train secretary	1 NYC conductor
1 barber	1 engineer
1 radio-telephone	1 fireman
attendant	1 head brakeman
1 Pullman bus-boy	1 rear brakeman
	1 baggageman

Some of the train personnel, however, do not make the entire trip between Chicago and New York. The engineer and fireman change at Harmon, Albany, Syracuse, Buffalo, Cleveland, Toledo and Elkhart. Thus there are eight engine crews for each Century. The conductors and brakemen change at Buffalo and Cleveland, making three New York Central train crews. This brings the railroad and Pullman personnel serving on a single Century trip to 65.

In addition to the actual train personnel there is a total of more than 40 U. S. Railway Postal Service clerks, during the entire run, sorting mail aboard the train.

In another chapter I will tell more about the Century's personnel, about their courtesy and helpful service in making the Twentieth Century Limited "your train."

The "Good Will Department" is the biggest and most important department on the Central. Working in an "office" 11,000 miles long, it is staffed by 136,000 men and women, each one of them knowing he has a personal stake in the success and prosperity of the railroad. Making friends is not only good job insurance but "company manners" pay dividends through customer satisfaction and the consequent good will of the traveler and the shipper.

The four million dollars that went into the creation of the twin Centuries was an investment made possible through Central service, public good will—and a smile.

Building The Century

The real building of the new Century began when George H. Daniels nursed into life that first faint spark that eventually flamed beneath a smoke plume of the now famous 999, the engine that on May 10, 1893, attained a speed of a shade over 112 miles per hour while pulling the Empire State Express between Batavia and Buffalo, New York.

George H. Daniels, called the father of the Century, later developed and promoted the train that was "a century ahead of its time." Through the years the Twentieth Century Limited has been featured in songs, plays, poems, on the radio, in the movies, and in countless articles. *Holiday* magazine, in the May issue of 1947, carried an article, "Train of the Tycoons," by Lucius Beebe; and "Meet the Century's Million Dollar Babies," by Michael Evans, appeared in the May, 1948, *Coronet*. "Bob Elson on the Century," interviewing famous people, has been heard by millions of radio listeners.

There is another story that seldom makes print which is the behind-the-scenes story of the building of the sleek and shiny cars of the Century in the great shops of the Pullman-Standard Manufacturing Company—the story of infinite research and planning, the assembling and molding and finishing of cars like the *Atlantic Shore* and the *Thunder Bay*, and all the others that go to make up not only the new Century but the New York Central's great train fleet.

It is too vast and intricate a subject to adequately report in these pages, for the Central's postwar building program is of titanic proportions. In another chapter we will review some of its many achievements, but here we are concerned with the art of car building.

The material authorized by railroad equipment engineers for an average 12-car train would fill 75 books, each book containing 90,000 words. Each car requires 900 separate drawings. From these drawings 3,000 wood or steel templates, or patterns, are made. When the patterns and specifications are ready the truck shop starts wheel assemblies, the steel erection shop starts work on the ends, sides, and roof. Another department starts fashioning small but essential items such as ash trays, soap dishes, wash basins, and other accessories.

To form the sleek, smooth sides of a car hundreds of corrugated stiffeners are welded to the 15 separate pieces which make up the side of a car. This requires thousands of welds. To do the job Pullman-Standard engineers developed a 90,000-pound spot welder. Operated by a "magic eye," this spot welder can make 1,400 welds per minute.

Meanwhile, at another end of the erection shop men are forming the 28 curved sheets of the roof over a frame which holds them rigidly in place. A traveling bridge then moves slowly along the 85 feet of car roof, making 8,000 spot welds and seaming the curved sheets together to form a single enormous piece of steel.

When the car ends and underframes have been fabricated the completed sides and roof join them in the assembling process. This is known as "laying down the car." A mammoth crane picks up the completed body structure, swinging it over the tops of other cars being assembled, and sets it on temporary wheels for movement about the 135-acre plant to various operation locations. Joiners, trimmers, electricians, painters, and other skilled craftsmen swarm over the car, converting it finally into a completed passenger-carrying unit, capable of carrying passengers at Century speed in the utmost comfort and luxury.

While huge machines and jigs are employed in the fabricating of these Century cars in the early stages, Pullman-Standard has not lost the beautiful art of hand craftsmanship that made the earlier Century cars decorative masterpieces. You have only to step into cars like the Twentieth Century Club's *Lake Shore* or the striking Lookout Lounge Observation to appreciate the fact that today, more than ever, the passenger car manufacturer operates on a special custom-building basis.

The lack of standardization in passenger car building—once known as the first mass production industry—stems from the varying traffic conditions under which different roads operate. New ideas incorporated in postwar equipment sprang from the particular needs and requests of the Central's clientele. The older equipment included few real luxuries, in contrast to the improvements and conveniences engineered into the cars of the new Century.

The complexity of construction of the modern de luxe passenger car is at once baffling and bewildering. The traveler takes all of the appointments more or less for granted, accepting the innovations offered without particular thought to the amazing "packaging" job that has been accomplished. There is, for instance, 52,000 feet or almost ten miles of electric wiring hidden in the walls and ceiling of the average 20-passenger sleeping car.

A Century car measuring 85 feet in length, 10 feet in width and 13½ feet in overall height will have 5,000 square feet of wall space which make up the partitions of the individual rooms. Installed will be 27 large doors, 20 small doors, 47 knob and lock sets, 17 wash basins and toilets, 91 lighting fixtures, and 4,142 feet of pipe. Five hundred ninety-three gallons of paint and varnish are used to finish a new car, or sufficient paint to do a very nice job, inside and out, on 22 five-room houses.

The Twentieth Century Limited is one of the favorite trains of "who's who" of business, politics, stage and screen. Many of its passengers ride the Century regularly, knowing its "on-time" reputation, its overnight comfort and convenience, its world-renowned cuisine, and the assurance of meeting friends, both among the passengers and crew.

From the moment at New York when passengers walk down the traditional maroon carpet they know that a quiet, conservative elegance, fostered by the most exacting service, will be theirs.

In addition to being an aristocrat of passenger-carrying renown, the Century holds high rank as a mail train. Important mail, demanding assurance of overnight delivery between New York and Chicago, is sent by business houses direct to departing Centuries for handling in the single mail car. In New York the number of pieces delivered direct to the train by messenger averages 7,500 daily. In Chicago this mail service averages around 3,800 pieces every day. The U. S. Postal Service makes late collections in the two cities of a daily average of 175,000 pieces of first class mail which is handled by the twin Centuries.

Dictaphone Service

Something entirely new was added to the "New" Century service in the fall of 1948, and that was dictaphone service. Leaflets are placed in each room of the train before its departure which read:

A Dictaphone Time-Master Dictating Machine is available for your use. The train secretary will place it in your room on request.

These dictaphone machines are available for the use of any passenger requesting them. There is absolutely no charge for the service. The machines are loaned and the Memobelts and mailer inserts are provided. When a passenger requests the use of a "Time-Master," the train secretary takes it to the passenger's room, plugs it in, instructs the passenger on the correct use and explains the details of the service. Once used, the Memobelts become the property of the passenger. He may mail them directly to his office for transcription or, if he requests, the train secretary will turn them over to the New York Central office either in New York or Chicago for transcription at the prevailing rates. A supply of Twentieth Century letterheads and envelopes are furnished specifically for this work.

Aside from the leaflets, lucite signs in the observation car, the lounge car and the train secretary's room also inform the traveler of this dictaphone service.

Almost all of this lengthy chapter on these fine new trains was dictated on No. 26's Time-Master by the author between Collinwood (Cleveland) and Rochester.

CHAPTER IV

BRAKE DEVELOPMENT

"HSC" Electro-Pneumatic Brake

To safeguard train movement, brake development must keep pace with the development of the ultra high-speed trains of today. Much has been accomplished by the Westinghouse Air Brake Company, as their engineers have attacked the problems of deceleration. The blazing rush of the modern passenger train has introduced new factors in brake control. Operating at these higher speeds, trains require a higher braking force, controlled at a very rapid rate and with a high degree of flexibility in order to accomplish acceptable stops.

The "HSC" Electro-Pneumatic brake was engineered for high-speed, streamlined passenger trains. This brake is basically an air brake with two systems of control, the one being electrical and the other pneumatic. All of the inherent safety features of the original Westinghouse Brake have been retained in this new brake. However, the "HSC" brake permits the air brakes on each car to be controlled to a great extent instantaneously by electrical means, thus providing a flexible and prompt control of brakes.

Shortly before World War II, a number of railroads began experimenting with passenger trains designed to operate at speeds up to 125 miles per hour. It readily became apparent that to stop trains traveling at such high speeds a new type of brake was going to be required.

The Westinghouse people then developed the "HSC" Electro-Pneumatic Brake. This brake has come into use on most, if not all, of the new streamlined passenger trains, and it has met with remarkable success.

In the "HSC" Electro-Pneumatic Brake several wires must run the length of the train. Because of the character of the service to which they are subjected, the nature of the connections between cars and the general problem of maintenance, faults are apt to develop in these electrical circuits. Thus a "circuit checking" mechanism is employed.

A mechanism is installed on the locomotive of the train, and this mechanism is busily engaged at all times in determining the integrity of the electric circuits in question. This device automatically switches control of the brake equipment throughout the train from the electrical system to the pneumatic system. Thus when the engineman moves his brake valve handle to application position he will obtain a brake application.

The development of this so-called "circuit checking equipment" presented some difficult problems, the solution of which required the employment of exceptionally ingenious electrical arrangements.

Starting with the first installations of the higher speed type of trains in 1932, continuous research and design in this new field of braking, supplemented by extensive road tests, have gone forward hand in hand with each new phase of high speed train operation. The "HSC" brake equipment thus has been developed to a standard basis, applicable to all types of equipment operating in high speed service. The basic elements of this brake were also made available for cars to be operated in conventional passenger trains, thereby facilitating later conversion to "HSC" if desired.

When operating electro-pneumatically in ultrahigh speed service, very high braking forces are available. These forces are prevented from producing excessive rates of retardation and wheel sliding by automatic control of the brake forces actually developed, through the medium of a controlling device by means of which the maximum practical retardation rate is utilized to effect the shortest and smoothest possible stop.

When operating pneumatically, the available braking force is automatically changed to the standard for general passenger

37

service, thus accomplishing harmonious operation in either class of service.

With electric control throughout the train the "HSC" electro-pneumatic brakes on each car apply and release almost instantaneously and simultaneously with the brakes on the locomotive. Large supply reservoirs on each car continuously charged from the brake pipe, provide a practically inexhaustible supply to sustain repeated brake application. Each set of brake cylinders is supplied locally through its control valve which builds up brake cylinder pressure directly from the supply reservoir, and when released, exhausts the brake cylinder air directly to the atmosphere. Consequently, the brake action is smooth, as changes in the brake force are simultaneous throughout the train.

The "HSC" brake system is suitable for passenger trains up to 24 cars. Pneumatic emergency brake application is instantly available from the brake valve in event of interference with the normal electro-pneumatic brake system, caused by interrupted electric circuits, ruptured straight air or main reservoir pipes, or other causes. It incorporates standard passenger pneumatic brake features which are available for handling trains to terminals in case the electro-pneumatic brake system fails through lack of electric current.

The braking ratio is automatically adjusted to that used on standard passenger equipment when the electro-pneumatic brake system is not used. Pneumatic emergency brake applications are available from the brake valve or conductor's valve at any time equipment is charged, and this is produced automatically if the brake pipe or its hose connections are ruptured.

The "HSC" has a higher braking force in emergency application, thus affording needed protection for unexpected emergencies, including those occurring during service stops. The pneumatic brake system has all the desirable operating features of standard passenger equipment cars when these cars are handled by a conventional steam or electric locomotive not equipped with electro-pneumatic control devices.

The improved functional characteristics of the pneumatic brake system include improved quick service, insured release, a more flexible graduated release, faster emergency transmission, accelerated release after emergency application and uniform brake cylinder pressure, which is maintained regardless of piston travel and normal leakage.

A pneumatic emergency brake application is produced automatically in the event the engineman becomes incapacitated. In the event an intended electro-pneumatic brake application does not apply within a fixed interval a pneumatic emergency brake application is produced automatically.

A further feature is the automatic sanding at the locomotive, and also at points in the train if desired, during emergency brake applications. To prevent breakage and loosening of pipe joints operating devices are equipped with reinforced pipe fittings.

A "self-lapping" brake valve provides the engineman with a thoroughly flexible control of braking pressure. He increases or decreases application pressure by merely advancing or retrieving the brake value handle. No "lap" position is employed, for the lapping feature is an automatic function of the brake valve itself. The application pressure rapidly builds up or reduces the required amount, corresponding to the brake valve handle position. The brake valve automatically laps at the desired pressure and then functions automatically to maintain the pressure.

The application pressure thus obtained operates an Electro-Pneumatic Master Controller which controls application and releases wires throughout the train. It makes and breaks contact with these circuits in accordance with the air pressure fixed by the brake valve handle movement and, consequently, acts as the point of transfer from pneumatic control to electric transmission.

A clutch is provided to condition the "HSC" brake valve for either electro-pneumatic or automatic control, thus making the locomotive brake equipment fully adaptable for operation of trains in either ultrahigh speed or conventional passenger service. An independent brake valve provides complete independent control of locomotive brakes.

Locomotives with standard "ET" equipment can be equipped for both classes of service by adding a self-lapping brake valve and related apparatus to the regular ET equipment schedule to provide electro-pneumatic control.

Application and release magnets on each car are energized or de-energized by the electro-pneumatic master controller on the locomotive, simultaneously applying or releasing a corresponding straight air pipe pressure on each car. The master controller is also self-lapping and consequently maintains the same pressure condition in the straight air pipe as set up by the brake valve handle position.

A control valve on the car provides the standard pneumatic brake features controlling the application and release of brakes in accordance with brake pipe changes as with conventional equipment. It provides higher brake cylinder pressure in an emergency and a very fast emergency propagation rate. It also provides the interlocking control between the electro-pneumatic and pneumatic brake systems.

Either the control valve or the electrically actuated elements act as a piloting device for the operation of one or more large-capacity, self-lapping type relay valves, as needed with any required number, size or arrangement of brake cylinders.

"AP" Decelostat Equipment

In stopping high-speed trains, especially from speeds as high as 100 miles per hour, powerful braking must be employed. The amount of brake force that can be applied to the car wheels depends upon the adhesion between fast-rolling wheels and the rails over which they roll. This adhesion is a variable factor which depends on the condition of the rail, weather conditions and other factors. The engineer, of course, cannot always know the amount of adhesion; as a consequence, the brakes may be applied with more power than is permitted by this rail adhesion. As a result, the brakes may lock some of the car wheels, causing them to slide. This wears flat spots on the wheels, rendering them unfit for regular service. The slip further reduces the effectiveness of the braking action.

To prevent sliding of the wheels because of too much braking power the Westinghouse Air Brake Company developed the "AP" Decelostat equipment. This equipment is built about an inertia device mounted on each axle of each car, which is arranged to detect incipient sliding of the car wheels and to soften and momentarily reduce the amount of braking on those wheels to prevent their sliding.

This equipment has been installed on many of the high-speed passenger trains now in service on a number of railroads, and it has been quite effective in preventing damage due to the sliding of the wheels.

"AB" Freight Brake Equipment

For a great many years the length of freight trains rarely exceeded 75 cars. But in the last two decades it became necessary for the railroads to haul longer and heavier trains at the higher speeds demanded in order to handle the mounting volume of freight traffic and to operate these trains with a greater degree of efficiency.

To meet this new development in railroading the Westinghouse Air Brake Company co-operated with the Association of American Railroads in creating a new type of freight brake equipment known as the "AB" brake, a brake that is now standard for all American railroads.

The development of the "AB" brake required many years of research and experimental work before it was perfected, at a cost of several million dollars. As a result, this braking system has become a valuable asset to the country's railroads, and it is now possible to haul heavy-tonnage trains of as many as 180 loaded cars at relatively high speeds in comparative safety. With the "AB" brake equipment the railroads were able, during the crisis of World War II, to haul a larger number of freight trains of greater length than ever before.

Because the "AB" brake represents an outstanding achievement in railroad development, the Franklin Institute, of Philadelphia, awarded a Certificate of Recognition to the engineers of the Westinghouse Company for their contribution in the development of this brake.

24-RL Lomocotive Brake Equipment

For many years certain types of locomotives were assigned to freight service and certain other locomotive types to passenger service. Because of this the brake equipment of freight and passenger locomotives was different. With the advent of the "HSC" Electro-Pneumatic brake for high-speed passenger trains it was necessary to develop an entirely new locomotive brake equipment to control this type of brake throughout the train.

In recent years there has been a tendency to design locomotives entirely suitable for either freight or passenger service. To meet this need the Westinghouse Air Brake Company developed the 24-RL equipment, which is a universal type of equipment as it can be adapted for any type of service. In other words, it can control the brakes in either freight or passenger trains, and can also control either electro-pneumatic brakes or all-pneumatic brakes. In addition, other features have been added to keep pace with recent developments in railroading such as employing various combinations of Diesel units for various lengths of trains.

Based on the principles of a sectional assembly the 24-RL brake valve is constructed in portions, two of which are of different types. Combinations of the basic sections with two changeable sections are made to suit the operating requirements of any particular service which involves steam, diesel, or electric road locomotives. Its design, therefore, is so arranged that supplementary control functions such as train control, safety control, overspeed feature and electro-pneumatic brake control for passenger service can be incorporated at any time by the insertion of supplementary parts.

42

Hot Bearing Detector

While the railroads make every effort to provide well-lubricated bearings, an absolutely essential factor in modern high-speed train movement, bearings, nevertheless, are occasionally bound to run hot and burn out. There have been instances where a burned-out bearing has caused wrecks, and this is a serious matter in the case of passenger trains.

With a desire to eliminate this hazard, so far as possible, the Westinghouse people and the Union Switch and Signal Company joined forces in developing a Hot Bearing Detector mechanism, which would, by means of signals, warn the engineer or members of the train crew that a hot bearing existed. Through their combined efforts hot bearing detection was removed from the questionable category by putting the bearing temperatures of a fast-moving train under the constant scrutiny of the train crew. The detector system positively identifies abnormal bearing temperatures and warns simultaneously in advance of the rise of such temperatures to a dangerous level.

Warned that a hot bearing exists, the engine or train crew can take the necessary steps to stop the train well in advance of possible serious trouble.

A train equipped with the Westinghouse-Union hot bearing equipment does not have to depend on the human element. The detective work is entirely automatic, and once installed the long life and integrity of the system is practically assured. The entire equipment, from the detector units installed in each bearing to the electro-pneumatic valves, is designed on the "closed circuit principle" and any irregularity in the system is self-detected by lamp indication and by the blowing of the whistle valve in the engineer's cab.

Let us examine for a moment the working of this modern trouble-shooter. In the first place, the equipment is margined to tolerate the normal expected temperature differential in the bearings. It does, however, immediately detect an unequal rise in the temperature of one bearing as compared with its associated bearings. Should all the associated bearings rise in temperature in a substantially equal amount, such as would result from a rise in encompassing temperatures, the detecting apparatus would not respond. In this manner, compensation is automatically obtained for surrounding temperatures, which effect the temperatures of all bearings on a car equally. At the same time, detection is provided for a dangerous rise in the temperature of one bearing as compared to the associated bearings, which denotes an impending hot bearing.

Each detecting unit on the car or locomotive is connected to a Wheatstone Bridge circuit in the relay unit. The amount of resistance in a detecting unit varies according to the temperature of the associated bearings and this factor is utilized to introduce resistance changes in the Wheatstone Bridge circuit.

With the bearing temperatures within normal limits the circuit is so organized that the detecting relays are alternately energized or de-energized in sequence to produce a continuous coding action. This coding action serves to compare the temperatures of each bearing with its associated bearings on the truck at periodic intervals. As long as the coding action is continuous a relay in the relay unit energizes a magnet valve and keeps it in a closed position, and also shows a green light.

Should a bearing attain an abnormally high temperature the increased resistance in the detecting unit unbalances the circuit and stops the coding action. This interruption de-energizes the magnet valve, venting the signal pipe pressure and blowing the whistle valve in the engineer's cab. As the signal pipe pressure reduces to a low point a relay valve connecting the main reservoir line to the signal whistle releases, with the result that the signal whistle blows continuously. Thus the engineman is warned of a hot bearing and can take immediate action.

Meanwhile, the green light in the panel of the car affected is extinguished and the proper red light is illuminated, both warning crew members and indicating the side on which the hot bearing is located.

The traditional safety of railroad passenger travel is greatly

44

enhanced through the development and application of the hot bearing detector, for it puts bearing temperatures of the speeding train under the constant scrutiny of the train crew. The indicator lamps are so located as to be readily observed by the train crew.

CHAPTER V

THE SANTA FE TRAIL

Famous Trains and Hotels

You can't go wrong on Fred Harvey any more than you can on the Atchison, Topeka and Santa Fe. The Santa Fe will carry you and Fred Harvey will feed you—not only feed you as you have seldom been fed before but sleep you in hostelries that are among the finest in the West. Of course, there is also the added attraction of the Harvey girl, who is closely woven into western tradition.

Nothing is too good for the traveler aboard the Santa Fe's hospitality trains. The roadway, motive power and personnel unite with the car-builders and designers to provide the traveler with perfect comfort and service. This book is concerned with modern rail transportation in its various phases and it is difficult to draw comparisons between the equipment of any of the top-ranking roads. Each has its own high standards, shaped to attract patronage.

The Santa Fe *Super Chief*, Nos. 17 and 18, now operates daily between Chicago and the West Coast. This train has equipment second to none throughout the U. S. What I have always liked about this train is its arrangement of lounge car accommodations. For instance, there is a lounge car on the head end. Then, there is the beautiful bar-lounge next to the diner, and the lovely new observation three-room car at the rear end, with adequate lounge facilities for some 15 people. Regardless of where you are aboard the *Super Chief* there is always a luxurious lounge compartment close by.

These lounge cars help to break the monotony of the trip.

You move about, you meet congenial people as you would in your own club. I feel that these lounge cars are one of the finest things about our "Railroad of Today."

The dining car service on the Santa Fe is always good with Fred Harvey serving the meals. You will read more of this astonishing Fred Harvey in the portion of this chapter devoted to mail trains.

To me, it is truly wonderful to follow the old Santa Fe Trail again—to travel the road our grandfathers pioneered—and to eat at a Harvey House, as they did. I like to be able to stop off, when I am in the mood, and find hotels of the sort that are famous on the road of the Santa Fe.

You want to visit a little in Las Vegas, New Mexico, in picturesque and charming Santa Fe, and you find hotel accommodations to suit the most exacting demands. In Albuquerque there is the Alvarado and at Winslow the La Pasada. Williams, Arizona, and Needles, California, offer the same excellent kind of hotels.

On the high rim of the Grand Canyon we find Bright Angel Lodge and the El Tovar, two of the most scenic locations it is possible to imagine. You ride to the very rim of this greatest of all natural wonders aboard cars of the Santa Fe.

As for *Super Chief*, this train now carries a "working" mail car along with its usual storage mail car. The Santa Fe never overlooks an opportunity when it comes to speeding Uncle Sam's mail through.

The *Texas Chief* is a beautiful modern train with lightweight stainless steel equipment. Its consist is usually three or four de luxe coaches, an unusually attractive lounge and dining car, four or five lightweight sleepers and a railway post office car.

The *Texas Chief* is handled by one 4,000-horsepower two-unit Diesel all the way through from Chicago to Galveston. The train is extremely popular and very much appreciated by a great many travelers to and from the great state of Texas.

The Santa Fe *Chief*, of which I have written about many times, is the same old *Chief*. It still carries its never-failing fine accommodations. It has excellent new equipment and operates

47

on its same daily schedule, which has been reduced to 44 hours in each direction.

The *Chief* carries the through sleeping cars from the New York Central's *Twentieth Century Limited,* as well as one daily from the Pennsylvania's *Broadway Limited* and one from Washington from the Baltimore & Ohio's *Capitol Limited.* This fine service has more than paid for itself. Proof of its popularity was the additional car from the *Century* in the latter part of 1948.

Travelers like this Coast-to-Coast service, and it is by all means well worth while.

The country's only extra-fare streamlined all-coach train, the *El Capitan,* Nos. 21 and 22, has been placed on a daily schedule and is booked to capacity on every trip. The consist includes coffee shop and dining cars, two attractive lounge cars and eight coaches. There is also a mail storage car.

The time of the *El Capitan* is the same as made by the fast-traveling *Super Chief.*

Mail Trains

Romance and adventure have been a part of the movement of United States Mail since the days of the stagecoach and the Pony Express. There has been thrill and excitement in the rush of the mail pouch across the mountains and the plains. There still is. It is simply an evolution from a man, a horse and a 20-pound load to a train and Railway Post-Office crew, 5,000 horses and hundreds of mail sacks. In 1860 the Pony Express was big business. Today the Railway Mail Service is still big business.

Every 24 hours some 9,000 trains, traveling an aggregate of more than 600,000 miles daily, roar down the rails with U. S. Mail. Playing an important part in this movement of mail we find trains 7 and 8 of the Santa Fe, the *Fast Mail and Express*—the only regularly scheduled daily exclusive mail and express trains running through west of the Mississippi River. No. 7, of course, is the westbound train; No. 8 is the eastbound.

By reason of the long distances they operate between Chicago

48

and Los Angeles—a total of 2,225 miles—trains Nos. 7 and 8 undoubtedly pile up more car-foot miles than any other like trains in the United States. The bulk of the mail moving through Chicago and Kansas City to California goes to Santa Fe, while the majority of mail destined to the East and Middlewest out of Los Angeles also rides the rails of the Santa Fe.

Besides the mail handled by trains 7 and 8, the east- and westbound Super Chief, Nos. 17 and 18, Chief, Nos. 19 and 20, and El Capitan, Nos. 21 and 22, haul two mail storage cars.

For well over 100 years American railroads and the U. S. Post Office Department have been working hand in hand at the business of transporting the mail. Together they have written much of the colorful history of the country and today combine their talents in producing the fastest, most reliable, and economical mail operation in the world.

Thus the strong arm of our government and the two-fisted railway systems of the nation, built on the solid foundation of free enterprise, have created the present Railway Mail Service, which includes the legendary "RPO"—the Railway Post Office, staffed by the finest type of men found anywhere.

It was back in 1862 that William A. Davis, then postmaster at St. Joseph, Missouri, conceived the idea of sorting the mail while in transit and having it ready for dispatch to various points immediately upon the arrival of the train at its terminal. Temporary cars were provided for the experiment and William Davis set out to prove that his idea was sound. He was accompanied by a clerk named Fred Harvey as one of his two-man crew. The first "traveling post office" was a success and the "Railway Mail Service" was born.

This Fred Harvey, the obscure mail clerk, later established the famous system of Fred Harvey eating houses along the Santa Fe. And so the London-born Frederick Henry Harvey not only had a hand in launching the present Railway Post Office but the present restaurants and hotels that bear his name. Undoubtedly these two services have produced more satisfied customers than any like institutions in the world.

The original RPO car was operated on the Hannibal & St.

Joseph Railroad between Quincy, Illinois, and St. Joseph, Missouri. However, this early experimental service, because of unfavorable road conditions, did not last out the year, and it withered on the vine. Later, the first assistant postmaster general, Selah R. Hobbie, was sent to England and France to examine and report on postal systems in these countries. England, at that time, had in use a "mail catcher" consisting of a net swung out of the side of the mail car to snare the suspended pouch and similar to the one still employed in the British Isles.

Hobbie's report on the traveling rail post office was unfavorable, for he felt that it was too expensive. He further declared that the railway clerk's work would be difficult because of the rough riding of our cars. The germ, nevertheless, had been planted in the minds of men of the Post Office Department and in August, 1864, two years after the first operation by William Davis, an official test was made between Chicago and Clinton, Iowa, on the Chicago and Northwestern Railroad, with a rebuilt baggage car.

This run was under the direction of George R. Armstrong, who later became the first superintendent of the Railway Mail Service. Upon the conclusion of this latest test it was decided to establish a permanent service over this route. During the year the service was extended to include the run between Washington and New York and between Chicago and Cairo, a distribution point for mail going to Union soldiers in the South.

Soon Railway Post Offices were operating on nearly every railroad in the country. The first full RPO car was built by the Chicago and Northwestern Railroad and placed in service in 1867. These early cars were 40 feet in length and without end doors. They had two windows and upper-deck lights on either side. A case for paper distribution was built into one end of the car. It was semicircular in shape and consisted of four rows of 13 boxes each, rising one above the other from the "opening" table where the pouches were emptied. Light was provided by two oil lamps.

Letter cases consisted of three sections, set in angular form, and having a capacity of 77 pigeon-holes each. The letter case, like the paper case, had two oil lamps and some drawers. A storage room at one end of the car had one lamp. The car was furnished with a chair, stove, lounge, wood-box, and ice cooler.

Wood racks to hold the pouches came into use in 1874. These were later replaced by the metal racks now in use. Prior to the introduction of the "Ward" mail-catcher, the mail clerk simply reached out precariously and snagged the pouch with his arm. The Ward catcher came into use in 1869 and provided a means of accelerating the service, now making it possible to dispatch a letter and receive an answer between almost any two points between New York and Buffalo within 24 hours, where it had formerly required two or three days.

The life of the Railway Mail clerk was far from rosy in the days of wood and coal stoves and coal oil lamps, but lighting and heating methods advanced until by the 1890s heating was accomplished by steam, and electric lights were beginning to be used. The first steel RPO car was launched down the steel rail in 1905.

Today the finest type of heating and lighting systems are employed in the cars of the Railway Mail Service, with air-conditioned cars in the immediate offing. Modern RPO cars for heavy runs are 60-footers, with smaller editions on shorter runs. In keeping with the modern trend, the Santa Fe is now operating streamlined RPO cars, built to Post Office Department specifications by the American Car and Foundry Company at St. Charles, Missouri. These cars are lightweight (43 tons), 60 feet in length.

Regardless of the latest lighting wrinkles, your modern RPO car carries a stock of candles as part of its equipment for emergency use. Each car, of course, has its wardrobe and toilet facilities. A 60-foot RPO car contains ten five-foot sections of metal racks, five along each side of the car, and arranged to hold 140 pouches for the clerks sorting the mail. There are also 50 overhead boxes and ten "bridges" of two separations each. These facilities allow for 210 separations of mail. Letter cases on each side of the car have a total of 744 boxes. There are several tables in the car—a stationary table along each letter case and five tables for sorting pouches and papers.

Let us examine the handling of mail on the famous eastbound train No. 8, the Santa Fe's "Fast Mail and Express." Eleven clerks are assigned to a full 60-foot RPO car. Early arrivals set up the racks for pouches and sacks, "stall" the mail which arrives by truck from the terminal post office and start "casing" letters. The mail cars are spotted at the Los Angeles Union Station several hours before the scheduled departure time and mountains of mail sacks are swallowed by the cars.

The great volume of mail which flows to train No. 8 by truck already has been separated in the terminal post office into pouches and sacks for the several types of cars that make up the train that soon will be hurtling East. Two of the storage cars are loaded with sacks and pouches going beyond Winslow, Arizona, and they are not opened until No. 8 reaches that point.

The other two storage cars remain open for taking on and discharging mail at various stations along the line. Two Santa Fe employees, a mail-piler and his helper, ride these cars. They take into the cars through an end door sacks and pouches which are filled by the clerks in the RPO cars as the train wheels East. Sacks and pouches of mail taken aboard the RPO cars at Los Angeles and other stops, or snatched up by the mail-catcher at non-stop points, are opened by the clerks and the mail they contain is sorted into other sacks and pouches for particular destinations.

Three of the clerks, for instance, work pouches of first class mail, one clerk handles newspapers, another has charge of registered mail, and one handles mixed mail. Of the remaining five clerks, one man handles mail for Illinois; another distributes mail for Colorado and New Mexico; one has charge of mail for California and Arizona points; one handles mail for Oklahoma, and the eleventh man handles mail for Texas.

Your RPO man leads a rigorous life, with little of the glamour that is often supposed to be attached to the job. In the first place he has to pass a stiff Civil Service examination. Having attained a sufficiently high rating, he is certified by the Civil

Service Commission to the general superintendent of the Railway Mail Service in Washington. He is then assigned, say, to the Los Angeles district as a substitute railway postal clerk. Now he is on his way.

For a year he works on a probationary basis in the Los Angeles terminal post office, all of the time learning distribution. During his first year he is required to pass two written examinations on space rules and regulations, as well as card-case examinations in which he has to distribute speedily and accurately a total of 2,100 cards representing post offices and railway post offices in his territory, as well as post offices contiguous to the line on which he hopes he will one day be running.

Having served his probationary period, he must take a written examination on postal regulations every three years. However, he must take a card-case test at least once a year until he is 60, or has been in the service 30 years. Once he has been assigned to this Los Angeles-Ash Fork run, he must take seven card-case examinations in three years—four for the city of Los Angeles, two for the state of California and one for the state of Arizona. These represent several thousand post offices the locations of which he must know well enough to distribute the cards with a high degree of speed and accuracy.

Some clerks, in the Middlewest, where post offices are more numerous, must know an even greater number. Thus, the average railway mail clerk is of a necessity familiar with four or five thousand post offices, in addition, in many cases, to streets and post office sub-stations within metropolitan areas. The card-case, or "sweat-box" as it is called, is an outstanding feature of the rigorous training these men of the Railway Mail Service must undergo in order to maintain the high standards demanded of them.

From the time these RPO men report at Santa Fe train No. 8 until the next morning when the Fast Mail and Express grinds to a stop at the railroad town of Ash Fork, Arizona, 485 miles east of Los Angeles, they work at a breakneck pace to keep up with the seemingly endless flow of mail.

Another RPO crew takes over at Ash Fork for the flight on

East aboard No. 8 as far as Albuquerque, New Mexico. Between Albuquerque and Chicago RPO crews change at La Junta, Colorado, and Kansas City. The crew arriving at Ash Fork check into a room provided for them in the Harvey house. Here each makes out a memorandum concerning the amount of distribution and any irregularities noted in the mail handled. The clerk in charge of the crew writes a trip report from this information which is forwarded to the chief clerk of the district. These reports not only serve as records of the type of work performed by each man, but also serve as a time and pay record from which the monthly pay roll is prepared.

Eight of the men who traveled to Ash Fork will leave for Los Angeles in a RPO crew on train No. 19, the Chief. The other three will lay over and return as part of the mail crew on No. 7, the westbound Fast Mail and Express.

The Santa Fe was running mail on trains to the West Coast as early as 1884 and to the Texas Gulf as early as 1887. Records indicate that as far back as 1892 the main line of the Santa Fe was the mail route from Chicago and Kansas City to Southern California.

During World War II, as now, train No. 7 operated in two sections practically every day, carrying an average of 21 cars into Los Angeles daily. A typical monthly total included 210 cars of mail, 400 cars of express and 32 other cars, in addition to 161 cars of express which were switched out at Barstow for Northern California.

To serve as a liaison agency between the railroad and the United States Post Office Department, an express and mail traffic department was established by the Santa Fe many years ago. This department, a division of the passenger traffic department, supervises the U. S. Mail and Railway Express Agency business over the rails of the Santa Fe.

It is the business of this part of the Santa Fe to clear details of the respective operations with the Post Office Department and to interpret the rules and regulations set up governing railroad mail service.

CHAPTER VI

THE NEW POWHATAN ARROW

Norfolk and Western's Crack Speedliner

One of the world's greatest coal-carriers—"Blue Chip" in the financial world—one of the nation's "busiest railroads," the Norfolk and Western, shortly after the close of World War II, began an all-embracing program, reflecting this road's faith not only in the future of the territory it serves, but also in American business.

The smoke of battle had hardly cleared away when the Norfolk and Western opened the throttle on its peace-time projects. The drafting rooms were flooded with tracings and blueprints touching on every phase of operation. Scarcely a single area in the territory did not come into the field of new construction and modernization. There were blueprints, too, of new locomotives, of new trains, of the new *Powhatan Arrow*.

This new speed queen, naturally, came in for a lot of planning, but it was not alone for the modern streamliner that this intensive track tailoring program went forward. Of course, so fine a train deserved the best but the Norfolk and Western was concerned with providing for many trains and every effort possible was expended for track and line betterments in the interest of better railroading as a whole, better railroad service, as a great "Railroad of Today" prepared for the traffic of tomorrow.

Before reviewing the makeup of the new *Powhatan Arrow*, we will go over the line for a quick look at the improvements which include, of course, that C.T.C. installation between Portsmouth and Cincinnati, covered in another chapter. We find a grade reduction at Beaver Pond Hill from 1.42 per cent to 0.52 per cent; a new bridge over Scioto Brush Creek; a new viaduct at

Cedar Fork Creek; cut improvements at Pine Gap Hollow; a new overpass at Peebles, eliminating a grade crossing; and other line betterments that will help speed and safeguard the flow of rail traffic over the main line between Norfolk, Virginia, and Cincinnati, Ohio.

Track, grade, and signal improvements alone between Portsmouth Ohio, and Cincinnati cost $3 millions. Bridges, yards and trackage near Kenova, Naugatuck, Iaeger and Devon in West Virginia; at Petersburg, in Virginia, and Sardinia, Ohio—all came in for major improvements. Probably one of the most striking track-side advancements was the rebuilding of the Norfolk and Western station at Roanoke, Virginia.

While the street-side portion of the station is pleasing and completely modern, the track-side view scales heights of architectural perfection not often achieved in the design of a railroad depot. We have become more or less inured to grimed and shabby railroad stations. The pity of it is that comparatively few travelers can see such truly beautiful stations as the one at Roanoke.

The station is a companion contribution to the new *Powhatan Arrow* in the trend toward better transportation facilities. Also being modernized at this writing is the Lynchburg station. Progressive advancement has always been the creed of the Norfolk and Western, and it is reflected in the work accomplished all along the line.

The first *Powhatan Arrow* was inaugurated and began operation in April, 1946. It was a fine train, an all-coach train—the last word for day travelers. The cars of this train were completely reconditioned coaches, travel-lounge cars, and dining cars. People all along the line received it with acclaim. They turned out in a manner that was "absolutely amazing."

That was yesterday. Today is the new *Powhatan Arrow*. Tomorrow? Who knows? Whatever it is, the Norfolk and Western will be among the leaders.

We have devoted considerable space in this book to the country's new trains and their interiors, but the spanking new cars of the new *Powhatan* deserve a special place in our review.

Cars of the New Powhatan Arrow

The coaches are equipped with rotating, reclining seats and adjustable foot rests, sponge rubber seats, backs and armrests. However, before you settle yourself into one of these amazingly comfortable seats, your eye will be filled with the beauty of the car's interior, from the striking floor design to the end wall art and the broad panoramic windows. The coaches are spacious and look so clean and fresh that the restfulness all immediately relaxes you.

The lighting is of the latest fluorescent type, consisting of a continuous light in the center of the ceiling over the aisle for general illumination and individually controlled fluorescent lighting in wash rooms and lounges. Each coach has its electric water cooler. Stainless steel toilet enclosures have ceramic tile flooring and all vestibule floors, walls and ceilings are lined with stainless steel.

The new dining cars are a little bit out of this world, with the spotless linens, the decorative mirrored paneling, the wide windows, the Venetian blinds, and the artistic border drapes. The seating arrangement is conventional, with tables for four on one side of the aisle and tables for two on the other. Seatings for thirty-six are provided.

Kitchens are provided with Electro-mechanical refrigeration. The kitchens also have chill boxes, frozen food storage compartments, and ice cube makers. Equipment includes electrically-operated garbage disposal units. All exposed surfaces in kitchen and pantry are of stainless steel. Facilities for washing and sterilizing the dishes, as well as for the storage and handling of all foods, complies with United States public health requirements.

Lighting of the dining compartment is by continuous-line light along the sides of the car at the top of the windows, with light being reflected to the tables as well as the ceiling.

The tavern-lounge-observation cars call for superlatives. You tread lightly and speak softly. This is an exclusive club atmosphere. Here, you undoubtedly will pass pleasant hours. You make the mental reservation that this is the ultimate in travel luxury.

There are seats for 36 passengers in the lounge section, including the sections which contain the upholstered wall seats and cocktail tables. Next to the rear of the car is the bar, the pantry and, beyond, the hostess room. The observation lounge seats 16 passengers in comfortable chairs. The furnishings include a writing desk and a magazine stand.

Fluorescent lighting in continuous line is provided over tables, seats and chairs. The pantry of the observation section is equipped with refrigerators and ice cube makers. All exposed surfaces here are of stainless steel. Other equipment includes an electric juicer, toaster, coffee urn, grilles and garbage-disposal unit.

All windows of the tavern-lounge observation cars are fitted with Venetian blinds and side drapes.

The hostess stateroom contains an upper and lower berth, wardrobe, lavatory, and toilet facilities.

A coach and locker car in the consist of the new *Powhatan Arrow* seats 40 in the coach section. Adjoining is a smoking room with spacious chairs. Beyond this is a steward's locker, which has a lavatory, toilet, and clothes locker. At this end of the car space is allotted the dining crew. Here are chairs, lavatories, a toilet, and a spacious clothes locker with a rod for coat hangers and a shelf above.

The opposite end of this coach has luggage lockers and toilet and wash rooms for men and women. This car, like the others, is shiny, spacious and completely restful.

All coaches, dining and tavern-lounge-observation cars are constructed of Cor-Ten steel, air-conditioned, and wired for public address system, radio, and recorded entertainment. Loud speakers are spaced at intervals in the ceilings to provide an even distribution of sound throughout the cars. Automatic control is used for maintaining a uniform sound level above ambient noises. Automatic door operators are installed on all end doors.

The makeup of the new *Powhatan Arrow* includes a 58-passenger coach, with a spacious and attractive women's dressing room at one end of the car, and a man's smoking room and toilet at the other end.

A two-compartment coach seats 42 in one section and 24 in the second section. Each section has individual women's and men's rooms.

The new N & W sleeping cars have ten roomettes and six bedrooms. Accommodations for 22 persons are provided in each sleeper. The facilities include hot and cold water, and also ice water. Complete toilet facilities are located in each roomette and bedroom.

These sleepers, like the coaches, have the latest type of airconditioning. Pneumatic door operators eliminate all of the tugging and straining that used to be part of moving from one car to another. Women and elderly people, as well as youngsters, find the pneumatic operators a blessing.

The still fine cars of the first *Powhatan Arrow* have been reassigned to other trains. This new speedliner of the Norfolk and Western, as we have seen, is not new in any figurative sense; it is *new* from front coupling to marker lights—a train of distinction.

The Norfolk and Western is a coal road. Fuel is no problem; the earth is full of it—some of the finest coal mined. In a world more and more becoming Diesel-minded, the Norfolk and Western trains are rolling behind the steam locomotive. We draw no comparisons. However, the locomotives are performing magnificently, from heavy-duty freight locomotives to the beautifully streamlined "J," or 4-8-4 type, engines in passenger service.

These 4-8-4's really pack a wallop and they are too handsome for words. Drivers are 70-inch. This "J" class is equipped with Timken tapered roller bearings and rods and they travel fast and effortlessly.

The *Powhatan Arrow* is a companion train to the famous *Pocahontas*. They are the glamour trains of the Norfolk and Western. They travel a scenic route that is second to none. The new *Powhatan Arrow* is making a name for itself on a road that is doing a hefty job in the transportation field.

And, to top it all, the Norfolk and Western has been awarded the coveted Harriman Memorial Gold Medal for the fourth time for its outstanding railroad safety record in 1947.

That is something to think about too when you are riding the new *Powhatan Arrow*. This Norfolk and Western is not only one of the busiest roads in the country, it is also one of the safest.

CHAPTER VII

UNION PACIFIC LOOKS AHEAD

Western Development—Retarder Yards

Before the Union Pacific has completed its postwar program the road will probably have spent as much as the system cost. From its inception, the Union Pacific seemed destined for greatness, and in 1949, 80 years after the driving of the Golden Spike, this pioneer of the old U. P. Trail stands out as a lusty stalwart among the rail giants of the West.

It is characteristic of the West that when there is a job to be done no time is wasted on dubious scenting of the wind for weather signs. Men simply roll up their sleeves and proceed to the business at hand. They have conquered time, distance, mountains, rivers and deserts. If these Western Railroads seem to swagger and strut a little, they have every right to; if they seem a bit heady and boastful, they have good cause.

The old Union Pacific of the seventies had faith in the growth of the West. The Union Pacific under the late E. H. Harriman foresaw continued westward expansion and began rebuilding the railroad shortly after the turn of the century. In the present postwar railroad era the Union Pacific is once more rebuilding and modernizing this great railway system under the able leadership of its president, A. E. Stoddard, and E. Roland Harriman, chairman of the Union Pacific board of directors, and a son of E. H. Harriman.

The Union Pacific serves 13 great Western states—California, Oregon, Washington, Idaho, Nevada, Utah, Montana, Wyoming, Colorado, Nebraska, Kansas, Iowa and Missouri—and since V-J Day some $200,000,000 has been authorized or spent for new equipment and fixed facilities to handle the increased flow of passengers, materials and finished products to and from the nation's newest, fastest-growing industrial areas.

With the end of World War II, students of history in America became increasingly aware of two things:

(1) American industry, divorced from the over-populated East, has gone West and could be counted upon to stay there.

(2) If that is true, some safe, certain lifeline must be found not only to keep it there but to link it even closer to the populous Eastern and Midwestern markets.

Union Pacific officials, with the experiences of the war years, had long planned for just such an eventuality. The result was that when the fighting was over the Union Pacific was ready with a long-range program designed to protect the future of the newly industrialized and increasingly agriculturalized West.

As always, there were railroad critics complaining loudly that the railroads were not progressive and still belonged to the horse-and-buggy days. The Board of Directors of the Union Pacific wasted no time replying to such carping but went ahead, sleeves rolled up, and took immediate action on the following program:

(1) Ordered an institutional advertising campaign in the nation's trade press pointing out the industrial advantages of the West. (Since the end of World War II, more than one thousand new industries have been located on UP lines.)

(2) Began placing orders for additional freight, refrigerator, and passenger cars.

(3) Started a purchasing program that resulted in complete "Dieselization" of the railroad's entire main line from Salt Lake City, Utah, to Los Angeles, California.

(4) On November 15, 1947, the Union Pacific had 272 Diesel units with a total of 358,980 horsepower. On that date the UP Board made railroad history when they ordered an additional 181 Diesel power units.

(5) Began a long-range construction program that resulted in construction of a new freight classification yard at Pocatello,

Idaho, and another at North Platte, Nebraska, to speed the flow of freight.

(6) Ordered construction of a new tunnel through the Wasatch Mountains at Aspen, Wyoming, which will eliminate the only section of single-track line between Omaha, Nebraska, and Salt Lake City.

(7) Ordered further centralized traffic control installations to provide faster, safer transportation.

(8) Instigated a new livestock dispatch service, eliminating the usual stop for feed, water and rest at Las Vegas, Nevada, and putting in livestock in Los Angeles from Ogden, Utah, in slightly more than 30 hours.

(9) Placed Union Pacific's entire fleet of five "Cities" streamliners into daily service between Chicago and Los Angeles, San Francisco, Portland, and Denver, and between St. Louis and Denver.

(10) Insisted that the problem of safer delivery of freight be solved by the employment of a container engineer whose job it is to see that all freight is properly packaged to cut down losses.

(11) Instituted an educational travel program designed to interest America's vast traveling public in the natural wonders of the West.

(12) Ordered an all-out effort to keep the railroad's service not only abreast of but also ahead of continued development of the Pacific Northwest, California, Idaho and other states served by the road.

(13) Demanded that all of this be accomplished by an ever-increasing vigilance against accidents through the installation of new safety devices and operation of an exhibition car in which not only the railroader but the public, as well, be given lectures on safety and railroad operation.

(14) Ordered the purchase of new type, high-speed 133-pound rail for use in a continuing program of track replacement of the road's main lines.

The Union Pacific believes the West is in for a long period of prosperity. Cheering words, indeed, and there seems little doubt but that the prophesy will be fulfilled. Certainly, great things are forecast in this West the railroads built.

It sounds wonderful, you say, but what has actually been done? It is easy to spend money on paper, and $200 million is real money.

Let us see how some of this money was spent: $2 million and one-half went into the classification yard at Pocatello, Idaho; $3 million and one-half was spent for the retarder yard at North Platte. When it is finally completed the Aspen Tunnel will have cost $8 million. Contracts had been let on seven UP construction projects in seven states in the spring of 1948 for $6,686,500.

Orders for the purchase of 50 new chair cars and 50 new all-room sleeping cars of lightweight construction were authorized in February, 1948, at a total cost of about $12 millions.

Some of the construction program included 59 miles of centralized traffic control between Los Angeles and Riverside, California, together with the extension of passing tracks and additional second main track; 110 miles of new color light signals between Ogden, Utah, and McCammon, Idaho, and the extension of passing tracks; 21.5 miles of new track from Fort Hall, Idaho, to a phosphate deposit at Gay, Idaho; automatic cab controlling circuits and new color lights between Laramie and Green River, Wyoming; the relocation and extension of tracks in the Nampa, Idaho, yards; Diesel oil storage facilities installed in nine cities; main line track changed at Strong, Bloom and Black Rock, Utah, and Farrier, Nevada, to eliminate sharp curves and their accompanying speed restrictions.

These are a few of the projects which will keep the Union Pacific well up in the forefront of the railroad modernization movement that is blazing the trail of "Railroads of Today."

The Union Pacific has 9,800 miles of railroad, plus all of its train and equipment, which adds up to a staggering figure. But that is not all. "The Union Pacific," says John Bridge in the *Wall Street Journal* of October 20, 1947, "operates more than a railroad. It owns or controls bus lines, hotels, oil and coal fields. Income from Union Pacific's non-railroad operations normally covers its fixed charges.

"Since 1937 when oil was first discovered on Union Pacific's lands, income from oil and gas operations has become the most important part of the company's 'other income.' Its oil operations are currently at record levels, running ahead of the $6.6 million net income from this source in 1946."

The same article points out that normally Union Pacific is the fifth U. S. railroad in total revenues from railway operations; adding that in the past few years it had been one of the top three railroad companies from the standpoint of net income.

During the war years, the UP spent $414 millions for maintenance and equipment to handle the war traffic, including the largest steam locomotives in the world, the giant 4-8-8-4 mallet types designed for mountain work, the well-known "Big Boys."

Late 1948 found the Union Pacific with about 1,200 passenger cars, more than 50,000 freight cars, more than 1,000 steam locomotives and around 417 Diesel units, with deliveries being maintained as this is written.

We find an example of the growth and development of the Union Pacific in the modern classification yard at Pocatello, Idaho. This yard was built as a 28-track classification yard. Looking to the future, the classification layout was planned for 40-track capacity. The Pocatello yard was completed in the fall of 1947, and before the fall of 1948 had rolled around it had expanded its classification facilities to their full 40-track capacity.

Modern Yard at Pocatello

In the good old days, which happily are gone beyond recall, it was claimed by the boomer fraternity that the qualifications required of a switchman applying for a job at Pocatello Yard largely depended on his ability to throw a ball switch with his feet while rolling a cigarette. If, in those days, a seer had told a switchman that the crystal ball indicated a future yard layout that included power switches, car retarders in place of "hump riders," teletype machines, talk-back speakers, radio telephone connections in the cabs of the Diesel switch engines, and inspection pits under the tracks, the switchman would, and not without reason, have declared that the crystal-gazer was crazy in the head.

But today these things are realities at Pocatello yard for the reason that, to expedite traffic, the railroads must employ every last wrinkle that science can develop to maintain their position in the transportation parade. The track is heavier; trains are faster; communications are far-reaching and positive, with this centralized traffic control performing feats that make the old-timer bat his eyes in amazement. An added piece of wizardry is the modern railroad yard.

Pocatello, Idaho, is a rail crossroads, a Union Pacific junction that finds lines converging from four directions. To the east, a line reaches to Granger, Wyoming, to tie in with the east-and-west main route of the road between Omaha, Nebraska, and Ogden, Utah. To the west, the rails extend through Boise, Idaho, to Portland, Oregon, and Seattle, Washington, with connections to Spokane, Washington. North of Pocatello, the track finds its way to Butte, Montana, and to the south there is the line to Ogden, Salt Lake City, Utah, and Los Angeles, California. This far-flung network originates a tremendous volume of products, moving into the hub at Pocatello. Foremost of these products are fruits, vegetables, lumber, phosphate and live stock from all parts of Washington, Oregon and Idaho. Moving into these territories are manufactured products and coal.

A large percentage of trains arriving at Pocatello must be classified and made up into new trains for departure. The traffic, of course, has its seasonal peaks, ranging up to 2,200 cars daily.

Switching once handled in two flat yards at Pocatello finally became entirely inadequate to meet the increasing demands. Delays and congestion of this rail traffic became serious, a condition that the Union Pacific set about correcting through the expenditure of more than two million and a half dollars. The plans that came off the drafting tables of the engineering department included a new gravity yard of a uniformly high capacity and designed to classify and make up trains with a minimum of delay.

66

#26 the N & W crack Powhatan Arrow running over CTC territory on the Scioto Division between Newtown and Ancor, Ohio, enroute to Norfolk.

Santa Fe 6000 h.p. EMC diesel #20 climbing the 3% grade up Glorietta Pass with train #20, the Chief, with fourteen cars, and no helper. Photo by R. H. Kindig.

Rear end of Santa Fe #20, hauled by #20, climbing the 3% grade up Glorietta Pass on the Third District of the New Mexico Division. Photo by R. H. Kindig.

The new North Platte, Nebraska, car retarder yard of the U.P. Classification of one train nears completion just as another heads for the receiving yard. North Platte Yard was placed in service in 1948, the one at Pocatello in 1947.

Baltimore & Ohio Sentinel Freight train with new B & O Class T–3 4–8–2 type, engine #5585 about to leave Deshler Yard en route to Chicago. Courtesy B & O RR.

Here are the classification tracks as the hump yardmaster sees them from his office on the second floor of the building at apex of hump. Union Pacific Pocatello Yard, Idaho-Utah Division.

Three-car cut of PFE cars gets its first retardation as it enters the first or hump retardor. Hump and trimmer signals are controlled by hump conductor located on first floor of building at the crest of hump. Hump yardmaster is located on second floor of the same building. Pocatello classification yards.

CTC machine with the Pocatello Glens Ferry Idaho Division CTC in the background which shows a portion of the fine dispatcher's office at Pocatello, Idaho. The second man dispatches the branches and the third man the line from Glens Ferry to Nampa. Small machine at right controls switches and signals at East Pocatello, permits routing freights operating east of Pocatello into and out of yard without stopping.

Flood lights aid inspectors both day and night. Mirrors make it possible to see parts of car which would otherwise be inaccessible to view even with the numerous vantage points provided in this modern inspection pit. Union Pacific Pocatello Yards.

Operator in tower A controls speed of cars as they pass through the first retarder. He also routes cars to the north or south side of the yard depending upon their destination. He is getting information from switch list under left hand and is kept advised of all movements by the teletype on his left at Pocatello Classification Yards.

The great features of the new U.P. Pocatello Yard are inspection facilities. Man on top floor inspects boxcar and reefer roofs plus lading of open cars. Inspectors under tracks between rails check brakes, rigging, insides of wheels, underframe, and other parts accessible to their view. Men in basement of buildings, one on each side of track, check journals, springs, brakeshoes, and other parts which cannot be seen from under center of track.

Cars are thoroughly inspected top sides and under carriages as they are pushed up the hump at Pocatello, Idaho, by Union Pacific diesel switches. Notice hump signal, inspection light, and high flood lights for the yard. A fine installation for the railroads of today.

Unloading mahogany logs from South Africa at the N&W's new Pier N at Norfolk from ship to railroad cars. Courtesy N&W RR.

The mahogany logs from South Africa are now moving through Roanoke on the N&W division of that name behind Engine #2166, class Y–3. Courtesy N&W RR.

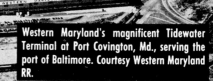

Western Maryland's magnificent Tidewater Terminal at Port Covington, Md., serving the port of Baltimore. Courtesy Western Maryland RR.

Eastward freight train hauled by a Class J–1 engine 4–6–6–4 type crossing the Salisbury Viaduct at Meyersdale, Pa., on the Elkins Division. Photo courtesy Western Maryland RR.

A river had to be moved, a hump built, grades calculated, floodlights installed, an electrical apparatus engineered into the layout and a general all-around remodeling and enlarging of plant and facilities had to be accomplished. This included 600,000 cubic yards of grading and the laying of 35 miles of track, involving a 14-track receiving yard, a 28-track classification yard, and an 11-track departure yard. Then there was a car repair yard and new tracks for yard engine fueling. The receiving yard tracks range in length from 2,025 feet to 6,310 feet. The departure yard tracks range from 4,640 to 6,245 feet in length.

The car repair yard has five tracks and is located to the south of the lead between the classification yard and the departure yard. South of the repair tracks are five caboose tracks about 820 feet long. A run-around track for freight trains is located to the north of the yards, and the double-track main line for passenger trains is to the south of the yards.

The original flat switching yards now form the new receiving yard. From the east end of this yard, eastward for about two miles, the construction on the present fill is all new. This area incorporates 75 additional acres. Four bends of the Portneuf river channel, totaling about three-quarters of a mile, were filled. Also several sections of new channel were dug. The entire yard area was graded to a level of six feet above record high water.

Culverts 30 to 40 inches in diameter provide for the necessary cross drainage. New 131-pound rail was laid for the new passenger tracks. All rail switches, frogs and turnouts in the retarder area are of 131-pound material. The rail of other yard tracks is 100-pound.

Two groups of eight tracks extended down the center of the original 28-track classification yard. To either side a space was left sufficient to accommodate six tracks each when additional tracks were required. Beyond these spaces, along each side of the fill, there was a group of six tracks. The reason for locating the latter six-track groups at the edges of the area, instead of adjacent to the two central groups, was that this procedure permitted the installation of tracks and switches in their permanent locations in the sections down the incline, making possible the subsequent addition of the two future groups without changes except the insertion of two switches in the main leads.

The classification tracks were thus arranged in groups, rather than being connected to ladders, which makes it possible for one car retarder for each group to be used to apply the final retardation for cars going to any of the tracks in each group. Sufficient area was available for length of tracks as required for various classifications without the necessity of using lap switches and, therefore, short ladders were used. The yard tracks are spaced on 14-foot centers, providing for a pathway between cars. The original 28 tracks placed in service had capacities ranging from 24 to 42 cars.

The Pocatello hump yard grade descends at about 0.2 per cent throughout the receiving, classification and departure yards. From the east end of the receiving yard a grade of 2 per cent ascends to the crest, the elevation of which is about 15 feet above that at the clearance points of the turnouts to the classification tracks. When cars are being pushed over the crest at the usual speed of about four miles per hour, the section of 4 per cent grade down the incline serves to accelerate the speed promptly, thus lengthening the separation between cars or cuts to allow space and time in which to operate the switches. From the bottom of this 4 per cent incline the grades were designed at gradually reducing percentages to about 0.2 per cent after passing the clearance points on the turnouts on the respective classification tracks.

Let us say now that a lightweight car, such as an empty stock car, has been dropped over the crest. This car will roll to the classification track at a speed of at least five miles per hour, even against the wind. For loaded cars or empty cars traveling too fast, the retarders are used to bring the speed to about three or four miles per hour as these cars leave the last retarder on each route. The 0.2 per cent grade on the classification tracks is just about right, under favorable conditions, to keep heavy cars moving without gaining speed. At the far end of each track there is 250 feet of ascending 0.4 per cent grade, which reduces the speed short of a hand skate placed on the track to hold the first car.

The power switch machines and car retarders—of the electro-pneumatic type—and the control machines were furnished by the Union Switch and Signal Company.

As the cars are pushed toward the crest from the receiving yard they pass a location at which men on each side use pressure equipment to shoot a stream of warm oil into the journal boxes. This aids the car to accelerate quickly when moving down the incline. Sheet-metal pans are provided to catch excess oil. Moving up to the crest, the cars to be humped past car inspection pits which house men who inspect the cars. At this point a concrete passageway about three feet wide and seven feet high extends through the fill. From this passageway a door leads to the inspection pit beneath the track where the car inspector sits looking through shatterproof glass windows, which face both up and down the track.

This inspector checks brake beams and other equipment. An automatic wiper, operated by air pressure, removes rain or snow from the glass. A steel roof covers the inspection pit between the windows at a level of two inches above the top of the rail. Ordinarily the inspector watches the running gear as it approaches but if he wants to take a second look he can turn around and glance through the opposite window. Floodlights sharply illuminate all equipment beneath the car.

In a pit at each side of the track there is an inspector who watches the wheels and trucks. These pits are glass-enclosed to prevent dirt from falling in the eyes of the inspector. Between the edge of the pit and the rail a mirror enables the inspector to watch for cracks in wheel flanges and possible flaws in journal boxes.

These side pits form the foundation walls for two individual inspection houses which are 22 feet high and six feet by 12 feet, the 12 feet being parallel with the rails. In the space in the upper section of each structure a car man looks through an opening, making an inspection of car roofs, running boards, grab irons and brake wheels.

When any of the five men on duty at this inspection station see a defect they use "talk-back" loud-speakers to announce the defect. The car foreman on the ground then marks the car and determines whether or not it must be switched to the repair tracks. If so, he informs the car-retarder foreman at the crest office, and he changes the switch list and informs the retarder operators accordingly.

About 100 feet in advance of the inspection pits there is a device which is actuated by any defective equipment hanging below standard clearance where it might strike the glass of the inspection pit. When this detector operates, a red lamp is lighted in the pit to warn the inspector to leave the pit. A special alarm is also given on the control panel in the office of the retarder foreman at the crest. He then uses his radio and signals to direct the engineman to stop the string of cars being pushed.

The Diesel-electric switching locomotives in the Pocatello yard are equipped with radios, which operate on two frequencies, the selection being made by the position of a toggle switch on the panel in the cab. These two frequencies represent two fixed stations, one of which is the yard office and the other is the building at the crest of the hump which is occupied by the retarder yardmaster and the switch foreman.

On the desk of the yardmaster in the yard office building near the departure yard there is a panel by means of which the yardmaster can connect his microphone and loud-speaker to any one of the 60 talk-back speakers, located at various places throughout the yard where men are working. On the desk of the switching foreman in the building at the crest there is a panel with indication lamps and toggle switches for the control of the two-way talk-back intercommunication between this office and the men in the car inspection pits, as well as the men in the three car-retarder towers. Also included in this system is a large outdoor speaker by means of which the foreman can issue instructions to the men who uncouple cars. The radio equipment here makes possible two-way conversation with the engineman in the locomotive which is pushing cars. The foreman, further, has a lever for controlling the signals which direct the pushing operation. Green indicates "push at normal speed"—about four miles per hour—while yellow indicates "push slower." Red, of course, is for *stop*, and flashing red for "back."

An important part of this arrangement is the fact that exact duplicates of these signal-control levers, radio equipment, and talk-back panels are located on the desk of the retarder yard-master, who has his office on the second floor of the crest build-ing, directly above the office in which the switch foreman works. This duplication was provided so that the retarder yardmaster can direct operation of crews when they are in the receiving yard, and also that he can speak directly to the car inspectors and the men in the retarder control towers, as well as to the foreman.

When the yardmaster wants to talk to the foreman of a switch crew he operates his panel key corresponding to the talk-back location nearest the crew. He presses his foot switch and calls the name of the foreman into his microphone; then releases his foot switch. If within 75 feet of the talk-back the foreman can hear the call, and the talk-back device will pick up his reply when he is 25 to 40 feet away from it. When the conversation is finished the yardmaster returns the key, corresponding to that talk-back location, to its normal position. If, however, the fore-man being called does not answer, the yardmaster connects his microphone to a set of three large "paging" speakers, located in the general area where the foreman should be. The paging speakers are located on 50-foot poles and can be heard several hundred feet. When the foreman hears his name booming out he goes to the nearest talk-back to answer.

When a yard foreman wants to call the yardmaster he pushes a button on the mast of a talk-back speaker. This sounds a buzzer and lights a lamp adjacent to the key corresponding to that field location. To answer the call the yardmaster throws that key and steps on his foot switch. Thus this loud-speaker system permits the yardmaster to keep in touch with activities throughout the yard, and to issue instructions as they are required. This yard-master, however, does not have supervision of the operation of the classification yard, this work being under the direction of the retarder yardmaster, who is located in the second floor of the building at the crest of the hump.

To keep the classification yard in operation as much of the time as possible two or more yard crews may be assigned to the work of pushing cars out of the receiving yard and over the hump to the classification tracks. Each of these crews consists of a foreman, an engineman, a fireman, and one or more men to throw switches, pull pins, etc. As each string of cars is ready for classification, the foreman of the crew involved goes to the office of the building on top of the hump and takes charge of the operation.

While trains are on their way to Pocatello from the last "in-advance" subdivision point, teletype equipment is used to transmit information concerning the consist of the train. This is received on a reperforator tape printer in the general telegraph office at Pocatello. The operator at the telegraph office runs each tape through a tape transmitter which operates page-type printers located in the retarder yardmaster's office in the second floor of the building at the crest of the classification yard, and also in each of the three retarder control towers and the general yardmaster's office. The printer in the retarder yardmaster's office makes two copies. He marks these lists to indicate the cuts of cars and the tracks to which they are to be classified. One copy of this list goes to the switch foreman of the crew that is to push the train onto the hump so that this foreman can direct his pin-puller. Also, the retarder yardmaster uses the intercommunication system to direct the men in the retarder towers to mark their lists to indicate the cuts and tracks.

An underground pneumatic tube was installed in the Pocatello yard to carry waybills from an office in the receiving yard to the yard office, a distance of 8,800 feet. A cartridge enclosing the waybills is pushed through the tube by air pressure, the movement being aided by pumping air out of the other end of the tube. About three minutes are required to transmit a cartridge.

The steel carrier tube is four inches in diameter. It is polished inside and was assembled from 20-foot lengths with square ends. Joints were made with six-inch sleeves, using a sealing compound. To reduce the possibility of moisture collecting in the tube it is enclosed in a fiber casing, impregnated with asphalt. The joints are taped and sealed. Where the tube passes under a track both the tube and casing are run through an eight-inch steel pipe. The tube is located a minimum of 30 inches below the surface of the ground. In order to repair defects quickly 14 manholes were installed.

The Pocatello yard is floodlighted throughout. Five 100-foot steel towers are located as required. Each tower has from nine to ten or more 1,500-watt floodlight units. Two towers near the crest illuminate the area down the incline through the switches and retarders. Other towers at the far end of the classification tracks illuminate this area so the retarder men can see where the cars are going. Floodlights located on buildings or special poles light the repair tracks, oil stations and other points. Illumination at ground level in the retarder area is 0.5 foot-candles and in the classification track area from 0.1 to 0.2 foot-candles.

Two important facilities in the yard are a 150-ton Fairbanks-Morse track scale and a 680-barrel tank for fuel oil to service the Diesel-electric switch engines.

The new Pocatello yard was constructed under the jurisdiction of W. C. Perkins, chief engineer of the Union Pacific, and J. A. Bunjer, now assistant chief engineer, who was resident engineer on the project. Installation of signals, power switch machines and retarders was under the direct supervision of L. D. Dickinson, general signal engineer, and G. R. Van Eaton, superintendent of telegraph, had charge of the design and installation of the communication facilities.

The Pocatello yard of yesterday served its purpose and old-time boomers remember it well. But times have changed. The boomer is gone with the chuffing steam switch engine to that realm of memory, the railroad Valhalla, while the Union Pacific has built at Pocatello, Idaho, a living monument to the Railroads of Today.

North Platte Yard

The second big modern retarder yard completed by the Union Pacific in 1948 was the one at North Platte, Nebraska. This yard follows the same general pattern as the Pocatello yard just described.

North Platte is 281 miles west of Omaha, Nebraska, on the UP's double-track main line. Previously, the yard facilities there consisted of 20 tracks on which cars were classified by the conventional flat-switching method. The new yard is five miles long and is divided into four major sections—a receiving yard, the incline, the classification yard, and a departure yard. It is designed for classifying both eastward and westward traffic.

Construction of the North Platte yard was in line with the UP's policy of modernizing its facilities and of consolidating classification work at fewer terminals, reducing detention and permitting an increase in the average tons per train. With respect to eastward movements, the classification of traffic at North Platte for the Council Bluffs, Iowa, and Kansas City, Missouri, gateways, and further classifying of cars for delivery to connecting lines, has resulted in reducing switching at the latter points and expediting deliveries to connecting roads.

In handling westward traffic at North Platte separate classifications are made for Colorado, the Southwest, the West and the Northwest, thereby reducing the amount of switching required at other terminals.

One of the most notable features of the yard is its network of communications, which would astound our old-time railroad man. A teletype system links the general yardmaster's office, the retarder yardmaster's tower, the three control towers, and the offices of the Pacific Fruit Express, located at the yard. Switch lists are transmitted by teletype from Grand Island, Nebraska, for trains from the East, from Hastings, Nebraska, for trains from the South, from Cheyenne, Wyoming, for trains from the West, and from Julesburg, Colorado, for trains from Colorado. These switch lists are received in the general tele-

74

graph office at North Platte on typing reperforators and are re-transmitted to various points in the yard.

This intercommunication system is truly amazing. It includes for the yardmaster's use 110 two-way, talk-back Racon speakers located at advantageous points throughout the yard. In connection with this system there are 23 Western Electric paging speakers divided into four groups covering various sections of the yard.

A separate intercommunicating and paging system is operated from the retarder yardmaster's tower. This system embodies four Racon speakers, two at each end of the classification yard, and four Western Electric paging speakers, two of which are placed at each end of the classification yard. A third intercommunication system provides a hook-up between the general yardmaster's office, the retarder yardmaster's tower, the three control towers for the classification yard, the locker rooms, and the inspection pit on the approach to the crest.

Eight Diesel switch engines at the yard are equipped with Motorola two-channel, two-way radio apparatus. For communicating with these locomotives there are two fixed radio stations. One of these, KBVH, is located in the retarder yardmaster's tower, with a triple skirt antenna mounted on the top of the tower. In the other fixed radio station, KBVI, the controls are located in the tower of the general yardmaster's office.

The antenna for this station is mounted on a 100-foot light tower about 200 feet from the yard office, and the radio equipment is contained in a steel case at the base of the tower. By manipulating a switch on the panel of the radio set in each locomotive the set may be made to operate on the frequency of either of the radio stations, depending on whether the locomotive is working under the supervision of the retarder yardmaster or the general yardmaster.

Eleven 100-foot steel light towers illuminate the incline, classification, and departure yards for night operations. The capacity of the North Platte yard, which is five miles in length overall, is 4,200 cars, divided into a 1,200-car receiving yard, a 1,400-car classification yard and a 1,600-car departure yard.

Aspen Tunnel

The Union Pacific's first Aspen Tunnel, a single-track 5,900-foot bore through a spur of the Uintah Mountains, a part of the Wasatch Range, was completed in 1901. The second Aspen Tunnel, built to eliminate a tight-throated bottleneck in the UP's 1,026-mile double-track main line between Omaha, Nebraska, and Salt Lake City, Utah, is scheduled for completion in 1949.

For close to 50 years the road was needle-threading east and westbound trains through the old Aspen Tunnel by control, but at about the time these lines will appear in print another Aspen Tunnel will be carrying double-track traffic through its 6,700-foot bore. By that time some 187,000 cubic yards of shale and sandstone will have been removed, 53,000 cubic yards of lining concrete poured, and 5,000 tons of reinforcing steel will be in, the rail laid—and that will be about the last of $8,000,000, the price of this new Aspen tunnel.

In these pages we will look at a river being "sidetracked" on the New York Central, a bridge being built on the Santa Fe, the ironing out of the right-of-way on the Great Northern, and here we'll examine briefly a little of the detail of driving a tunnel —the longest tunnel on the Union Pacific.

Aspen Tunnel is located between the stations of Aspen and Altamont, just east of Evanston, Wyoming, at which point the right-of-way reaches a little better than a 7,000-foot elevation and goes through the mountain around 460 feet below the rim. The new tunnel is north of and roughly parallel to the old tunnel.

This is pretty rough country and was tough country in the old days, with many pitched battles between citizens and desperadoes. In fact, in one of these battles the *Frontier Index*, a newspaper which followed the building of the Union Pacific, was destroyed in the notorious town of Bear River.

Summers are cool, up there, and winter snows often block the road to Evanston. Before the tunnel was started a town of sorts had to be built, including living quarters, mess halls, shops, first-aid station, construction offices, and facilities to take care of a trailer village. An old passenger coach was even provided for a school room, with desks in place of seats.

Twelve miles of road had to be built and a lot of equipment moved in. When the tunnel gangs were ready to attack the mountain, the equipment included a three-deck drill carriage, called a "Jumbo," two mucking machines, four narrow-gauge electric locomotives, two narrow-gauge Diesel locomotives, 45 narrow gauge muck cars, two drag lines, one standard-gauge, 20-ton gas locomotive, a 840-horsepower stationary Diesel power plant, three stationary air compressors, a portable air compressor, bulldozers, a fleet of trucks, machine and blacksmith shop equipment, and a mountain of explosives, drills and shovels.

The work went ahead 24 hours a day, six days a week. A tunnel bore progresses in "bites." The Jumbo is trundled to the tunnel face and drillers nip out "pigeonholes." Into these explosives are tamped. Then the "shooting" begins. The number of shots varies, but generally the objective is to loosen the face to a depth of six or seven feet. After the shooting, the muckers move in and the loose rock and earth is raked back and funneled into the dump cars by a mucking machine. A narrow-gauge track leads out to a dump half a mile or so from the tunnel mouth.

Shoring up the roof and sides of the tunnel with heavy timbers and steel ribs follows closely on the work of the men attacking the tunnel face. Then comes the installation of concrete forms, the placing of reinforcing steel; then the pouring of the cement.

Finally there is the laying of the track, the spiking down of the steel, and a train goes rumbling through. And No. 6 of the Union Pacific's 14-point postwar modernization program has been checked off. This railroad's traffic vice president, Ambrose Seitz, is also one of this country's top traffic experts, and is a real go-getter all the way. So it is no wonder the U.P. handles the volume of business they do.

CHAPTER VIII

WESTERN MARYLAND

A Railroad of Today

The Western Maryland is one of the great railroads of America—not great in miles of track and gleaming glamour trains, but great as a champion is great in his division. The Western Maryland is a road of brawn. It is a freight railroad and shows on its emblem the picture of a locomotive and freight cars, and the words "Fast Freight Line."

Throughout the United States too little is known of the Western Maryland, unfortunately, and not enough by the railroad fraternity of the country. The Western Maryland operates 1,260 miles of track—717 miles of main track, 110 miles of second track and 453 miles of sidings—through the states of Maryland, Pennsylvania and West Virginia. It is a highly strategic road, and during World War II one of the largest ordnance plants in the East was built adjacent to its rails.

Five thousand people work for the Western Maryland. The payroll is around a million and one-half dollars per month. During an average day, the Western Maryland handles over 2,000 cars, carrying every commodity under the sun, from toothpicks to great steel girders 285 feet in length. The road owns a fleet of 12,000 cars of every description. Due to varied operating conditions, ranging from water level to the heaviest mountain grades, the Western Maryland has 230 locomotives of various classes.

One of the finest operating men I have ever known is at the head of the operating department of the Western Maryland, and the road is maintained superbly by the chief engineer and a well-trained force. The track and roadbed are excellent in every respect, as they have to be to carry safely both heavy mountain traffic and the high-speed manifest trains.

The earnings of the road are remarkably high and, fortunately, it is blessed with very little passenger traffic. However, the passenger trains it does operate are first-class in every respect, serving the needs of the line and its communities, some fine towns and cities, in an excellent manner. The Western Maryland family has over 5,200 members and it maintains offices in the major cities throughout the country to give better service to its patrons and to secure business for the road.

The right-of-way of the Western Maryland includes the water-level route west out of the Port Covington Terminal in Baltimore, Maryland, and ranges upwards to the heaviest of mountain grades, some of which are 3 per cent in the Alleghenies, and at one point even 3.75 per cent.

Rail in the main track ranges from ninety to one hundred and thirty-two pounds, with an average of 102.31 pounds. Because of its amazingly fine clearances, the Western Maryland is able to handle any type of high and wide load, a fact that proved invaluable during World War II when the road played a prominent and able part in the war effort. All of the main traffic divisions of the line employ complete automatic block signals of the latest type. A great many spring switches are used and a large number of the open telegraph offices are provided with high-speed train order stands. All bridges of the road are maintained in A-1 shape and they were built to take care of all motive power in operation anywhere on the line.

An outstanding feature of the Western Maryland is the fact that its power was selected for special jobs. Each class of locomotives was designed to handle a certain type of load in a certain district, with the result that their performance is the apex of perfection.

Motive Power

Beside the eastward coal movement from the Pennsylvania and West Virginia fields into the port of Baltimore and also east to Lurgan, Pennsylvania, where connection is made with the Reading, the Western Maryland operates a great fleet of redball freight trains. Among the most famous of this fleet we find the WM-1's, WM-2's, WM-3's and the WM-4's east and westward into Baltimore, as well as the CSD (Central States Dispatch) 94 and 97 connections from the Baltimore & Ohio at Cherry Run and the Reading at Rutherford. This train operates over the Western Maryland tracks, Cherry Run to Lurgan, thence has trackage rights over the Reading to Rutherford.

A large amount of manifest freight is also received from the Pittsburgh and Lake Erie at Dickerson Run, Pennsylvania, their yard at Connellsville and from the Pittsburgh and West Virginia at Bowest, Pennsylvania, the name of their yard there.

These trains then go booming over the Alleghenies to Cumberland behind 12 fine examples of the 4-6-6-4 type of coal-burning locomotive. They then move behind great 4-8-4 fast freight engines from Cumberland to Rutherford through Hagerstown, or from Cumberland to Baltimore.

The Western Maryland owns the most powerful 2-10-0 Decapod type locomotives in the United States. These engines have a tractive effort of 96,300 pounds. They also boast the largest coal and water capacity tenders ever used on these locomotives. These work-horse engines handle some of the coal trains through the mountains. They are also assigned to some of the manifest trains operating between Hagerstown and Port Covington over the Blue Ridge Mountain grades.

Another high rating that we have to give to the Western Maryland is for their 40 Consolidation 2-8-0, Class H-9 locomotives. They have 23-ton coal capacity tenders and 15,000-gallon water tanks. These astonishing engines have a tractive power of 71,500 pounds. They weigh 287,910 pounds on the drivers. Driving wheels are 61-inch. They carry a steam pressure of 220 pounds. It is a lot of engine for a 2-8-0.

These locomotives, together with an additional 20 of the H-8 Class, which have a tractive effort of 61,000 pounds, are used on mine-run service, mine pick-up work and on divisions with great curvature. This power, even with 9,500-gallon tanks and 14-ton coal capacity tenders, is able to negotiate 30 degree curves. On two of the coal divisions in West Virginia the Western Maryland has the sharpest curves of any Class 1 railroad in the United States.

Mountain Railroading

In searching out railroad information across the United States a writer is constantly being faced by hitherto little known facts and figures that seem almost incredulous. For instance, we learned while preparing the material for this chapter on the Western Maryland that this road hauls the heaviest tonnage of any Class 1 railroad in the United States over a 3 per cent grade. And it is almost certain that this feat is accomplished nowhere else in the world.

This is not a stunt or a once-in-a-lifetime exploit. It is simply a part of a day's work—the night's work. Nightly, trains with 80 loaded cars of coal leave Webster Springs, bound for Elkins, West Virginia, a distance of 105 miles—105 mountain miles. And mountain miles in the West Virginia coal country are tough.

Eighty loaded coal cars! An average train means 5,500 tons. These trains are handled over 3 per cent grades for fourteen miles from Laurel Bank to Spruce, West Virginia. They move from Elkins with various helpers on lesser grades to Haddix, up over the grade to Thomas, which is 2 per cent all of the way, much of it averaging 3 per cent. These work-horse coal drags then top it off with a 3.75 per cent pull for a distance of two miles.

These trains are handled by 800 Class locomotives—Class H-9 —and they are given six helpers over these grades on both divisions. The Western Maryland figures one engine for 800 tons.

Let us ride one of these coal drags out of Elkins.

We are called at 2:30 P.M. We have engine number 823 and 80 cars. 5,565 tons.
We couple onto the train at 2:50.
Leave Elkins at 3:01.

81

Arrive Montrose, 12 miles east, at 3:30, picking up two
helpers to assist us up the 2 per cent grade over Haddix.
Pass Parsons 4:24.
Arrive at Hendricks, the helper station, at 4:40.
Here six helpers are cut in.
We then attack the track from Hendricks to Thomas, a dis-
tance of 11 miles, making the run in one hour and 13
minutes over a wet and slippery rail in the rain.
We arrive at 6:09. One helper continues to Fairfax where
there is another slight grade east of Summit.

This is an excellent, well-planned move. It is much cheaper
to operate trains of this size with this number of locomotives
than to have a lot of light trains clogging up the division and
helper engines running back and forth. The crews are all well-
trained veteran railroaders and their judgment and methods of
train handling are exceptional. I feel that not too much credit
can be given to the Western Maryland for this type of operation,
one of the most difficult in the country and yet one which is accomplished at a profit.

The line between Webster Springs and Cheat Jct. near Bemis
was once a standard gauge lumber road. Now with a good roadbed and 110-pound rail it accomplishes its purpose as a coal
road. The cost of straightening the curves and reducing the
grades, no doubt, would be prohibitive. As it stands, the coal
starts its journey to market in one of the most colorful and
spectacular operations in the nation.

A typical day's coal movement by districts is as follows:

From the Thomas District	173	cars
From the Connellsville District	20	"
From the Georges Creek District	12	"
From Somerset	35	"
From Fairmont	261	"
From Belington	12	"
From Durbin	8	"
Where interchange is made with the C. & O.		
From the Elk River District	124	"
Total	645	cars

Coal loading on some days totals over 1,000 cars and it rarely drops under 500. It provides a fine income for this splendid road, the services of which are vastly appreciated by the coal miners, the producers, and the shippers alike.

It is good to stand beside the rails of the Western Maryland and listen to the cannonading exhausts of those powerful Consolidations moving the coal trains through the mountains. When the last steam locomotive has departed and there is only the memory of their deep-throated chant, the hills will have lost a stout and goodly friend.

Pilots for Pushing Rocks

Unique to the extreme are the pilots on Western Maryland locomotives. These were built to perform adequately the service for which the first "cowcatchers" were designed, but which seldom did more than discourage undue familiarity. The operating department feels that this pilot of theirs is just about the finest thing there is for pushing rocks or some foolhardy motorist off the track before they become tangled with the engine trucks. Beside being able to cope with smaller landslides, the pilots perform well as snowplows.

The Western Maryland fast freight line follows the Potomac River from Hagerstown to Cumberland on the opposite bank from the rails of the Baltimore & Ohio. The beauty of this Potomac Valley is unequaled. From Hagerstown to Baltimore the Western Maryland is served by two lines. The line from Highfield, Maryland, to Emory Grove, Maryland, which crosses the highest point of the Blue Ridge, and the line from Highfield to Porter's Pennsylvania, thence to Emory Grove which is somewhat longer, but the eastbound traffic has the advantage of more favorable grades. The northern line passes through the historic city of Gettysburg and also serves the metropolis of York, Pennsylvania.

The manifest trains are handled by the new J-1 Class 4-8-4 locomotives, which are equipped with roller bearings. Like other engines of the road they serve a definite purpose in the scheme of things, and their handling of the red ball trains is superb.

Port Covington Terminal

The Port Covington Terminal at Baltimore is one of the finest in the country. Baltimore has never had the recognition it deserves in connection with its fine harbor facilities. Other ports consistently get more acclaim, but it would be hard to find better deep-water docking accommodations for ocean-going steamships than those provided in Baltimore's natural, ice-free harbor.

The Western Maryland's Port Covington Terminal is located along the Patapsco River in Baltimore Harbor, adjacent to Hanover and McComas Streets. It is served by a 35-foot channel. The terminal has four merchandise piers with a combined floor area of 486,000 square feet. Three of the piers are modern two-story structures with large-capacity elevators and covered bridges connecting the second floors. The piers are completely equipped with gantry cranes and cargo masts.

The Port Covington Terminal coal pier is capable of transferring a car of coal a minute, with minimum breakage. The bulk cargo pier is equipped with a cantilever gantry crane for transferring ore and other bulk freight from ship to railroad car. It has a fine modern grain elevator with a capacity of 4,000,000 bushels. This elevator is equipped with all of the latest modern facilities for handling grain from and to cars and vessels.

Port Covington Terminal can berth 23 ocean-going vessels at one time. The floor space of the terminal's warehouses reaches the amazing total of 125,000 square feet, a wonderful installation which provides plenty of employment not only for Western Maryland but for the residents of the grand city of Baltimore.

In addition to its merchandise piers and warehouses, the terminal includes a locomotive repair shop, an excellent roundhouse, a car repair yard, track scales, and two transfer bridges. The marine equipment includes nine all-steel car floats, numerous launches, open lighters and scows for use in Baltimore Harbor.

A surprising amount of coal and ore moves through this great waterway. Most certainly this great freight road and its fabulous Baltimore terminal deserves a chapter in the story of American transportation.

The Western Maryland's major car and locomotive shops are maintained at Hagerstown, Maryland. The shops are extremely modern, with up-to-date equipment and complete facilities for handling every type of repair and construction.

I don't know of any railroad in the United States that is more underrated or one that has been so completely overlooked by everyone connected with the industry as the Western Maryland. The Western Maryland is as remarkable a piece of railroad property, from tidewater to the last coal mine spur, as you will find in many a day's journey. You judge a railroad not only by its plant and its performance but also by its officials. In my opinion, the law and traffic vice-presidents of the Western Maryland rank high. As I pointed out earlier in this chapter, the operating vice-president is a thoroughly capable railroad man. His name is G. R. Haworth.

Eugene S. Williams, president of the Western Maryland, is the type of executive you would expect to find at the head of a perfectly coordinated and completely successful railroad. He has left no stone unturned to provide for the well-being of the road, its shippers, its stockholders, and its employees.

There is something else that goes into the fabric of a well-ordered railroad, and that is its personnel. It would be hard to find a better trained or more loyal and efficient railroad family than the men and women of the Western Maryland.

In conclusion. Size and miles of track are not everything in this American railroad picture. More than anything else, there must be timber. Quality. The Western Maryland has it, and through it has achieved greatness. The Western Maryland, definitely, is a "Railroad of Today."

CHAPTER IX

THE POSTWAR EMPIRE BUILDER

First of the New Streamliners

There is one feature of the modern trains that we particularly like and that is the reproduction on the walls of some cars of scenes that tell the story of the country through which the train is speeding.

On board the new Empire Builder we find Indian pictures by the late Charles M. Russell, once a Montana cowboy, and one of the really great Western artists. Thus while enjoying the comfort and conveniences of an ultra-modern train we are given a glimpse into the past, as we take in a page from the country's colorful history. There is even romance in the columns of this Great Northern timetable when we run down the names there—Cutbank, Gunsight, Sundance, Fort Piegan, Triple Divide, Spotted Robe, Bison, Rising Wolf, Blacktail, Singleshot.

This is the land of the Empire Builder, the nation's first de luxe postwar-built transcontinental streamliner, one of the famous train fleet that provides daily 45-hour passenger service between Chicago and Seattle-Portland.

Five trains, each having a consist of 12 cars and Diesel power, costing $7,000,000, began operation over the Great Northern lines on February 23, 1947, as was pointed out in another chapter. This inaugurated a 45-hour service that clipped 13½ hours from the best previous schedule on this 2,211-mile run. When new equipment scheduled for delivery in the fourth quarter of 1949 is received each train of the Empire Builder fleet will have 14 cars instead of 12.

The Empire Builders were the first postwar-designed transcontinental trains to carry coaches; also to these trains were assigned the first sleeping cars built and delivered to any railway after the war ended. The bright orange and dark green trains offer a variety of luxurious accommodations for the traveler in both sleepers and coaches.

The consist of each train includes a baggage-mail car; one 60-seat coach; three 48-seat coaches; a coffee shop-lounge car; a diner; four sleeping cars; and an observation-lounge. Accommodations provide for 307 passengers. To say that the cars were built by the Pullman-Standard Car Manufacturing Company is to say that they are unexcelled in quality, workmanship, and styling.

Many unusual features have been built into these trains of the Empire Builder, which were the first to utilize duplex-roomette sleeping cars. The Pullman-Standard people built an experimental car of this type before the war and it was thoroughly tested in wartime service.

An ingenious staggering of the duplex roomettes affords private-room accommodation at only slighty more than the cost of a lower berth. The Empire Builders also offer double bedroom, drawing room and open section facilities. Each of two cars on each train provides four open sections, eight single-occupancy duplex roomettes, and four bedrooms.

In addition to the conventional running hot and cold water, Empire Builder sleepers were the first to have ice water on tap in all rooms, including the duplex roomettes. The bedrooms on the sleepers were the first to have the postwar wardrobe at aisle side for hanging clothes, etc.

The three day-night coaches in each train have chaise-longue reclining seats. Leg-rests fold down from the back of the seat ahead, providing added comfort and reclining position when desired. The double-paned "picture" windows have a vacuum space between outer and inner glass, providing fog-proof view under all weather conditions. This further aids in insulating against outside temperature, and cold or heat radiation from window panes is eliminated.

The coffee shop car offered an innovation in the form of a

lunch counter seating ten persons, and a lounge seating ten. Each train's consist includes a complete dining car seating 36.

Through a "dinner-by-reservation" service, Empire Builder passengers are saved the annoyance of standing in line for the evening meal in the diner. During the afternoon the passenger representative asks travelers to name their choice of meal time; then each receives a card for presentation in the dining car at the hour chosen. You have your ticket and you have your seat, without delay or inconvenience—another service of the Great Northern.

The interior decoration of each of the Empire Builders reflects the coloring and the scenic beauty of the Northwest. Dining car draperies, for instance, are of the blues and the greens found in the lakes of Glacier National Park, combined with the tans and darker hues of the Cascade and the Rocky Mountains. The dainty colorings of the native flowers found in the region are variously expressed in the car interiors, and throughout the train runs the motif of the Blackfeet Indians.

The china service for each dining car is decorated with Glacier Park scenes, including reproductions of the wild flowers in natural colors. This is one of the little touches that goes to make the Empire Builder more than just another de luxe train, and it becomes a train of distinction and individuality. The road packages the beauty and the tradition and the background of this Northwest country and brings it to the traveler aboard this great train.

The kitchen equipment and dining car accessories—china, silverware, glassware and linens—added $10,000 to the cost of each diner, but it was money well invested.

Murals reproduced from original portraits of the Blackfeet Indians make up the panels of the observation lounge. These were done by Winold Reiss. Here also are reproductions of the work of Charles M. Russell.

In the opening chapter we spoke of "John Jones," the train passenger agent, aboard our *Mountaineer*. We find an added crew member of similar station and attributes on the Empire Builder. This uniformed passenger representative of the Great

Northern announces important train information and indicates points of scenic and historic interest along the route. The primary function of the passenger representative always is to assist travelers. His voice is heard frequently over the train's public address system.

The Empire Builder is equipped with the modern electrically-controlled brakes and brake-shoe control equipment which gives graduated maximum braking ratio at all speeds and eliminates wheel sliding.

The cars have a new type folding vestibule step with lights at foot-level to provide a clear view of the steps at night.

Safety features include an oscillating red light on the rear of the train which cuts in automatically when the train speed drops below a certain point. It also operates while the train is standing. The locomotives have oscillating white beams, visible over a considerable distance, which serve as a warning when the train is approaching stations and crossings and also provide protection when safety is involved.

Radio, of course, is part of the train equipment. Also, train communication between the engineer and conductor's office.

The exterior of the streamlined Empire Builder has a background of dark green. A broad window band of brilliant orange, and a narrower band of the same color edged in yellow, below the windows, provide a striking combination, which is set off by a stripe of silver at the car bottom. And, of course, there is Old Bill up ahead, leading the Empire Builder fleet.

The power on the Empire Builders is an Electro-Motive Diesel, as has been indicated before, and has been since it was inaugurated in February, 1947. Five two-unit 4,000-horsepower locomotives handle the five trains between St. Paul and Seattle. A fresh Diesel is coupled on No. 2, eastbound, and wheels through to St. Paul. This locomotive then takes out that day's No. 1, westbound, for Seattle. Upon arrival in Seattle at 8 in the morning, it is readied for the Empire Builder leaving at 3 in the afternoon. This locomotive pulls No. 2 to Havre, Montana, and is changed out.

On the electrified segment in the Cascades the electric locomotive pulls the trains but the Diesel stays on.

The Empire Builder, with a schedule of 45 hours between
Chicago and Seattle, provides full passenger comfort and convenience, but it is not an extra-fare train. Through its connections at Spokane, Washington, Portland, Oregon, is also afforded
the same 45-hour service as Seattle. Two cars of the streamliner
are dropped at Spokane to move over the rails of the Spokane,
Portland & Seattle Railway to Portland. These return to Spokane
to rejoin the streamliner run eastward.

The Oriental Limited

The "Oriental Limited" is one of the proudest name trains in
the colorful history of Western railroading. Honorably dis-
charged in 1931, two years after the Empire Builder began
rolling over the rails of the Great Northern, the Oriental Limited
has returned to again take its place among great transcontinental
trains.

The Oriental Limited began operation way back in 1905 in
the empire-building era of James J. Hill, providing an important
link with the trade of the Orient. New equipment in 1924 made
it the finest train of its day. The name of the Oriental Limited
designates the train fleet which, since 1929, has operated between
Seattle and Chicago as the Empire Builders.

The Oriental Limited was brought back to give transcontinental travelers on this route their choice of two daily depar-
tures, and also to provide added service to lovely Glacier Park.

Now let us take a look at the ever-changing picture as it stands
as of late 1948.

Purchase by the Great Northern of 66 new, lightweight passenger cars at an estimated cost of $8,500,000, was authorized, and
brought expenditures for new passenger and freight cars and
Diesel locomotives, authorized in 1948, to $37,500,000.

The railway's directors at about this time also declared a
dividend of $2 per share, payable December 10, 1948, to stock-

holders of record November 10. The directors indicated the intention to pay future dividends, if declared, on a quarterly basis instead of a semi-annual basis, which had been the practice previously.

The acquisition of additional modern passenger equipment was encouraged by the consistently heavy patronage of the new Empire Builder, F. J. Gavin, president of Great Northern, explained. "The public acceptance of the streamlined service between Chicago and Seattle has been extremely gratifying," Mr. Gavin stated at the time he announced the authorization of the new equipment, "and the railway management believes the patronage of the Empire Builder clearly justifies purchase of additional modern passenger equipment for the expansion of streamliner service in its territory."

At this writing it was expected that the new equipment would not be available until sometime in 1951. The new equipment will include 30 sleeping cars and six each of coaches, dining, coffee shop, observation, baggage, and baggage-mail cars. Existing plans call for the replacement of the cars of the Empire Builder with entirely new equipment. The Empire Builder equipment is expected to be used to streamline the Oriental Limited, at this time pulled by Diesel power but with standard cars.

The plans now outlined calling for a 14-car consist in each of the new trains are as follows: One baggage-mail car, four coaches, one coffee shop-lounge car, one diner, six sleepers and an observation car. Details, of course, in this early stage are not settled, depending, more or less, on the relaxation of the jam in passenger equipment construction.

When the time comes for the Oriental Limited to inherit the current Empire Builder equipment, the Oriental will get the 12-car Empire Builder consist, plus two sleepers on order for each. This will mean a basic 14-car Oriental Limited, but it will not be a tight consist. At times it will get up to 17 or 18 cars as the Oriental has had before. However, there is nothing absolutely final about some of this, but this is how the trend seems now.

The remarkable part of the Empire Builder fleet operation, considering the rugged country traversed and the severity of the winter weather on occasion, is the fact that in the first year of operation it turned in a 98 per cent on-time terminal arrival performance. A good record has been maintained to the present late 1948.

The first year the five trains traveled 1,300,487 miles between Chicago and Seattle-Portland. 160,905 revenue passengers were carried the initial year of a streamlined operation, 76,886 rode on No. 1, the westbound Empire Builder, and 84,019 rode No. 2, the eastbound.

Public acceptance of the Empire Builder has been outstanding, as clearly shown by the patronage figures. Reservations are made for both Pullman and coach space on the trains, and very frequently since their inauguration they have been unable to handle all the patrons who wanted to ride. This was particularly true, of course, during the summer vacation seasons. However, it was also very often true at other times during the year.

Demand for space on the new Empire Builder generally has been very heavy. The earnings for the streamlined fleet have been substantially better than for the old-type trains, and the Great Northern officials consider the investment definitely worth while.

CHAPTER X

THE ROCK ISLAND STORY

"Planned Progress"

The character of a railroad is a reflection of the character and ability of its leaders. The triumphant battle waged by the Rock Island in achieving its present place among the railroads of to-day was the result of a "planned progress" program by a great operating man.

This man came to the Rock Island as chief operating officer in 1936. The road at that time had been in receivership for three years. In 1942 he was made chief executive officer and was elected president of the system at the termination of the road's reorganization proceedings.

In 1936 the Rock Island was in bad shape. Weeds were literally growing between the rails of as run-down a railroad as you would find in a long time. The Chicago, Rock Island & Pacific Railroad Company was a hay-wire outfit—all of the 8,100 shabby miles of it.

The first requisite in the rehabilitation of the road in 1936 was a long-range improvement plan. Plant and equipment had to be modernized if the railroad was to make the grade. It didn't seem then that the road could ever hope to become really great again.

When you start remodeling a tumble-down piece of property you must have money. A scrap drive was begun, and certainly there is no more lucrative place to look for scrap than around a run-down railroad. Gangs cut up obsolete locomotives, junking the useless items and reclaiming other parts to repair the newer locomotives. That first year netted $1,465,000 from the scrap drive. The next year the scrap brought in $2,579,000.

From that point on the Rock Island story was a veritable American "rags-to-riches" story. The Rock Island very well fitted a term familiar to all railroaders—a "streak of rust." People don't care about riding a streak of rust. The road began laying new rail—2,041 miles of it in the 12-year period ending December 31, 1947. 1,550 miles of reclaimed rail was spiked down. In 1945, because of the constant increase in traffic, the use of 131-pound rail in areas of heaviest traffic density was adopted, and this program is constantly moving ahead.

The first orders for the beginning of the Rock Island's fleet of Rockets were placed in 1936. They went into service between Chicago and Peoria, Illinois, and proved that fast comfortable service could win patronage back from the highways.

However, there was the problem of getting new Diesel power.

Bankers are a cautious lot and they were by no means sold on this new Diesel locomotive, certainly not to the extent of loaning good money to a sad-eyed road in the throes of bankruptcy. Here Electro-Motive stepped in. Electro-Motive had just turned out the first locomotive in their new La Grange plant—a 600-horsepower Diesel switcher—and the Rock Island proved exactly the demonstration field they were looking for, a struggling road, searching for ways and means of rebuilding its fences.

The Electro-Motive division of General Motors Corporation soon convinced the Rock Island that their new kind of motive power would pay for itself. Full of hope and having confidence in the future of the Diesel, the chief executive of the road put the matter up to the trustees. Once they had been sold on the idea, they hustled out and scraped together enough money to make a 10 per cent down payment. The General Motors Acceptance Corporation—best known for its financing of private automobiles—took care of the balance on the installment basis.

The Rock Island placed an order for ten 600-horsepower switch engines and six 1200-horsepower passenger Diesels for their new Rocket fleet. That's the story of the Diesel and the Rock Island. Today the Rock Island's main line freight and pas-

senger trains are practically all moving behind Diesel locomotives.

The Rock Island story is the story of a man with vision and
determination, a man who saved the road in its darkest hour.
In 1941 the Rock Island showed its first net profit report in 11
years—$4,644,000.

On January 1, 1948, the Rock Island Lines emerged from the
quagmire of bankruptcy, terminating bankruptcy proceedings
instituted in June, 1933. At that time the road had put $100
million into physical improvements and another 35 million dollar program was begun. The road had $58 million cash and a net
working capital of $46,834,000.

Track and Bridge Projects

The Rock Island's improvement program included profile
improvements, the cutting down of grades, the elimination of
curves, and otherwise shortening the line. We will present some
of these projects as an indication of the enormous amount of
work accomplished, starting with the Cimarron Bridge, near
Liberal, Kansas. This great bridge is called the "Sampson of the
Cimarron."

The cost of the Cimarron project was around a million and
one half. The immediate savings are approximately $100,000
annually, or 7 per cent on the investment.

The project involved the construction of 8.43 miles of new
line, which permitted abandoning 11.99 miles of old line. The
ruling grade in each direction was reduced 0.5 per cent, curvature
was reduced 353 degrees, and 113 feet of rise and fall was eliminated. The bridge proper is 1,250 feet long, of modern type.
The distance from rail to streambed is 98 feet. This new structure has eliminated the threat of future washouts, a big factor
in securing dependable rail transport in all weather conditions.

Another project involved a major line change of 15.10 miles
of new construction between Mercer and Mill Grove, Missouri.
The cost ran around two million. It produced a line 1.28 miles

95

shorter, reduced the maximum grade from 1.58 per cent to 0.5 per cent. It reduced the maximum curvature from 6 degrees to 1 degree and 30 minutes.

The improvement has permitted passenger train speeds to be lifted from 40 miles an hour to 90 miles an hour. It makes possible increasing tonnage from 2,400 to 6,300 tons behind a 4,500-horsepower locomotive. The Rock Island uses 4,050-horsepower locomotives, but the mathematical ratio remains the same. Helpers were used in this territory prior to the line change, but they are not required now. The saving in operation is estimated at $175,000, or 8 per cent on the investment.

A line change between Eldon and Perlee, Iowa, involved 20.74 miles of construction, shortening the line 1.95 miles. It reduced an eastward grade of 1.65 per cent to 0.5 per cent, and reduced the curvature from 4 degrees to 1½ degrees. Passenger trains benefit by stepping up from former 55 miles-per-hour speed to 90 miles per hour. Freight train tonnage went from 2,250 to 6,300 tons. The estimated annual savings of $360,000 on this $2,500,000 project earns 14 per cent on the investment.

The Centerville-Paris, Iowa, project involved a segment of line 18.13 miles long. It included a large steel bridge over the Chariton River and two other smaller steel bridges. It shortened the distance 3.87 miles and reduced the maximum grade from 1.0 per cent to 0.5 per cent. The maximum curvature was reduced from 4 degrees to 1 degree, lifting permissible speeds from 55 miles per hour to 99 miles per hour. The project cost about $2,700,000 and produced an annual saving of $413,664, or 15 per cent on the investment.

The Rock Island's planned progress program had for its aim an over-all picture that would have no grade between Chicago and Dalhart, Texas, in excess of 0.5 per cent. In this connection, 16.40 miles of line were ironed out between Paris and Eldon, Iowa, shortening the line 1.43 miles and reducing the eastward grade from 1.4 per cent to 0.5 per cent; also easing the curvature from 4 degrees to 1 degree and 30 minutes. Locomotive tonnage was doubled, as a result, and again passenger train speeds were raised from 55 to 90 miles an hour. For the $1,882,910 spent

96

there was an annual saving in operation of $267,000, or 22 per cent on the investment.

There were other line changes and betterments in this vast program, including changes at Imogene and Fowler, Kansas; also at Herrington, Wellington, Colfax, and the Truman Bridge at Kansas City, constructed jointly with the Milwaukee Railroad, providing a better entrance into and through Kansas City and saving about 30 minutes running time.

In addition to the bridges already mentioned, the Rock Island improvement program included work on the bridge over the Red River at Terral, Oklahoma, the lengthening and strengthening of the bridge over the Canadian River at Bridgeport, Oklahoma, the Mississippi River bridge, near St. Paul, and others. Altogether, bridges in 30 districts were strengthened. The total number of bridges decreased from 5,723 to 5,365, which meant 358 bridges less to maintain. In 1936 the Rock Island had 109 miles of bridges and ten years later only 90 miles of bridges, representing a big saving in maintenance. For instance, open-deck trestles decreased 102,218 feet or 21 miles.

In ten years the Rock Island spent 28 million dollars in new rail, rail relaying and all of the accessories connected with such a project. Eleven million, three hundred eighty-three thousand pre-adzed, pre-bored, and creosoted cross ties with a life expectancy of 30 years were placed in service. This did not include 4,600,000 board feet of switch ties installed.

In the period of which we write, 7,050 miles of track were ballasted, or more than 92 per cent. 660 miles was ballasted with stone, 3,000 miles with gravel, 460 miles with granite, 1,230 with chats and 295 with slag. Chats, as you know, come from the tailings of lead mines. It makes a fine ballast and is used where it will not wash out. It has enough mineral in it to prevent weeds from growing.

Signaling

During the ten-year period of rehabilitation automatic block signals were installed as follows: (Data is not at hand for the year 1946 when important additional improvements were made.)

Herington to Tucumcari (On main California line)	467	miles
Manly to Newport	93	"
Bureau to Peoria	47	"
El Reno to Oklahoma City	23	"
Iowa Falls to Allerton	147	"
Sherwood to Polo	33	"
Miscellaneous Installations	41	"

Centralized Traffic Control

Seven hundred thirty-seven miles of C.T.C. were installed on various parts of the Rock Island System. Some of the principal centralized traffic control installations were made as outlined on the opposite page.

This, now, is something to note. It indicates the general forward-looking attitude of the Rock Island. Other roads have increased the capacity of single-track by C.T.C. installations, but the Rock Island is one of the few roads that have installed C.T.C. on busy double-track lines.

With this double-track installation trains can be run around each other. During certain times of the day traffic might be light in one direction and then both tracks may be used to relieve the congestion on the more heavily traveled tracks.

A positive automatic signal system was installed between Omaha and Limon, in which power switches were not used, but if the traffic warrants the additional expenditure it may be completed into full C.T.C. by adding the power switches at some future time.

This type of signalling was developed for use on medium density lines that cannot support the expense of C.T.C.

Cab signals have been installed in the locomotives operating over the Illinois Division between Chicago and Rock Island.

Also, in connection with modern signalling, the Rock Island is working on experimental installations of electronics, which include radio communication with trains, yard installations, and

Rock Island #507 Twin Star Rocket south of Albert Lea, Minn., with diesel 825 on the Cedar Rapids Division. Photo courtesy Rock Island Lines.

New observation lounge car on the Empire Builder, Great Northern #1 and #2. Decorations stem from the Blackfoot Indians. Courtesy G. N. RR.

Interior of new deluxe lightweight coach in through passenger service on N.Y.C. This is typical of the new coaches on the railroads of today. Courtesy N.Y.C. RR.

New Fiesta dining car with club lounge seats on opposite end from kitchen. Patterned after old Mexico patios. It also contains a bar. Courtesy Rock Island Lines.

On 107 miles of the N&W's Radford Division between Radford and Bristol, CTC coordinates train movements so closely that 50% of the meets are nonstop. Here #45, the westbound Tennessean, passes east end of Glade Spring, Va., hauled by #606, Class J–1, 4–8–4 type.

Western Maryland train WM–2 eastbound Time Freight at Williamsport, Md., waiting to be pushed into Hagerstown up the 1% grade. The engine is Class M–1 4–8–4 type latest of the W.M.'s great motive power fleet. Note the Western Maryland pilot. Courtesy Western Maryland RR.

Center of new dining section on latest twin-unit diners in service on the new Twentieth Century Limited between New York and Chicago. Courtesy N.Y.C. RR.

Coffee-shop lounge of the Great Northern's new Empire Builder for coach passengers feeding ten at the counter and ten in the lounge. Courtesy G. N. RR.

G. N. #442, eastbound manifest freight train descending the 1.6% grade near Chumstick, Washington, running over the electrified portion of the First Subdivision of the Cascade Division. Photo by W. J. Pontin, Railway Photo Service.

S.P. first #824 with new S.P. 4-unit Electro Motive diesel passing Alhambra, Calif., with solid fruit block for the Rock Island at Tucumari and eastern markets. Courtesy Southern Pacific RR.

New Rock Island Line testing laboratory recently completed in the 47th Street Yard in Chicago. In this laboratory over 60,000 items are tested before, during, and after using on the railroad's 9000-mile system. Courtesy Rock Island Lines.

CTC machine at Clifton Forge, Virginia, governing movements between Staunton and Clifton Forge on the Mountain Subdivision of the Clifton Forge Division.

WM—3 Western Maryland Time Freight attacking the Alleghenies on the 1.75% grade, 3 miles west of Cumberland going around Helmsteder's Curve with I—2, 2—10—0 type helper on the Elkins Division. Courtesy Western Maryland RR.

Upper and lower duplexes which cost only a trifle more than a lower berth in service on many new lightweight trains today. Courtesy G. N. RR.

The C & O new coal-burning steam turbine locomotive being coaled and watered at special coaling stations that were built to service these engines at Clifton Forge, Va., and Hinton, W. Va. Courtesy C & O RR.

CHICAGO, ROCK ISLAND AND PACIFIC RAILROAD COMPANY

C.T.C.—C.R.I.&P. As of January 1, 1949	Miles of Road	of Track	Cab Signaling Blue Island, Ill. to Rock Island, Ill.
Blue Island, Illinois, to			166 Miles of Road
Joliet, Illinois	24.15	48.30	332 " " Track
Rockdale, Illinois, to			
W. of Morris, Illinois	20.20	40.40	
Spring Valley, Illinois, to			
Bureau, Illinois	12.80	25.60	
E. of Atkinson, Illinois, to			
Silvis, Illinois	24.00	48.00	
Eldon, Iowa, to Polo, Mo.	161.00	185.60	
*Polo, Mo. to Birmingham, Mo.	37.70	75.40	
*Birmingham, Mo. to Air Line			
Junction, Kansas City, Mo.	4.45	8.90	
**Manly Iowa, to Albert Lea,			
Minnesota	28.17	28.17	
Faribault, Minn. to Comus, Minn.	6.52	6.52	
Inver Grove, Minnesota, to			
Newport, Minn.	1.8	1.8	
Little Rock, Arkansas, to			
North Little Rock, Ark.	.78	.78	
***Briark, Arkansas, to			
Hulbert, Arkansas	4.33	4.33	
Hot Springs Junction, Arkansas,			
to Biddle, Arkansas	1.2	1.2	
Herington, Kansas, to			
El Reno, Oklahoma	231.0	231.0	
Fort Worth, Texas (Dalwor Jct.)			
to Dallas, Texas (North Jct.)	31.6	31.6	
TOTAL	589.70	737.60	

* Joint with Milwaukee
** Joint with M. & St. L.
*** Joint with Missouri Pacific

devices that tell an operator 100 miles away the arrival and departure of trains.

Radio, of course, has been employed by the railroads for communication in yards and on main lines, as well as between head and rear-ends of long freights, for some times. The Rock Island is interested in the further development of radio in railroading, as are all progressive roads.

Shops and Engine Houses—Laboratory

Power for shops at 14 points was converted from steam to electricity, permitting the power plants to be shut down in warm weather when it was not necessary to heat the buildings. Modern machinery was installed at six points, roundhouse stalls and turntables were lengthened to accommodate heavier locomotives, and facilities were installed to care for Diesel locomotives. A new electric shop was installed at Silvis, Illinois, and two 150-ton cranes replaced old 50-ton cranes. The new cranes effected a saving of 10 per cent on the investment, as did the cost of consolidating locomotives and car-repair facilities at Cedar Rapids.

New car-repair and coach servicing facilities, including a new car-washer, were installed at Chicago. A new research laboratory was erected on 47th Street in Chicago. This modern laboratory was both for making tests and conducting basic research.

During the Rock Island's period of rehabilitation, 111 steam locomotives were modernized, including 18 of the 4,000 Class Mountain-Type passenger engines, 65 of the 5,000 Type 4-8-4 locomotives, and 28 (K-37) Mikado Type freight locomotives. Lightweight side-rods, roller bearings and other improvements created the following results:

Cost of repairing 4,000 Type locomotives equipped with roller bearings produced a saving of 48%. In the case of the 5,000 Type, the saving was 29%.

The monthly mileage run was very substantially increased:

	Friction Bearings	Roller Bearings
4000 Class	7,000	14,000
5000 Class	5,000	7,000
K67 Mikado	4,300	7,000

The above figures speak for themselves.

The Rock Island Lines testing laboratory is in line with the road's planned progress. High train speeds and greater emphasis on Diesel power have brought new importance to high quality fuel, and lubrication oils and greases. A department of the laboratory is devoted to their study.

Quality and uniformity of protective coverings used on equipment are of the utmost importance. Part of the laboratory is devoted to the testing of paints, varnishes, lacquers, and other protective coatings under conditions simulating weather extremes of cold, heat, dampness, rain and sunshine.

In the machine tool section of the laboratory various specimens are prepared for physical and chemical tests.

John D. Farrington

John D. Farrington, president of the Chicago, Rock Island & Pacific Railroad Company, was solely responsible for the "planned progress" program that brought greatness to a sadly depleted, wasted, and run-down railroad empire. He not only built up the road's cash assets, he rebuilt the road, as you have seen in these pages, he bought new equipment, new motive power, new trains; he invigorated the personnel with his own spirit and determination.

There isn't much fun railroading on a broken-down stretch of rust. Men and women on the Rock Island today are proud of the road, proud of the things that have been accomplished. John D. Farrington gives much credit to Rock Island railroaders for their part in aiding in the rebirth of this really great system.

Though he is the son of a Great Northern vice-president, Farrington began at the bottom of the railroad ladder as a trackman, slowly working himself up on various railroads to general superintendent for the Burlington, a position he held until he joined the Rock Island in 1936.

When you ride one of the Rock Island's fleet of 20 Diesel-powered streamliners that speed over the western prairies, you will see the result of the efforts John Farrington put into the road.

From the beginning, Farrington's emphasis was on a well-tailored roadbed, reduced grades and curves, heavier rails, and stronger bridges. He hired W. H. Hillis (now vice-president-operations) to do the job. The work was begun and the Rock Island laid the foundation for the now famous "Rockets" and the "Rocket Freights."

Other railroads have been brought back from the "stretch-of-rust" stage, but probably no other railroad was ever in so sad a state as the Rock Island when John Farrington picked up the reins in 1936.

In order that the system may continue to occupy its present high place in the industry, Farrington plans to continue the modernization program, including the purchase of new freight cars and new Diesels.

Other improvements will include yard modernization. An example is the new Armourdale yard near Kansas City, Missouri. This yard has 40 classification tracks, with ten retarders, installed by the Union Switch & Signal Company.

The Armourdale yard will make possible the classification of approximately 4,500 incoming and outgoing freight cars daily. The cost is estimated at about $2,000,000. The improvement is located down a one-half-mile corridor that extends over a distance of five miles just southwest of Kansas City, Kansas.

Radio communications between yard office and switch engines have been installed in principal classification yards and between engines and cabooses on *Rocket Freights*.

Jack Farrington is not related to the author of this book, but it is an honor to bear the name of such a smart and very popular all around railroader.

CHAPTER XI

UNION SWITCH & SIGNAL COMPANY

Coded Track Circuits Developed

Coded track circuits have made possible the modern signal systems which safeguard today's high speed trains, and they represent one of the most important advances in the history of railway signaling.

The coded track circuit was developed and introduced by the Union Switch & Signal Company. The first installation was placed in service in electrified territory in March, 1933, and in steam service territory in October of that same year. The original or steady-energy track circuit, invented in 1872 and applied to the practical needs of railway signaling by the Union Switch & Signal Company since its organization in 1881, constitutes a safe and reliable medium through which a train may automatically control a signal or other device provided for its protection.

This steady-energy track circuit operated what we know as the automatic block signal. In this system the electric current from a track battery feeds over the rails, energizing a relay at the base of the signal mast and holding the semaphore arm at "clear." When any part of a train is present in the section, or "block," the shunting action of the wheels and axles deprives the track relay of the current and releases the relay. Through this release the signal light or arm is placed at "stop."

When the train leaves the section, or block, the shunt is removed and pick-up energy is restored to the track relay, causing the signal to show "clear," indicating that the section is again vacant.

Signal systems employing track circuits of this steady-energy type have been extensively used by many railroads all over the world, and still are. These systems perform faithfully and well the task assigned to them. Coded track circuits, however, go further, performing magically many functions in train signaling beyond the range of the steady-energy track circuit.

We shall make no attempt to cover all the highly technical aspects of the coded track circuit and its applications, but rather indicate in as simple language as possible what it is and what it accomplishes.

The basis of the coded track circuit is the same combination of elements used in the steady-energy track circuit. It differs from the steady-energy circuit in that the rail current is broken up into recurring pulses to form a code. By using codes of different characters the current in the track rails can be employed not only to detect the presence of a train and protect against broken rails, but also to perform a great variety of other functions which higher train speeds, more powerful locomotives, longer trains, increased traffic density, and other factors demand.

The coded track circuit is a circuit in which the rail current is broken up into recurring pulses to form a code. This is done by a code transmitter, which is a continuously operating electric mechanism installed between the source of current and the track rails and produces in the track circuit a code made up of "on" period energy pulses, separated by "off" period intervals. This system employs a code-following track relay, which picks up during each "on" period of the code and releases during each "off" period; a track-circuit detector relay, which is held picked up continuously during the code-following operations, but which releases if the code-following track relay ceases to follow the code due to the shunting action of a train.

The older steady-energy track circuit and the modern coded track circuit perform the same functions, viz., that of detecting the presence of a train in the track-circuited section. Notwithstanding the similarity of the function, the coded track circuit has certain marked advantages over the steady-energy circuit, and these include: greatly improved sensitivity to train shunting; greater immunity to false operations by foreign currents; and extension of the length of the track circuit which may be reliably operated without the necessity of using cut sections.

Train-detecting operation is only one of the many functions which coded track circuits are designed to perform. When applied to systems of automatic block signaling they are capable of additionally controlling three or more aspects, either or both wayside signals and train-carried cab signals, and of doing this solely through the medium of rail-transmitted energy and without the aid of line wires.

Let us consider the control of a wayside signal in which the signal-code track circuit is amplified to include: (1) continuously-operating coders for supplying the rails with a "clear" (180 pulses per minute) or with an "approach" code (75 pulses per minute); (2) a relay which selects the clear 180 code when the block next in advance is vacant and the approach 75 code when that advance block is occupied; (3) decoding apparatus for distinguishing between 180 pulses per minute and 75 pulses per minute operation by the code-following track relay; and (4) means for controlling the signal in accordance with that distinction.

Such a two-code track circuit thus performs the independent functions of: (1) detecting the presence of a train in a particular block and (2) selecting between the "proceed" and "approach" indications of the wayside signal for that block.

If four indications are desired instead of the three which are available with two different code frequencies, a third code of intermediate frequency, such as 120 pulses per minute, may be employed, and a still greater number of indications may be obtained by the use of additional frequencies.

In addition to the arrangement thus far mentioned in which a number of controls may be communicated from the exit to the entrance end of the block the coded track circuit may also be arranged to perform other functions usually requiring separate line wires with the steady-energy track circuit. These additional functions ordinarily require communication from the entrance to the exit end of the block and may include approach lighting of the signals, approach application of cab signal energy, approach locking and the like. These controls are accomplished with the coded track circuit by means of reverse codes which are automatically supplied to the rails so that the reverse-code pulses occur during the "off" energy intervals of the normal code supplied at the exit end of the block.

Coded track circuits, as we have pointed out, may be used to perform a great variety of functions as compared with the distinctly limited capacity of the steady-energy track circuit. With requisite apparatus, the basic form of the coded track circuit may be expanded to accomplish all elements of control required by certain signal systems, and, when so used for system operation, the term "coded track circuit control" is applicable. This flexibility is an important factor, not only in automatic block signaling but also in connection with installations of centralized traffic control, remote control, interlocking and other systems of signaling.

Thus far mention has been made only of coded track circuits employing the well-known frequency code system. Because the frequency code system as well as the apparatus required for its operation are relatively simple it has been highly developed and widely installed. In the frequency code the distinction between the different codes is based upon the rate or frequency at which the "on" pulses recur and discrimination between different codes is accomplished by apparatus which is selectively responsive to these frequencies.

Other types of codes are usually known as the "time code," the "polar code," and the "count code." The time code is characterized by "on" and "off" code periods of varying lengths, and discrimination is accomplished by suitable timing apparatus. Polar codes are made up of recurring energy pulses of distinctive polarity which responds selectively to the polarity of the pulses. Count codes are characterized by the number of pulses, separated by cycle-defining intervals. Suitable counting apparatus distinguishes between codes.

Aside from the frequency code, these three types, or some combination of them, appear to be the only practical ones suitable for use with direct-current track circuits. It is claimed by many signal authorities that the time, polar, and count codes, are less desirable than the frequency code, which is installed extensively on a great many railroads in this country as well as abroad.

Coded track circuits are adaptable for use in steam territory using either direct-current or alternating-current track circuits, or in direct-current or alternating-current electric propulsion territory where alternating-current track circuits must be used. They can be employed for single-direction running on multiple tracks or for either-direction running on one or more of these tracks. They may be effectively combined with remote control and centralized traffic control systems, and for use with automatic block signaling on single track.

The coded track circuit may, further, be used for wayside signals alone, for cab signals where there are no automatic wayside signals, or where a combination of wayside and cab signals are used. They are also utilized for special purposes, such as securing improved shunting sensitivity in interlocking, and in isolated locations in automatic block signal installations where difficulty has been experienced in the operation of steady-energy track circuits.

In a steady-energy track circuit a train shunt must reduce the rail potential below the track relay's release value in order to effect track release. In a coded track circuit, however, the shunt need only reduce the rail potential below the relay's pick-up value to stop the track relay from following code. As the latter value is considerably above the former, coded track circuits inherently have a shunting sensitivity which is much higher than that of steady-energy circuits under equivalent conditions. In addition to this basic improvement, the coded track circuit lends itself to use with impulse codes of comparatively high voltage, which still further improve the shunting sensitivity where required by unfavorable conditions caused by various kinds of rail film.

It sometimes happens that foreign currents are present in the track circuit and it is highly important that these foreign currents shall not cause improper energization of the track relay. The track relay in the coded track circuit follows the code and such relay cannot set up an improper signal indication because it is inconceivable that any foreign current present would have the code pattern of a regular trackway code. Every stoppage of the code-following track relay operation, either with the relay picked up or released, immediately causes the code-controlled relay to release and consequently puts the signal to "stop."

So many factors combine to determine the maximum operable length of a track circuit that no rigid limits for either the steady-energy or the coded type can be stated. However, since the coded track circuit shunts against the pick-up rather than the release value of the track relay, and for other reasons established by engineering analysis, laboratory test, and field experience, it can be operated with complete satisfaction and without sacrifice of "broken rail" or other essential forms of protection, over a greater length of track than a steady-energy track circuit. Track circuits using coded direct current are, in fact, regularly operated over 11,000-foot track lengths. Because of this extended operating range, cut sections are seldom necessary and additional insulated joints plus energy-repeating devices and housing facilities for these are eliminated.

An important factor of the coded track circuits is the reduction, or complete elimination, of line wires for signal control and thus affords a high degree of immunity against interruption by storms.

C.T.C. and Coded Carrier Control

We have examined the application of the coded carrier impulses in connection with the rail, and now we will examine the functions of the coded carrier as applied to line wires, where it performs further miracles for the railroads of today.

Coded carrier control, as developed by the Union Switch & Signal Company, has increased enormously the capacity of centralized traffic control systems for any number of sections may be operated simultaneously over a two-wire line.

Centralized traffic control is a system of train dispatching whereby the dispatcher seated at his C.T.C. control machine has at his finger-tips complete control of switches and signals over his district or division. Coded carrier control is employed principally for large C.T.C. installations where it is desirable to divide the territory into two or more sections. Ordinarily this would require the use of a separate pair of wires for each section.

However, with coded carrier control all sections can be controlled independently from the same control point over one pair of wires. Coded carrier control is a carrier system designed for the purpose of remotely controlling "time code control" systems, and it consists of carrier equipment that is used to transmit codes in both directions between the control points and the remotely located control apparatus.

In general, the coded carrier equipment generates—transmits directly to—and receives directly from the line an individual carrier frequency for each carrier-operated control and indication code. Frequencies in the 10-30 kc. range are usually employed. In some instances, frequencies as low as 4 kc. and as high as 56 kc. have been utilized, while for special applications carrier equipment operating in the voice range can be used for modulating communication carriers.

With coded carrier control the section adjacent to the office is usually controlled directly by means of a conventional D.C. code line circuit. The second section, which is installed as an independent D.C. code line circuit, is controlled by coded carrier frequencies transmitted over the first section. A third section can be readily controlled by means of a different pair of carrier frequencies transmitted over the first and second sections. It is thus apparent that additional sections, if required, can be controlled in a similar manner to extend the territory to any desired practicable length, or to handle any number of functions in a particular territory.

Coded carrier control can be readily coordinated with other communication facilities and may be superimposed on the same wires with other facilities. This very important application affords great latitude in locating the control point of the control installation. For example, the desired control point may be so far from the actual C.T.C. territory that it may not be considered practicable to extend the wires of the line circuit to that point.

In such an instance it is usually possible to transmit coded carrier currents over an existing communication line and thus permit the control point for the C.T.C. territory to be at the preferred location. This flexibility in choosing the control point has resulted in an increasing tendency to centralize the control of C.T.C. territories by locating the control machines at Division Headquarters.

Where the C.T.C. territory includes a large number of controlled switches and signals, the entire territory can be divided into sections and all sections can be operated over the same two line wires extending from the office. Let us say that the territory is 180 miles long. Three sections controlled by conventional equipment would involve 720 miles of code line wire, with sections evenly divided. With coded carrier control only 360 miles of line wire would be required.

Another important advantage of coded carrier control is its use in territory where code delay makes it desirable to divide the territory into groups which can be operated independently.

In general, the carrier frequencies for the coded carrier system are selected above the voice frequency range so that the two wires for the C.T.C. system may be used also for a physical telephone circuit. Furthermore, if necessary, the frequencies are selected in a way that other carrier communication systems may be operated on the same pair of wires. If a new line is installed for the time code control system, particularly if it is on a Western Union pole line or railroad communication line, the new line should be transposed so that it will be suitable for frequencies up to 30 kc. This provides for the coordination between the coded carrier control system and other carrier frequency systems, such as carrier telephone and telegraph.

It is standard practice to install duplicate sets of carrier equipment in the office and at the field carrier locations, one set serving for stand-by purposes. Stand-by equipment is essential to a C.T.C. installation for the following reasons:

(1) A complete section of C.T.C. is dependent on the proper operation of the carrier equipment. Stand-by equipment guards the section against being inoperative through a fault in the carrier circuits.

(2) With stand-by carrier equipment in use, it is not necessary for a maintainer to be sufficiently well acquainted with the details of the apparatus to be able to repair it.

(3) Since it is advisable to have spare equipment, it is most logical to have it wired in place ready for service.

Change-over circuits are provided for shifting from the normal to the stand-by equipment. The change-over is under control of the operator, enabling him to place either set in service as desired.

The standard carrier equipment is usually adjusted to deliver a higher voltage to the line than the normal units and to respond to a lower received voltage. Thus the stand-by equipment may be able to operate under emergency conditions, such as a broken line wire, when the normal units, adjusted for a lower power level, could not operate. For this reason, the field changeover relay is usually so controlled that the field stand-by equipment will be placed in service automatically in case of a line fault in the carrier circuit.

Included in the stand-by equipment we usually find a "coded carrier repeater," which is not normally used in the circuit, but is there to amplify coded carrier frequencies under emergency conditions. This coded carrier repeater is an electron tube device for amplifying carrier frequencies. It has two particular applications in coded carrier control. Its most extensive application is to overcome emergency conditions, such as severe sleet storms or a broken line wire which produce a large amount of attenuation or thinning out of the carrier current. In this application, the coded carrier repeater is cut in to amplify the coded carrier frequencies under the existing emergency conditions. The second application of the repeater is employed to extend the distance over which it is practicable to transmit coded carrier frequencies.

On a carrier system, a disturbance on the line, such as a severe lightning surge, may stall or blank out a step of an indication code and cause the office and field units to get out of step. In such a situation synchronizing circuit relays are employed to reset the field and office units.

Unusual Installation

A coded track circuit control system of unusual interest was installed between Norfolk and Forest, Virginia, by the Norfolk & Western. The territory included over 400 track-miles, with several stretches of preferential grade single-track making up part of the double-track line. Coded track circuits are employed exclusively.

On double-track, the coded track circuits effect conventional signal control and, through interlocking, they provide detection. On single-track stretches, either C.T.C. or A.P.B. signaling is used. For these locations, several adaptations of the coded track circuit control system were employed with interesting results and important advantages.

In general, the installation employs the well-known two-block, three-indication system with signals spaced about 9,000 feet. Sections of three-block, four-indication signaling were installed on both single- and double-track where local conditions made it necessary. The signals in approach to interlocking were usually equipped with a fourth ("approach-medium") indication. The installation was planned to permit future cab signaling operation without change to wayside installation, simply by the addition of the necessary locomotive equipment.

In double-track territory where the signaling is required to accommodate traffic movements in only one direction, the coded A.C. track circuits are comparatively simple. The necessary controls are provided by the selection of the code frequencies applied to the rails and this selection is governed by traffic conditions. Basic circuits of the type used for this purpose were discussed earlier in this chapter.

Most of the single-track sections which intervene between extensive stretches of double-track are equipped with absolute permissive block signaling, using coded track circuit control. The great flexibility of this arrangement made it possible to operate the system with a smaller number of line wires than would be required with steady-energy track circuits. All "approach" signal indications are exclusively controlled by coded track circuits, as well as many "proceed" indications.

The operation of the system is accomplished over two line wires used for centralized traffic control of the switches and signals and also for telephone purposes. Because coded track circuits were used, no signal control line wires were required in the C.T.C. territory.

CHAPTER XII

SANTA FE C.T.C.

Plains Division Installation Speeds Freight

In my book, *Railroading from the Rear End*, I told the story of centralized traffic control on the famous Pecos Division of the Santa Fe. This heavily-traveled freight line, with the completion of the Plains Division installation before the close of 1948, was then almost all C.T.C. controlled, from Belen, New Mexico, to the Middle Division double-track at Ellinor, Kansas.

There are, of course, some sections of double-track in this territory, and when the Panhandle Division installation will be completed, probably in the fall of 1949, the entire line over which the Grand Canyon and the Scout operate, together with the majority of transcontinental Santa Fe freight, will be dispatched by the modern magic called centralized traffic control.

The First District of the Plains Division of the Santa Fe extends from Waynoka, Oklahoma, to Canadian, Texas, a distance of 107.6 miles. This is entirely C.T.C. controlled. The Second District reaches from Canadian to Amarillo, Texas, 97.8 miles. Of this, Canadian to Pampa, 36 miles, is C.T.C. The remaining distance, Pampa to Amarillo, is double-track.

The Third District extends from Amarillo, Texas, to Clovis, New Mexico, 103.6 miles. The first 17 miles out of Amarillo are double-track to Canyon. From Canyon to Texico, 77 miles, the trains are under centralized traffic control. The nine miles from Texico to Clovis, New Mexico, are double-track.

This Plains Division is quite a division. Yes, it's a great division. Operations are directed from division headquarters at Amarillo, Texas, which is 98 miles away from the nearest point on the Canadian-Waynoka C.T.C. installation. It is a little difficult for the layman to understand how a train dispatcher can efficiently operate a busy railroad division from an office one hundred miles away; it still mystifies some railroaders at times, and even the veteran can find the thing a bit awesome and intriguing.

"You flip a diminutive switch on a panel before you," explains the train conductor on board the *Plainsman* in the opening chapter of this book, "and miles away at some lonely desert siding, there is a clatter of switch-points and the rail is lined for a train to head into the passing track."

In the chapter on Coded Track Circuits you read how this thing is done, but you are still amazed by the magic of it. It is a great age we are living in—a great railroad age. And the more you know of your railroads, the more you are forced to marvel at their accomplishments.

Out at division headquarters at Amarillo they have some of the best train dispatchers in the business, and one of the finest division superintendents you can find anywhere. Before I take up the more detailed description of this C.T.C. installation I want to set down something of the picture of train movements on this teeming division and offer one or two incidents in connection with the many advantages offered by centralized traffic control.

When Booming Trains Are on the Move

All of the sidings on this Canadian-Waynoka District are 12,000 feet in length, or longer. The Santa Fe has one 4-mile siding; another 3-mile siding and at least three sidings on each district are equipped with the new double or intermediate crossover, which enables them to handle very heavy traffic with a minimum of delay at meeting or passing tracks.

It is not unusual for a heavy freight train to be moving through one of these long sidings, with a passenger train on the main track moving past it, and neither train losing any of its maximum speed. It requires skill by the dispatcher, skill and judgment by the enginemen, but it is part of railroading on the Santa Fe.

Likewise, stations that have a double cross-over enable the dispatcher to "meet" two opposing freight trains at the same time allowing a passenger train to pass one freight and meet the other. This has been accomplished in many cases without delay to any of the three trains. Incredible as it may seem, it is a bit of the day's work just the same. A pretty fancy piece of railroading, but after you have had the privilege of sitting beside some of these C.T.C. dispatchers, watching them work, nothing seems impossible. They become so expert, their knowledge of the division, its trains, and enginemen so complete that they make the most difficult situations seem simple.

The case history of every double-track railroad mentions somewhere a major derailment on one of the main tracks which, before proper flag protection had been accomplished, resulted in the derailed cars, fouling the adjoining track, being struck by a second train and other results often more serious than those caused by the original derailment. Such an accident could not occur on a single-track with C.T.C. in operation.

However, simply installing C.T.C. equipment on a railroad is by no means the complete answer to the problem of handling heavy traffic at high speed. Various other factors must be considered. The Santa Fe, for instance, has used excellent judgment in lengthening all sidings, and other roads are bringing their tracks up-to-date in the same manner. Important to top utilization of these long sidings is the installation of No. 20 switch turn-out assemblies with 30-foot points. Of further importance is the placing of three cross-overs near the center on at least three sidings on each district. Each such cross-over, in my opinion, is equivalent to an additional siding. It is amazing what a crack C.T.C. dispatcher can do with these long sidings with a center cross-over.

Let us take a typical morning at Amarillo. We are going to ride No. 2, the *Scout*, eastbound. We have engine number 3781 and 14 cars and we are out on time.

Here is the line-up over the district, which Chief Dispatcher Horn has sent to Superintendent Stuppi.

Two red ball trains are moving west on the Third District. 2-53-T, engine 5012, 100 cars, 4,250 tons, reach Amarillo at 5:20 A.M. We met them, of course, before leaving Amarillo. 49-T, engine 3776, 79 cars, 3,360 tons, reach Canadian at 7:00 A.M. We met him at Miami, non-stop. 81-V, engine 3752, 72 cars, 3,100 tons, reach Canadian about 8:00 A.M. We met him at Clear Creek, non-stop.

MX-53-U, engine 5011, 73 cars, 3,210 tons, leave Waynoka at 5:48 A.M. We met him at Glacier, non-stop, at 9:35 A.M.

Borger Oil Special, engine 3812, 75 cars, 2,800 tons, leave Waynoka at 6:00 A.M. He was stopped at Gage when we met him.

53-U reported in at Waynoka at 7:30 A.M.

59-U reported in at Waynoka at 8:15 A.M.

We met these two trains, both non-stop, at Fargo and Gerlack. They had engines 5003 and 3777.

2-81-V reported in at Waynoka at 10:30 A.M.

91-V reported in at Waynoka at 12:45 P.M.

Three more red ball trains were behind them. Besides these westbound red ball freights we also met First No. 23, the Grand Canyon, with Diesel 165 and 11 cars, at Mendota, Texas, and Second No. 23, engine 3782 with 8 cars, which was on First No. 23's block into Waynoka, at Shattuck.

Moving east that morning over the First District were two red ball freight trains. We ran around Extra 5002 East at Clear Creek.

Moving east on the Second District there were two red ball trains, and on the Third District one red ball train. There were also six more red ball trains reported in at Clovis. Two more C-34 trains were ready to leave Clovis.

There was one 5000-Class locomotive out of service at Clovis that morning, with two en route to Clovis and two en route to Waynoka.

The great 5000-Class locomotive of the Santa Fe is still as popular as ever on the Plains and Pecos Divisions. These powerful 2-10-4's do a really remarkable job and there is no call for Diesels in this territory.

That morning, in addition to all of the other booming trains flashing their lights on the C.T.C. boards, there was also a Hereford turn moving 38 cars of beets to Amarillo and running extra up to Boise City, Oklahoma, on the Boise City Branch. This, incidentally, is an excellent shortcut for freight movement to the North-Western Districts, and if passenger service were run over it, it would cut the time to Pueblo and Denver, Colorado, very substantially. It could easily be made into a crack piece of railroad, a great deal better than the Colorado Southern, which now handles some of the business from Denver to Amarillo and Fort Worth direct.

C.T.C. Railroad Watchman

A centralized traffic control installation has other advantages and possibilities aside from dispatching trains—advantages that for the most part escape our attention, unless we get the story from some railroad man. Here are one or two incidents.

A C.T.C. dispatcher had headed a local way freight into a long siding to meet a westbound red ball freight and the local was standing at the east switch when the red ball came through. The local's head-end crew noticed that some 20 or 30 cars behind the engine a carload of pipe had shifted and that some of these heavy pipes apparently were protruding beyond a safe clearance.

The head brakeman of the local hurried to the C.T.C. telephone, located near the switch, and notified the dispatcher of the hazardous condition aboard the speeding red ball train.

The train dispatcher had only to reach out and flip a switch on the panel of the C.T.C. machine before him to take the green signal at the west end of the long siding away from the red ball. The fast freight stopped and its head brakeman went to the telephone at the switch to inform the dispatcher that they had a red signal. The brakeman was instructed to go back and look at the car of pipe.

He found that one of the stakes supporting the load of pipe was broken, allowing the load to shift in such a manner that the ends of four lengths of pipe had a dangerous overhang. Section men were contacted and the pipes were rearranged and secured.

From another road we heard of a somewhat similar occurrence. It was during a heavy fog that a section foreman notified a dispatcher from a C.T.C. telephone of a blazing hotbox on a coal train that had just passed him. It was clear that none of the crew were aware of it.

Once more the dispatcher snapped a red light on in place of a green. When a brakeman called in he was instructed to make an inspection of the journals on the train. Trainmen soon found the hotbox, thanks to the alertness of the section boss and the dispatcher's instant action.

The journal had burned off and dropped down as the coal train came to a stop. It was impossible to estimate the amount of damage that might have occurred in both of these instances if these trains had been operating on double-track and with no immediate means of communication other than open telegraph offices over long distances.

C.T.C. Motor Car Indicators

The Santa Fe's new type motor car signals, built by the Union Switch and Signal Company, are an exceptionally fine addition to their C.T.C. installation on the Plains Division.

In sections where sighting distances are short motor-car indicators are provided, by means of which men on motor cars can be warned of the approach of trains. Where A.C. power is available the indicators are of the electric lamp type, each indicator consisting of an electric lamp previously used on the old semaphore signals. These indicators are mounted on signal cases, the lamps being directed at an angle across the track so that, as a man approaches on a motor car, the indicator he sees applies to the territory into which he is going to proceed.

Each indicator has a 3.5-watt, 13.5-volt lamp which is normally lighted. The relay which controls each indicator is normally energized by a line circuit which breaks through front contacts of the track or line relays for the limits of the control of the indicator. The indicator line circuits are taken through contacts in the directional-stick relays so that the indicators will clear for a man on a motor car to follow a train.

At locations where A.C. is not available to feed a lamp, the indicators are semaphore type with 500-ohm coils which are normally energized by the line circuit. In most instances the line circuits are fed from the D.C. side of the rectifiers. When the A.C. power fails, the line circuit is de-energized but this is of no consequence because with the A.C. off, the lamp in the indicator would not be lighted.

These motor-car circuits are entirely independent from the signal circuits, so that any grounds or crosses will not interfere with the signaling. An important part of the improvements was a motor-car set-off, built of old ties, provided at every power switch and every intermediate signal as well as at others placed not more than an average of one-quarter mile apart.

The distance of the track circuit in both directions is indicated on these signals. Thus, a trackman can tell at once how far he is protected. Where signal lamps are employed the lamps are only lighted when a train is in the circuit.

C.T.C. Machine Combinations

The C.T.C. machine in the dispatcher's office at Amarillo has a center panel five feet long and on each side there are two 2-foot-5-inch panels which are set at angles to form a "U" shape having a total length of 15 feet.

Another five-foot C.T.C. machine is in the same room. This is for the control of the 40-mile section from Canadian west to Pampa, from which point the double-track extends into

Amarillo, and 18 miles beyond to Canyon. The C.T.C. project between Canyon and Texico is controlled by a second 15-foot machine arranged in a "U" shape, with its open end facing the open end of the Waynoka-Canadian machine.

Between the two U-shaped machines is the one five-foot machine for the Canadian-Pampa section. The five-foot machine is on four large casters which are equipped with toe-operated jacks by means of which the weight of the machine can be raised up on pads which lock the machine and prevent it from rolling. The floor is covered with sheet iron, on which the machine can be readily pushed about.

By this means the five-foot machine for the Canadian-Pampa 40-mile section can be operated by a separate dispatcher; in periods of light traffic, it can be turned to face the open U-end of either the Waynoka-Canadian or the Canyon-Texico machine, and can be operated by the dispatcher in charge of either of the larger machines.

The wires entering the five-foot machine come from the rear through a flexible metal conduit to a pipe extending up through the floor, with slack in the length of the conduit and sufficient wire to allow the machine to be moved in either direction as far as may be required.

Fewer Break-In-Two's

Under the former timetable and train-order operation on the Plains Division there was a tendency for trains to bunch toward the far end of the district; then pull into Canadian, for example, one after another, blocking the yards and generally causing delays. C.T.C. eliminated this bunching through its speed and flexibility, allowing for a more desirable spacing of trains on the division.

Another feature has been the reduction of train stops, and this eliminates many break-in-two's. For the division as a whole there were 56 pulled drawbars in November, 1943, against nine in November, 1946, or after C.T.C. had been installed.

On the average, a break-in-two not only delays the train involved for about an hour, but it also delays other trains as much as five or six hours.

With train orders, several hours were required to get all the trains rolling again, but, with C.T.C., the signal aspects, which are the modern equivalent of a train order, can be controlled instantaneously at innumerable places by the dispatcher. Therefore, all the trains are on their way soon after the train with the break-in-two has corrected its trouble.

Helper locomotives, used on tonnage trains westward from Waynoka to Curtis, formerly lost time in returning to Waynoka under timetable and train-order operation. Four helper crews worked 12 to 16 hours daily. Now, with C.T.C., these helpers can be moved back to Waynoka promptly and, as a result, only three helper crews are needed and they seldom work more than eight hours.

Centralized traffic control is by no means a cure-all for all railroad ills, but it has worked major miracles at every location where it has been installed. And right here we want to say that the magic of C.T.C. has its counterpart in the master miracle worker who operates it—the man with a "thousand-track brain." The train dispatcher.

CHAPTER XIII

THE CINCINNATIAN OF THE B.&O.

"Armchair on Wheels"

Typical of trains of today is the Baltimore & Ohio's sleek and modern *Cincinnatian.* This train maintains the fastest train schedule ever made between Baltimore, Maryland, and Cincinnati, Ohio, covering the 570-mile run in twelve and one-half hours, making 11 scheduled stops. And this, in a few words, tells the story of your modern high-speed luxury travel down the steel rail.

Wheeling swiftly between two great American cities, it places at the disposal of the traveler "armchair" comfort and service de luxe, leaving the passenger completely relaxed and refreshed at the journey's end. For many travelers it provides a completely new experience in transportation, in courtesy, and in personal attention. Nothing can be more irritating to the passenger than a lack of courtesy by railroad personnel. With disposition ruffled by gruffness, the passenger is further irritated by unpleasant surroundings and various annoyances, including bodily discomfort and indifferent service.

Hospitality goes hand in hand with speed and luxury on the Cincinnatian. You feel that you are the road's honored guest, and not just another passenger. You leave the train at your destination a "satisfied customer," convinced that neither private automobile nor bus can compare even remotely to travel on the railroads of today. While airplane travel offers greater speed, it is governed to a certain extent by weather conditions, which do not affect trains. Also, travel by rail allows the passenger to become more intimately acquainted with the country and the communities along the way.

123

The east and westbound *Cincinnatians* were placed in operation January 19, 1947, and immediately established a new standard for coach travelers aboard these five-car daylight trains. It may be pointed out that daylight trains all over the country are becoming increasingly popular, as they allow the passenger to watch the miles unroll in a constantly changing panorama of our America.

The twin *Cincinnatians* were designed by men of the B.&O. and built at the railroad's Mt. Clare shops, having a particular styling adapted to the modern trend, with service features that appeal to the traveling public. These include advances in passenger-car design and equipment of proven value, developed by the railroads and manufacturers of coach specialties, and of pleasing interior and exterior decorative treatment and styling usually associated with extra-fare train accommodations.

Some technical developments incorporated in these trains are comparatively new; others take the form of applications of materials and equipment that have been previously available but which have not enjoyed widespread use in passenger cars. Some features are obvious to the traveler, while others, hidden from view, contribute directly or indirectly to the passenger's comfort or to the service. Among the former are the reclining chairs, the fluorescent lighting, the individually-controlled seat lights, air-conditioning, radio and public address system in each car, the full-view windows, the Venetian blinds and electric water coolers.

Less obvious but tending to provide greater comfort are the sound-deadening and vibration-eliminating materials on the trucks, the air-filters, the rounding of the corners to promote cleanliness, the roller bearings on car trucks, the telephone system for train crew communication, and other ingenious equipment built into cars and running-gear.

On many trains the "coach" passenger is denied the use of other more luxurious cars of the train. This is not so on the Cincinnatian and the traveler finds that every luxury of the train is available for his use and enjoyment. He can move around on the train, relaxing in the buffet-lounge section to read or enjoy a light lunch or beverages. The diner-observation gives him an opportunity to enjoy a complete dinner, to write, or enjoy the scenery in lounging comfort.

Before examining in detail some of the train's appointments, let us consider the make-up of the train. The *Cincinnatian* consists of a baggage-buffet-lounge car, three coaches and the dining-observation car. The first car has a 20-foot baggage room, and a seven-foot by eight-foot room with lockers and toilet for the crew. Then comes a buffet and the lounge, seating 24 persons. At the end of the car the conductor has a five-and-one-half-foot office.

The following three cars are coaches. The middle coach contains the quarters of the stewardess. About three-fifths of the last car is devoted to the kitchen and dining room, and the remainder is the observation lounge. It has a seating capacity of 21.

A very trim streamlined steam locomotive of the Pacific type is pulling the Cincinnatian. Even when standing it gives an impression of movement, of speed. From pilot to the curved observation, the train is rather breath-taking in appearance and Roy B. White, president, and the Baltimore & Ohio have every reason to be proud of these striking and beautiful examples of today's trains, dressed in B.&O. royal blue with aluminum striping.

Supplementing the attractive folders which are given to the passengers, there are loud speakers over which comes the pleasant voice of the stewardess, announcing various points of interest. The folders are entitled "Sightseeing along the route of the *Cincinnatian*"; they contain maps and place names and the train's schedule, enabling the passenger to identify the country through which he is passing. There are also thumbnail sketches of cities and villages and other locations of historical and geographical significance.

A maximum amount of window space is provided throughout the train. Windows of the coaches, as well as those of the buffet-lounge and the observation-diner, are approximately five feet wide, with double-glass breather-type sashes and safety glass on the inside. "Da-lite" blinds allow the passenger to control at all times the amount of light coming through the window.

The three coaches of the Cincinnatian are nearly identical in basic design and arangement of facilities. Two have a seating capacity of 60 persons; the other seats 56 because of the space set apart for the stewardess. The seats are of the Sleepy Hollow type, designed by Heywood-Wakefield and first installed on the B.&O. To insure plenty of leg room the seats are spaced at 42-inch intervals. This also allows for convenient adjustment of seat backs and foot rests. At no time does one have a sense of being crowded. A button adjusts the back to ten different positions and the depression of a lever moves the foot rest to any one of four positions. This makes for body comfort, which is essential on a day-coach train.

Another feature that plays an important part in attracting the traveling public is the color scheme and the interior decorating. Boarding the Cincinnatian, you are impressed by the spotless high-gloss walls and panels, by the artistic color selections which are pleasing and restful. Let us take, for example, the color scheme employed in one of the coaches. Here we find a royal blue base with suntan walls, trimmed in royal blue, merging with a ceiling of white faintly tinged with suntan. The seats are rust colored. The floor is marbleized Linotyle with an aisle design in ivory.

Another coach employs a forest-green base, lighter green walls trimmed in forest green, with a ceiling in a tinted green shading. The floor is marbleized black with an attractive aisle design of block ivory. The seats are soft green in Chase needlepoint.

The buffet section of the first car has stainless steel appointments. The lounge is equipped with two tables seating four persons each, plus numerous chairs conveniently grouped around small tables. Food and beverages are served to any location in the car at all hours. Indented aluminum-lined circles on the tops of the smaller tables act as glass holders and ash trays. The color scheme of the buffet-lounge utilizes black base wall and trim, Persian red walls and a ceiling of white tinted red. Chairs and couches are upholstered in leather, and the colors include blue, red, green and rust. The flooring is of modern design in black and white.

You have had a snack and spent a little time in the buffet-lounge, and now you move back through the coaches to the observation section of the last car with its deep-pile carpeting in red, gold, and black. You find restful chairs and sofas in Chase needlepoint or leather in light green, yellow, blue, or red. Current magazines are stored in a rack. There is a writing table and stationery for your convenience. There are mirrors or pictures on the end walls, and attractive drapes in fabrics of romantic design and in shades which blend with the car's color scheme.

The train is equipped with both radio reception and a public address system. The radio in the buffet-lounge is controlled for local reception by the attendant. Another receiving set is located in the observation car and may be hooked up with the public address system for reception of general programs or important news items.

The public address system extends to every car on the train. It includes a microphone in the conductor's office at the end of the buffet-lounge; another one located in the steward's compartment of the dining car, and a third one in the compartment of the stewardess in the middle coach. Each car has two speaker units, one power amplifier and a rotary converter. The speakers are installed in the bulkheads at the ends of each coach and in the air-conditioning ducts of the other two cars.

In the buffet-lounge and in the dining-observation section the equipment consists of a radio receiver, mounted on a panel with tuning and volume controls, a control box including an output-level meter, an "in use" light, a three-position switch and a microphone. When the switch in either car is in normal position, radio programs are reproduced over the amplifier and speakers in that particular car. When the switch is in a locking position the programs are distributed throughout the entire train. If the switch is moved to nonlocking position announcements can be made to the entire train.

The conductor's desk is furnished with a control box, microphone and a monitor speaker. When the switch is in nonlocking position the conductor can make announcements to the entire train, automatically cutting off radio programs being transmitted. The same facilities are employed in the stewardess' room.

Transmission throughout the train is accomplished over four wire conductors. Two carry the signal and the other two are used for relay control purposes. Use of the level meter insures satisfactory volume conditions. Each radio is operated from train antennas located on the top of that car in which the receiver is located.

The train telephone system for the crew includes a station at the rear of the observation car and one at the forward end; two are in the baggage-buffet-lounge car—one in the conductor's office and one in the crew's quarters. Another station is located at the engineman's side in the locomotive cab. The system is a party-line arrangement with the signaling accomplished by bells operated by a hold-down switch at each station. The telephone wiring is incorporated with that of the sound system, four wires being allocated to the public-address system and two to the telephone.

Each car is equipped with two 7½ kw. axle-driven generators and batteries of 1,000-amp-hour capacity. Two 1,200-watt capacity motor alternators are located under the baggage-buffet-lounge and diner-observation cars and one of 1,200-watt capacity in each of the coaches to furnish 110-volt current for the fluorescent lighting system. One 225-watt rotary converter under each car furnishes the current for the radio and public-address system.

In addition to the fluorescent lighting the cars have 25-watt incandescent lamps located in the fluorescent troughs for night and emergency lighting. The individual seat lights have both a 15-watt incandescent bulb for night lighting and a 25-watt light bulb for the purpose of reading.

Quarters for the stewardess are located at one end of the middle of the train's three coaches. The accommodations include a wide berth-type seat on which an ailing passenger can lie down, a closet for the stewardess' personal belongings, cupboard space for her supplies, a small table at which she can fill out her reports, and a private toilet and wash room. Two toilets are located at the opposite end of this coach. The remaining two coaches have two toilets for men at one end and two toilets for women at the other end.

All coaches are fitted with steel tubing baggage racks and flat metal slats that run the length of the cars over the seats. Electric water coolers in the coaches eliminate the need of re-icing at station stops and also do away with the problems of waste water from melting ice. Bottled spring water is served in the dining room and buffet.

All cars of the Cincinnatian are air-conditioned, the conditioned air being distributed through ducts running down the center of each car ceiling. Heating is by means of cycle-modulation, zone-control equipment which includes fin-type radiation units and thermostats and humidistats, permitting the modulated control of the air-conditioning. Each outlet is equipped with an exhaust fan.

The Cincinnatian in its flight down the shining rails travels through a country rich in scenery and tradition. The train appointments provide the traveler with every comfort and convenience. The six-wheel roller-bearing trucks cradle the fleeting cars in their strong arms of steel, carrying the west-bound passenger swiftly up the beautiful Potomac River Valley to traverse the Alleghenies and rush on toward Cincinnati.

The traveler has a look at Harpers Ferry and the Shenandoah and Cheat River Canyon, perhaps for the first time, and retains cherished memories of the trip long after the sleek Cincinnatian has eased to a stop at its Western terminal. Following its introduction, surveys seemed to indicate that much of the Cincinnatian's patronage was new business. More and more, people are turning to the restful ride on a train in preference to fighting highway traffic in their own car or traveling by bus. Certainly the railroads of today are selling the finest kind of transportation, and well up among the leaders we find the progressive Baltimore & Ohio Railroad with a train that has won national recognition for its beauty, comfort, fast schedule and on-time performance.

CHAPTER XIV

THE C.&O.'S "500"

Steam Turbine-Electric Locomotive

The forward looking Chesapeake and Ohio has come up with something new in motive power—a steam turbine-electric locomotive. In this writer's opinion, it is, by all odds, the best turbine-type locomotive ever built, and miles ahead of its closest competitor.

The C.&O.'s "500" is so entirely different that it is almost like something from another planet. You accept this vivid orange and aluminum locomotive, with its strange, unorthodox design, with the same slow wonderment you would accept a startling creation that just rolled down the rails from Mars.

America has come to look for and, generally, to take to heart the bold pathfinding adventuring of the C.&O. The impact of its advertising is something you do not forget; the impact of your first look at this "500" will remain with you for a long time.

In December, 1947, more than 40,000 people eagerly took advantage of the opportunity to inspect the revolutionary locomotive. Their interest aroused by newspaper and radio announcements, crowds were on hand at Washington, D.C.; at Charlottesville, Waynesboro, Staunton, Clifton Forge, and Covington, Virginia; at Hinton, Charleston and Huntington, West Virginia; at Cincinnati and Columbus, Ohio; at Ashland, Kentucky, and Richmond, Virginia. An inspection stairway and platform was provided at these various stops, enabling the crowds to climb up and inspect the controls of the world's first coal-burning, steam turbine-electric locomotive. Meanwhile personnel of the C.&O.'s Public Relations Department kept up a running description of the "500's" features over the public address system.

Special guests of the C.&O. at many stops were local coal operators, who were greatly interested and impressed, both by the appearance of this new locomotive and its possibilities. For, appearance to the contrary notwithstanding, this locomotive was a new type of coal-burner, boldly pioneering startling innovations at a time when general opinion held that the steam locomotive was singing its swansong. We make no predictions concerning the C.&O.'s "500" future, but it is here; it is in operation. There is no test tube like operation in service. Later we will know more about this steam turbine-electric motive power and its ability to "take it," out there on those mountain grades.

There is a strange fascination about this C.&O. "500," probably because of its radical departure from standard design. When the Pennsylvania road began experimenting with the turbine idea, they turned out something that still *looked* like a steam locomotive. The C.&O., on the other hand, threw out of the window all accepted designs and started from scratch. The Pennsylvania turbine had a more or less conventional 6-8-6 wheel arrangement, keeping to old standards. The C.&O. went far beyond that and came up with a 4-8-0-4-8-4 type of locomotive.

This is about the equivalent of a good 4-8-4. The C.&O. "500," however, has many advantages over the conventional steam locomotive. For one thing, it is easy on the rail; you know, of course, that the old-type steam motive power was heavy-footed and hit the rail hard while going. The constant-torque electrics and Diesel-electrics, on the other hand, are easy on the rail.

Now let us take a look at the C.&O. "500" close-up. Remember, we are not examining an experimental locomotive. This "500" is pulling trains in regularly scheduled service, and thousands of people will have seen this coal-burning, steam-turbine C.&O. locomotive in main line running before you open this book *Railroads of Today*.

The most radical departure from the standard design we find in the locomotive's fundamental arrangement. The "500's" 29¼-ton coal bunker is forward of the cab, or where you normally would look for the boiler. The boiler of the "500" is at the rear of the cab, where, you feel, the tender should be. Coupled back of the locomotive is the water tender.

All of the engineer's operating controls, of course, are located on the forward wall of the cab compartment. All of the boiler controls are located on the rear wall or the boiler head. The trailing water tender has a 25,000-gallon capacity.

The length of the "500" is 140 feet, 3¾ inches. The weight is 411½ tons.

Coal is automatically fed from the bunker at the front, back under the cab floor to the fire-box. The boiler has a working steam pressure of 310 pounds to the square inch. There are 20 pairs of wheels under the engine alone, and eight pairs, or 16 wheels, are driving wheels, 40 inches in diameter.

How the "500" Operates

The "500" locomotive boiler produces superheated steam that is conducted to the power plant's 6,000-horsepower turbine. This turbine drives twin generators, which produce 4,000 kilowatt-hours of electrical energy. These generators power eight motors, which deliver a total of 4,960 horsepower to the 16 driving wheels.

There is little to be seen outside of the "500's" cowling. Inside of the cowl, at the front, we find the air pumps, a blower, a dynamo and the engine bell; also, the stoker engine. The turbine is located beyond the smoke-box and stack, toward the rear. Then, there are the gear case and the generators. Many of the accessories on the "500" are the same as those of the conventional reciprocating steam locomotive, including lubricator, ash-pan dump blower, boiler blowdown, low-water alarm, etc.

The boiler supplies 85,000 pounds of steam per hour at 290 pounds per square inch gauge pressure and 750 degrees Fahrenheit. With this flow and with 15 pounds per square inch gauge back pressure, the turbine is capable of developing 6,000 horsepower at 6,000 r.p.m. The smoke-box is of the standard master mechanic's style with the turbine exhaust producing the draft, as in a conventional locomotive.

When the highly super-heated steam leaves the Type "E" super-heater units, it flows through a seven valve steamchest to an impulse type steam turbine, which consists of a velocity-compound, impulse-control stage followed by four-full admission impulse stages. The turbine is connected through a helical gear reduction unit (6 to 1) to two generators (each double armature) 2,000 kw. 580 volts, operating at 1,000 r.p.m. Each of the four kw. generator armatures furnishes power for two Westinghouse 620-horsepower, 720 r.p.m. traction motors permanently connected in parallel.

Advantages of the C.&O. "500" over the conventional locomotive rests chiefly in the operating flexibility assured by its electric drive, smooth starting, and full power at all operating speeds.

The power of the locomotive is controlled both by varying the strength of the separately excited fields of the main generators and by speed control of the turbine. The electric transmission produces smooth-as-silk acceleration at the desired rate with close regulation of locomotive speed.

The control equipment for the main generators and the rear four motors is mounted in a control cabinet at the extreme rear of the locomotive. The control equipment for the four front motors is located in a cabinet under the coal box on the right side of the locomotive.

The controller is located in the operator's cab on the right side. A large lever on the top controls the speed whereas a small lever on the side controls the direction of travel. When the speed control lever is moved to "idle," steam is admitted to the turbine, bringing it to the idling speed of 3,850 r.p.m.

The traction motors are connected with the generators by electro-pneumatic unit switches. The fields of the traction motors are connected with a drum type reverser, which in turn is controlled by the reverse lever on the controller.

The traction motors and generators are cooled by turbine-driven propeller-type blowers. Super-heated steam is used to drive the blower turbines. A 9,000 CFM blower mounted in the nose ventilates the motors on the front unit while a 15,000 CFM blower mounted on the left side directly back of the smoke box ventilates the motors on the rear unit. A 25,000 CFM blower mounted on the right side in back of the smoke box ventilates the generators.

The 24-RL brake equipment with automatic and electro-pneumatic operation is part of the "500's" equipment. It uses the same general principles as the equipment on the earlier standard locomotives, providing all of the functions in an equal or improved manner, with the extra feature of being permitted to limit the equipment to those functions required by the service in which the locomotive operates. With the "self-lapping" electro-pneumatic control fast application and release is made possible for high-speed passenger service. There is no dynamic brake, however.

The lateral restraint on the leading and intermediate trucks is produced by a combination of small rollers on small inclined planes and lateral restraining springs. As the bolster moves laterally, the initial movement is restrained by the rollers on inclined planes and any additional lateral movement is restrained by lateral restraining springs. The restraining device is designed to permit a lateral movement of nine inches. With this new arrangement superior stability is obtained at high speeds, particularly when traversing a curve, since the mechanism has the non-lift feature. The zero lift is the result of a combination of the truck spring deflection and tilting of the truck frame.

The underframe is supported on the frames of the running gear by two center pins and nine spring loaded plungers. The spring plungers, which slide on horizontal plates attached to the underframe, are arranged in such a manner that additional support is obtained for increased stability of the cab structure. All draft and bumping strains are transferred from the front running gear unit to the rear running gear unit through the center pins and underframe. The spring plungers are lubricated by force feeds from the Nathan mechanical lubricator.

The wheel arrangement of the C.&O.'s new "500" provides the

flexibility necessary to negotiate all curves with the smoothness of a "Chessie" streamlined coach.

The locomotive is equipped with a speed governor control which graduates the brake pressure to match the train speed. This equipment is part of the electro-pneumatic brake equipment and receives its power from the auxiliary generator or storage batteries.

The diameter of truck wheels, front and intermediate, is 36 inches, and all driving wheels 40 inches. The overall length of engine and tender is 154 feet. The rated tractive force of the engine is 98,000 pounds; the continuous tractive force is 48,000 pounds.

Three of these "500" class locomotives were built in 1947—500, 501 and 502. This type of motive power was born of the C.&O.'s program to develop more effective use of bituminous coal, an important contribution to the railway's freight revenues.

The introduction of the C.&O. "500" is an adventure in motive power engineering by a progressive railroad. What it will lead to we do not know, but it is new and it is thrilling. Years may elapse between the inception of an idea and its full adoption. In the meantime, the painstaking process of experiment moves forward as your railroad of today constantly strives to produce greater transportation efficiency.

The C.&O. turbine-electric is a fine engine to ride. It is very clean and has excellent visibility; it is easy on the track. There has been no trouble with the last two built and this is probably the answer if a railroad desires to build a coal-burning steam-turbine locomotive. As we have pointed out, it is way ahead of the others that have been built today. It will probably be an excellent locomotive for many years to come.

The crews are getting used to the "500" and turn in an admirable performance, not only on the Allegheny grades but on the 90-mile-an-hour territory between Russel and Cincinnati, Ohio, on the Cincinnati Division. It does not use too much coal, is easy on water, and has handled passenger trains up to 15 or 16 cars, making the time with all the C.&O. fast trains. All in all, it has proved itself.

CHAPTER XV

THE EAGLES

New Equipment on Missouri Pacific—
Texas & Pacific

The "Eagles" have spread their wings in the Southwest. The Missouri Pacific and the Texas & Pacific together have made a contribution to the development of passenger service along their combined lines to the tune of over $14,000,000, spent on new equipment since the close of World War II.

The large postwar equipment program was undertaken after exhaustive preliminary study. Officials of both roads worked through the research department of the Missouri Pacific in conducting a detailed study of the advisability of entering upon such an extensive modernization. The conclusion was reached that new trains and equipment were essential if the MP and the T&P were to meet the accelerated postwar competition offered not only by other roads, but also by other types of transportation. It was believed that attractive streamliners would both check any losses of traffic and attract considerable new business.

The decision was based on the experience of the first Missouri Pacific streamliner, the "Missouri River Eagle." This six-car day train was established between St. Louis, Kansas City, Missouri, and Omaha, Nebraska, on March 10, 1940. The first nine months of operation of this train between St. Louis and Kansas City, (excluding head-end revenues), showed that passenger revenues had increased 129.6 per cent over the 1939 earnings of the standard train which it had replaced. For the same comparative period, system passenger revenues increased only 7.3 per cent. The per cent increase in 1941 over 1939 was 191.4 for the "Missouri

River Eagles," while the system increase was but 69.3 per cent. By October 28, 1942, after two years, seven months and 18 days of operation, the two sets of equipment making up this train had earned $1,137,727 in *net income*, equalling their entire initial cost.

People will pay for speed, comfort, and service. Riding these new Eagles the first time is an adventure in itself. The thrill will, perhaps, wear off after a few trips, but the kind of service these trains render remains a solid factor to be considered in the transportation field in the great Southwest.

The "Delta Eagle," a two-car streamliner placed in service on May 11, 1941, between Memphis, Tennessee, and Tallaluah, Louisiana,—a run over which no comparable service had previously been offered—paid for itself within four years and two months. The third train, the "Colorado Eagle," which went into service on June 21, 1942, cost $1,467,663. Net earnings reached that amount in 290 days. Up to December 31, 1947, it had earned $4.10 net per train-mile.

As a result of this showing, the Eagle service was expanded to include the "Louisiana Eagle," operating between Fort Worth and New Orleans, the inauguration of which took place in September, 1948. The "Valley Eagle," an all-coach streamliner, was established late in 1948 between Brownsville and Houston, Texas, connecting with the "Texas Eagles" to and from St. Louis.

These fine all-coach trains operate on accelerated schedules. The southbound "Valley Eagle" leaves Houston at 10:45 A.M., permitting passengers from St. Louis on the Texas Eagle to make unhurried connections to continue their journey to the Rio Grande Valley. This train arrives in Corpus Christi at 4:25 P.M. and in Brownsville at 7:40 P.M.

The northbound "Valley Eagle" leaves Brownsville at 6:30 A.M., arriving in Houston at 3:15 P.M., affording easy connections with the northbound Texas Eagle, leaving Houston at 4:00 P.M. Northward, the coach leaves Corpus Christi at 9:35 A.M.

Coach passengers between Corpus Christ and St. Louis need

not leave their seats, as this one coach is a through car in both directions.

The Valley Eagle also carries a grill coach, providing a luncheonette service at a grill in the center of the coach. There are seats for 28 in one section and 24 in the other. Wash rooms for men and women are located at both ends of the car.

All coaches feature revolving, fully reclining, individually controlled seats, deeply upholstered, with adjustable foot-rests. Individual fluorescent reading lights are located above each pair of seats. These lights are recessed into the fully enclosed luggage racks overhead. Windows are of the wide-vision type, affording unobstructed views of the passing scenery. Soundproofed walls and modern heating and air-conditioning equipment assure a clean, quiet, and restful ride. The spacious interiors are decorated in tastefully blended pastel colors, with harmonizing drapes at the sides of the windows. All cars are radio equipped.

Both the south and west Texas Eagles have replaced corresponding sections of the "Sunshine Special," which previously provided the roads' top passenger service on these runs. The "South Texas Eagle," train No. 21, operates southbound and splits at Palestine, Texas, for San Antonio and Houston, respectively.

The following represents the assignment of new Eagle passenger cars.

Assignment	No. of Cars
"West Texas Eagle"	39
"South Texas Eagle"	30
"Louisiana Eagle"	20
"Valley Eagle"	10
"Sunshine Special" x	4
"Colorado Eagle" xx	10
"Sunflower" x	4
Train Nos. 116 & 125 x	2
Train Nos. 219 & 220 x	1
Unassigned	14
Total	134

x "Eagle" cars in regular trains
xx New cars replacing earlier "Eagle" units

B & O #5303 — 4-6-2 type, Class P-5 descending Cranberry grade near Rodemer, W. Va., Cumberland Division with train #75 the Cincinnatian—daily all-coach streamliner from Washington. Photo by R. H. Kindig.

Nearly all the U.P. CTC control machines are located at DIV headquarters where train movements are coordinated on division-wide basis. Two machines shown in this picture at Salt Lake City, Utah, control the longest CTC installation in the world—325 miles from Salt Lake City to Caliente, Nevada, on California Division. Note new board in foreground has division profile underneath track diagram.

U.P. #37 westbound Pony Express passing the east end at Milford, Utah, automatically sending an "OS" to Salt Lake City illuminating track model light on CTC machine. Such up to the minute "OSing" of trains helps dispatchers plan meets accurately. It is one of the advantages of CTC. "A" on signals means absolute.

Rear end of the new lookout lounge on Twentieth Century observation car, one of the finest in the country. Courtesy N.Y.C. RR.

Santa Fe #2923, the great 4–8–4 type, descending Curtis Hill with #2 the Scout on the new line between Belva and Heman, Okla., at 60 miles an hour with thirteen cars on the First District of the Plains Division. The old location is in the left background. Photo by Preston George.

U.P. Extra 3800 east with helper 5505 — 2–10–2 type—solid train of Idaho potatoes. Meets Extra 3830 4–6–6–4 type west at the west end of Max, Idaho, Division CTC. There is very heavy freight traffic over this division and in addition considerable local work is handled and a large amount is fed over this territory from busy branch lines.

Fine new motor-car signals now in use on U.P. and Santa Fe CTC districts. When track ahead is clear for sufficient distance to permit motor car to proceed, the indicator is energized and two green disks are aligned vertically. Center disk is always black. When track is not clear, indicator becomes de-energized and red disks are lighted horizontally. Disks are covered with Scotch light material and reflect motor-car headlights to produce distinctive indications at night.

Magnificent new club lounge cars in service on many of the New York Central's newly moderized fleet of passenger trains. Bar and tables in café are enclosed with attractive glass windows. A fine, all-around car. Courtesy N.Y.C. RR.

The most photographed spot on the B & O — Altamount, Maryland, with eastward coal train starting down the 17-mile 2% grade after the retainers have been put up. Photo by R. H. Kindig.

SUMMIT OF ALLEGHANIES
ALTITUDE
2628 FT

Missouri Pacific's new lightweight lounge, four-bedroom sleeper in service on the Texas Eagle, a typical car of the railroads of today. Courtesy Missouri Pacific RR.

C & O #500, the new steam turbine, at the opening of the new Fort Spring Tunnel on the Alegheny Subdivision of the Clifton Forge Division. Courtesy C & O RR.

Santa Fe #5015, 5025 coupled, 2–10–4, the famous 5011 class with an eastward green fruit block climbing the 1.14% grade in Abo Canyon, N.M., with eighty-seven cars on the Second District of the Pecos Division CTC territory. Photo by Preston George.

B & O diesel #63 with #6, the eastbound Capital Limited, at Kensington on the west end of the Baltimore Division. Photo by Bruce D. Fales.

Eastbound Nickel Plate Manifest train running over CTC territory between Ripley and Westfield, N.Y., with engine #742 — 2—8—4 type. Courtesy Nickel Plate RR.

The West Texas Eagle, train No. 1, follows No. 21, the South Texas Eagle to Longview, Texas, then heads west over the Texas & Pacific to Dallas, Fort Worth, and El Paso. Its makeup is as follows:

RPO mail-baggage	Texarkana-Dallas
RPO mail-baggage	St. Louis-Fort Worth
Baggage-dormitory	St. Louis-Fort Worth
De luxe coach	St. Louis-El Paso
Divided coach	St. Louis-El Paso
Diner	St. Louis-Fort Worth
Sleeper	St. Louis-Fort Worth
Sleeper	St. Louis-Fort Worth
Sleeper-lounge	St. Louis-El Paso
Sleeper	Washington-Ft. Worth (from B&O)
Sleeper	New York-El Paso (from PRR)
Sleeper	Memphis-Fort Worth
Divided coach	Memphis-Fort Worth

The sleeping cars are preponderantly of the 14-roomette, four double-bedroom type, and none contains open sections. The dormitory cars provide overnight accommodations for train personnel. The divided coaches differ from the de luxe coaches principally by being partitioned to comply with state laws in the South.

Train No. 31, formerly the third section of the Sunshine Special, continues to operate under the latter name but on an improved schedule and with Diesel power. All of its equipment has been modernized, "skirting" added to the car bodies and the blue and gray color scheme of the Eagles applied. One new Eagle car—a 14-roomette, four double-bedroom sleeper—is included in the consist between St. Louis and Hope, Arkansas, where it is cut out for movement to Shreveport, Louisiana, over the rails of the Louisiana & Arkansas.

The balance of the Sunshine handles cars for Mexico City, including, for the first time, a through coach; an El Dorado, Arkansas, sleeper; coaches and sleepers for Hot Springs, Arkansas, and Lake Charles, Louisiana; and a Memphis-Houston sleeping car.

139

The "Louisiana Eagle," westbound, has the following consist:

RPO mail-baggage	New Orleans-Fort Worth
Baggage-dormitory	New Orleans-El Paso
Divided coach	New Orleans-Fort Worth
De luxe coach	New Orleans-Fort Worth
Diner-lounge	New Orleans-El Paso
Sleeper	New Orleans-Fort Worth
Sleeper	New Orleans-Fort Worth
Sleeper	New Orleans-Fort Worth

Factors in Faster Schedules

The expedited operation of the new and sparkling Texas trains has been made possible mainly because the trains are Diesel-powered and are made up of lightweight equipment; also all cars are equipped with electric braking. The use of Diesel locomotives has eliminated water and fuel stops—enormous time-wasters. The servicing now is confined to principal stops where the necessary work can be done during train time.

Important improvement in the physical plant, predicated at least in part on the Eagle passenger program, included three line revisions in 1945, 1946, and 1948, respectively, on the Missouri division between St. Louis and Poplar Bluff, 165 miles. A fourth such project was at Tip Top and Gads Hill. The Tip Top relocation reduced the maximum grade at this point from 2.45 per cent southward, and 2.15 per cent northward to 1.25 per cent, compensated for curvature, in both directions, and replaced one eight-degree curve and several only slightly less severe. Now, none is greater than two degrees.

The relocation reduced mileage 0.7, and, together with other projects, cut three miles from the total distance over the division. Diesel-powered trains, before the change, negotiated the Tip Top grade unassisted with 13 passenger cars. Steam-powered trains required a helper above 11 cars. With the completion of the Tip Top-Gads Hill project, passenger helper service, and the

140

facilities required to maintain it, were virtually eliminated on the division.

New Coach and Front-End Cars

The cars of the Eagles are sleek and striking in appearance, conforming to all Association of American Railroads contour standards, and they could be used in interchange service on any streamliner. The predominant exterior color is blue, accentuated by gray window pier panels and gray skirts, with a band of cream just below the drip rail the full length of the car. The design gives continuity to the trains in which the equipment is used.

With a view to serving a particular need in the creation of a new daylight streamliner, six de luxe coaches of unusual design were ordered. Seating 64 passengers, they include a stateroom in each car and have windows on either side of the non-vestibule end so each car can serve as an observation coach when properly placed in the train. Two of these are used with a grill coach between, and when combined with a baggage-mail car and a Diesel-electric locomotive they will provide an observation-equipped train of which only the engine will need turning.

Yellow ceilings, tan sidewalls, rust-upholstered de luxe reclining seats, gold-colored silk-faced curtains, and two-tone turquoise carpeting provide the color scheme. There are appropriate photo-murals on the bulkheads against the men's and women's lounge rooms. The stateroom is similarly decorated except that the walls are green. This private accommodation has a lounge chair and a lounge sofa for four, and a private annex with toilet and washstand.

The 60-passenger coaches and the 64-passenger divided coaches are equipped with revolving, reclining coach seats with sliding type cushions, individual adjustable foot-rests and drop-center arms. The color schemes follow the pattern of the other coaches. The women's lounge has a canary-yellow ceiling and green walls. The men's smoking room is done entirely in tan. Both rooms are equipped with wash basins, lounge settees, mirrors and dental bowls. The women's lounge has a special vanity table with chair and mirror. A built-in water cooler and a radio receiver serving two loud-speakers, one in each bulkhead at the ends of the coach section, are added refinements. Photo-murals add attractiveness to these cars, and a lighted poste frame for railroad and other announcements is just inside of the vestibule door on the facing partition.

The divided coaches, seating 40 passengers in one section and 24 in the other, are decorated in a manner similar to those just described. These cars are also radio-equipped and have light-weight revolving and reclining coach seats.

The so-called "dormitory" coach points up the trend toward longer runs for dining-car crews, and it was with this in mind that this type of car was designed. A 10-bunk dormitory has been built into this car. It is equipped with every convenience for the comfort and cleanliness of the crew. There are three 3-tier bunks, a clothes locker, wash stand, mirror, shelves and dental bowl. A private toilet annex is provided. Each of the nine berths has its own individual reading lamp. A shower has also been built into one end of the dormitory quarters.

Slightly more than half of the dormitory coach is given over to revenue space. This is divided into two sections, one of which is a smoking section. The car also has a conductor's office with a desk and chair. A microphone is provided for making train an-nouncements.

The "baggage-dormitory" cars combine a completely equipped baggage space 40 feet long, and an air-conditioned dormitory section for 15 crew members. A conductor's stateroom is also included in the design.

The crew dormitory is a complete living area in itself. The five three-tier folding bunks have individual lighting. The crew lava-tory has a crew locker, two toilets, a shower with vapor-proof lighting, dental bowl, and three wash basins with individual mirrors and electric razor outlets.

Outside of the crew quarters at the end of the car are a coach-lunch, top-iced refrigerator, switchboard, broom and cleaning locker, and a pillow locker. The baggage section has fish racks on either side for half its length, water cooler, folding wash basin, toilet, and desk and letter case.

The "baggage-mail" car has an inside length of 82 feet, of which 30 feet is devoted to the Railway Mail Service, which completely conforms to all RMS requirements. In addition to the necessary postal equipment the post-office clerks are provided with facilities for their comfort and convenience, including a completely equipped lavatory, refrigerator, steam cooker and water cooler. The baggage section is similar to that in the previously described baggage-dormitory car.

New Sleepers for the "Eagles"

The Missouri Pacific-Texas & Pacific passenger-car improvement program included a substantial number of modern sleeping cars. They consist of three types—roomette-bedroom, bedroom-lounge and roomette-bedroom-drawing-room combinations.

Thirty-eight of the cars have 14 roomettes and four bedrooms each. Of these cars, 22 belong to the Missouri Pacific and 16 to the Texas & Pacific, but all are in the Texas Eagle pool.

All of the new sleepers present a uniform outward appearance, but the interior decorations are of various groupings. For instance, one group has roomettes with yellow ceilings and medium gray walls; another one complementary blues, and still another one tans and greens. Appropriately colored curtains and window shades are used in roomettes and bedrooms. Seats, sofas and chairs are done in harmonious shades in keeping with the particular decorative pattern involved. Carpeting, of course, is employed in bedrooms, roomettes and passageways. Red rubber floor tile is used in annexes and porter's sections.

Three cars of the new group are combination bedroom and soda-fountain lounge cars. One belongs to the Missouri Pacific and two to the Texas & Pacific. Each car contains five bedrooms, a soda fountain adjoining the bedroom near the center of the car and a lounge seating 26 passengers at the nonvestibule end.

At the entrance end there is the general toilet and washroom and the porter's section.

Bedrooms in these cars have light-blue ceilings and medium-tan walls. Window shades are light blue, and seat coverings a darker blue; the floors are covered with two-tone blue carpets. In the lounge section light yellows and light blues prevail in pleasing shade variations. There are blue Venetian blinds with gold tapes. The window draperies are also blue. Settees and chairs are done in red, gold, and blue fabrics. The lounge includes magazine tables, table lamps and smoking stands. The soda fountain is a standard dispensing unit. At the end of the lounge section are large illuminated transparencies mounted on both sides of the door.

Another group of sleepers offer an arrangement that consists of 14 roomettes, two bedrooms and one drawing room. The roomettes face each other across the aisle at the forward end of the car, seven on each side. The drawing room and bedrooms adjoin along the right side of the car. The porter's section and a small general washroom take up the remaining space at the vestibule end. Again the decorative treatment is pleasing and restful, with rust and gray shades prevailing. The drawing room draperies are blue. Five cars in this group were assigned to the Missouri Pacific and one to the Texas & Pacific.

The new sleeping cars have superstructures of Pullman-Standard riveted girder-type construction in aluminum alloy. Underframes are made of low-alloy high-strength steel. The trucks are cast-steel, four-wheel, single-equalizer, all-coil-spring type, with Timken roller bearings, Houdaille vertical shock absorbers, bolster anchors, bolster stabilizers and truck-mounted air-brake cylinders. It is estimated that there is a saving of about 5,500 pounds weight per car due to the use of aluminum in the superstructure.

General Features of New Equipment

Fluorescent lighting is used for general illumination in the cars of the Eagles. Incandescent lighting is used for individual lighting as required and in vestibules, toilets and for poster frame lights.

The air brakes are Westinghouse throughout, with the exception of two grill coaches, six de luxe coaches and two baggage-mail cars for use on the St. Louis, Brownsville & Mexico, a subsidiary of the Missouri Pacific, which are equipped with New York Air Brakes.

All brake equipment is "HSC," fitted with electro-pneumatic straight-air control. Brake cylinders are truck-mounted, four per car. With 100-pound cylinder pressure braking power is 250 per cent of the light weight of the car. Arrangement has been made for future application of wheel-slide control.

End equipment features Waughmat Twin-Cushion draft gear and Tightlock type couplers of the A.A.R. design. All walking surfaces are Alumnalum, while vestibule steps are of streamline design. When in closed position, the back of the step is protected to prevent clogging from ice and snow, which would keep the trap door from opening and the steps from lowering.

With the exception of the floor, all cars are insulated throughout with three-inch Fiberglas with asbestos covering where the thickness is two inches. The inside of the cars is finished in sheet aluminum, Prestwood and Plymetal for such work as partitions, panels, headlining and ceilings, with an application of stainless steel wherever there is possible danger of damage from baggage or splashing. End and vestibule doors are aluminum and interior doors for lockers and toilets are ½-inch Plymetal. Windows are of the aluminum breather type, double-sash.

Water supply has been provided for with 200-gallon capacity in the coaches. The air-pressure-operated water systems are from Westinghouse Air Brake Company, with Vapor anti-freeze protection and hot water supply. General Electric water coolers are in all cars, usually one in each of the men's and women's lounges. Air-conditioning by Frigidaire complements the Vapor zone system of steam heat, which is supplemented by an overhead heat unit built into air-conditioned equipment.

Car trucks are four-wheel, single-equalizer type, with the exception of baggage and mail and the baggage-dormitory cars, which have six-wheel trucks. The multiple-wear wheels are 36 inches in diameter. They are wrought steel and semi-finished for balancing, with rims ground after mounting. With the exception of the Hyatt roller bearings on the grill and de luxe coaches for the St. Louis, Brownsville & Mexico run, all roller bearings are of Timken manufacture.

Strength has been built into the cars to comply with the specifications of the Post Office Department and the Association of American Railroads.

"The enthusiasm with which the traveling public greeted the 'Missouri River Eagles' and the 'Colorado Eagles' prior to and during World War II," says P. J. Neff, chief executive officer of the Missouri Pacific Lines, "convinced us that 'Eagle' service should be provided in our Southern territory as quickly as equipment could be made available.

"Studies were made during the war, and immediately after VJ-Day orders were placed for sufficient equipment to operate the 'Texas Eagles' between St. Louis-Memphis and the principal cities of Texas, and the 'Valley Eagles' between Houston and Brownsville."

As has been recorded in this chapter, the Eagles are paying off, and the Missouri Pacific and Texas & Pacific lines are to be commended for their fine contribution to the development of the railroads of today in the great Southwest. A fine road with fine personnel and officials headed by Paul Neff, a crack railroad man.

CHAPTER XVI

THE NICKEL PLATE

Road of Fast Freight

When you look up the "Nickel Plate Road" in the Official Railway Guide, you are referred to "(See N. Y. C. & St. L.)"; this stands for New York, Chicago & St. Louis Railroad. Just how and why the N. Y. C. & St. L. came to be called the Nickel Plate Road is a bit obscure, but it seems that the name was first employed in a jocular way by a newspaper editor. It was good publicity and the name stuck. Few people could tell off-hand what road the Nickel Plate represents, but the name itself is a famous railroad trade name in America—a name today made even more famous because of the speed of its fast freight.

First, let us consider the physical description of the Nickel Plate system. It is a product of a 1923 consolidation of the Toledo, St. Louis & Western (Clover Leaf) and the Lake Erie & Western with the New York, Chicago & St. Louis, which created a 1,687-mile system serving a six-state area. The principal lines extend like a three-pronged fork from Buffalo, New York, through Cleveland and Bellevue, Ohio, to Chicago and Peoria, Illinois, and St. Louis.

This highly concentrated, heavily-traveled area is a vastly important part of the nation's railway system, and the Nickel Plate is a vital piece of this steel-woven fabric of America.

The regional trend of traffic is predominantly eastward over the principal routes named. These three east-west lines, which funnel traffic to Buffalo, are supplemented by branches from Sandusky and Toledo, Ohio, and are intersected by branches

147

running north and south from Fort Wayne and Connersville, Indiana, and from Michigan City and Indianapolis.

The remarkable part of the Nickel Plate is the fact that its heavy fast freight movement, except for 250 miles, is single-track over the 1,687 miles operated. Where traffic density is greatest, the line is either double-track with automatic signaling, or single-track with Centralized Traffic Control. Automatic train control is employed in the territory between Chicago and Fort Wayne.

The Nickel Plate moves each freight car it handles at a greater average distance per day than any other large steam railway in the Eastern district of the United States. In June, 1948, the average was 78.4 miles per day.

Through 1948 and the latter part of 1947, the average speed of Nickel Plate freight trains, including branch-line locals and switch runs, was 19.2 miles per hour, or about 20 per cent higher than the national average. In April, 1948, the gross ton-miles per freight train-hour over the system equaled 51,659 miles, and on the busy Buffalo Division—less than half of which is double-tracked—it reached a record of 94,941 miles.

During the first six months of 1948, Nickel Plate freight locomotives ran an average daily mileage of 138.9, compared with a national average of 91.8 miles. In the very severe month of February of that year the average was 156.7 miles daily, excelling the locomotive mileage performance of any of the 56 roads included in the Interstate Commerce Commission's monthly "Operating Statistics of Large Steam Railways."

These remarkable operating results were the product of a very effective modernization program, which was carried out through close integration of the functions of several departments of the Nickel Plate system.

Now we will turn back the pages to learn a little of what went before and what led up to the present high standards of train performance on the Nickel Plate. Not long after the Van Sweringens acquired the road in 1916, the newly elected president, John J. Bernet, gave his attention to the relatively unsatisfactory performance of fuels poured under the boilers of Nickel Plate locomotives. What Mr. Bernet learned, in effect, was that a horse pulling half a load consumed practically the same amount of hay as when it pulled a full load. The same truth applied to the "iron horse." The result was the heavier loading of loco-motives.

In order to maintain the schedules of heavier trains it was necessary to improve the Nickel Plate's physical plant, including modern signaling practices, which would eliminate stops and slow-downs. It doesn't cost much to stop a train, but to start a train you have to pour on the coal, and a few unnecessary stops and the corresponding starts can play havoc with the fuel bill.

The effort to improve fuel efficiency, started by Nickel Plate president John J. Bernet in 1916, set in motion a general rehabili-tation and modernization program which continues to this day. The increased efficiency of the operations produces service more attractive to the shipper, with the result that the increased vol-ume of traffic has enabled the road to improve further its trans-portation of volume traffic.

In a program begun in 1938, over $33 million was spent for equipment and $19 million for improvements on the road. The benefits from these expenditures, carefully planned to improve transportation practices, were clearly reflected in the general improvement of the system.

In 1947, and through the first half of 1948, despite great in-creases in the unit cost of doing business, the Nickel Plate's posi-tion was relatively better than in the boom year of 1929.

The regularity of freight train operation is of distinct economic advantage to the road because it enhances its competitive posi-tion. The high utilization of locomotives and cars is made pos-sible by a quick turn-around. Expedited handling reduces *per diem* payments, since few cars in overhead traffic remain on Nickel Plate rails long enough to accrue more than a single day's charges. Hopper cars in coal traffic released empty in the Chicago area are often returned to connections as far east as Fostoria, 243 miles, before midnight of the day of release.

Freight train schedules are set up to favor eastward movements, as approximately 63 per cent of the net ton-miles handled move in that direction. The average speed of all eastbound trains during July, 1948, was 21.2 miles per hour, while the westbound average was 18.7. Although eastbound traffic is given preference, as has been pointed out, the average speed of westbound freights is well above the national average. The average gross tonnage of all trains in July, 1948, was 2,975 eastbound and 2,197 westbound. Eastward trains averaged 53 loaded and 6.8 empty cars, while westward trains averaged 28.3 loaded and 27.5 empty cars.

Fast freight schedules are maintained in both directions between Chicago, Peoria, and St. Louis, on the west, and Cleveland and Buffalo, on the east. Chicago-Buffalo trains are made up at Calumet yard, about 12 miles from Chicago; pick up from the Indiana Harbor Belt at Osborn, 11 miles farther east, and from the Elgin, Joliet & Eastern at Hobart, 12 miles east of Osborn. Under ordinary conditions, non-stop runs are made to West Wayne yard at Fort Wayne, Indiana, 151 miles east of Chicago.

The motive power is changed here and the freights continue eastward as soon as inspections are completed. Normally the runs over the division to Bellevue, Ohio, 125 miles, are made without stops. Bellevue is the Nickel Plate's principal classification yard, and both east- and westbound trains are classified here. Bellevue is not a big yard, having a combined east and west capacity of 3,200 cars. However, it frequently handles more than that number in a single 24-hour period.

The next two divisions, from Bellevue to Conneaut, Ohio, 132 miles, and Conneaut to Buffalo, 113 miles, are covered generally without coal or water stops, the locomotives operating through Conneaut on the same trains.

Trains from St. Louis and Peoria are consolidated at Frankfort, Indiana. Primary classifications are made at this point, and, when schedules permit, pre-classification for connections at Buffalo is performed. This further breakdown, however, is not allowed to interfere with the on-time operation of the trains.

Motive Power

A remarkable feature of the Nickel Plate's fast freight service is the speed of these booming trains. Manifest rolls at maximum authorized speeds of 60 miles per hour over most of the main line. Two-eight-four, or Berkshire type, steam locomotives with a rated tractive force of 64,100 pounds, have been adopted as standard for road freight service. These engines develop a high speed and they have proved very satisfactory.

Seventy of these locomotives are in service on the Nickel Plate as this is written, and ten are under construction at the Lima Hamilton Works. Thirty of the earlier locomotives are equipped with roller bearings on engine trucks and drivers and the ten new engines will be similarly equipped. Tenders are mounted on two six-wheel trucks and have a capacity of 22,000 gallons of water and 20 tons of coal.

Diesels are used in passenger service on the Nickel Plate, and eleven 2,000-horsepower units of this type of power were purchased in 1948. On the heavy Chicago-Cleveland-Buffalo trains two units are coupled into a 4,000-horsepower locomotive. On the lighter Cleveland-St. Louis run single units are used, and these have proved exceptionally well adapted to this service. Their rapid acceleration permits the fastest possible schedules on runs that require many intermediate stops for mail and passengers.

Yard work on the Nickel Plate is pretty well Dieselized with engines of 1,000-horsepower. These switchers are grouped at various points according to builder in order to simplify maintenance. Forty-three were in service in the latter part of 1948. At that time six switch engines at Buffalo and six at Cleveland were equipped with radio on an experimental basis. The results were so satisfactory that it was expected expansion of this service would be but a matter of a short time.

All motive power on the Nickel Plate is designed to such high standards that road failures are greatly minimized, with the result of high availability. Engines are built to stand the gaff of continuous high speed with tonnage trains.

Speed recorders have been installed on all locomotives in

manifest service. They are valuable not only as protection against excessive speeds, but they also take advantage of permissive speeds in order to lose as little time as possible in operating trains at less than permissible speed.

Water for steam locomotive operation is chemically treated at points where the local supply is not of a desirable quality. Coal purchases are carefully supervised to maintain grades of a standard that will give the utmost in steaming quality and will also alleviate the necessity of cleaning fires between regular engine terminals.

The Progressive Nickel Plate

Some 75 per cent of the Nickel Plate's freight is received from connecting lines and it is essential to maintain a lively and aggressive traffic department with real service to sell. The road maintains 42 traffic offices—31 of which are at off-line points. The Northern Ohio food terminal at Cleveland, constructed in 1930, and the Niagara Frontier food terminal at Buffalo—operated jointly with the Erie—coupled with its fast freight schedules, have enabled the Nickel Plate to secure considerable perishable traffic for termination on its own lines, as well as for delivery to eastern connections.

Under the able administration of the late J. W. Davin, president, a great railroader, the policy of rehabilitation and improvement was greatly accelerated, enabling the road to produce the kind of transportation that appeals to shippers—the kind of transportation that is noted for its dispatch and its efficiency.

In the latter part of 1948, in addition to the 10 modern steam freight locomotives, the Nickel Plate had on order 25 streamlined passenger cars, of which 13 were sleepers, two were sleeper-diner-lounge cars and ten were coaches. These, upon delivery, completely modernized the road's main line passenger service. Another progressive program included replacing with steel the wooden sides of 1,890 box cars at the Frankfort shops. This work began immediately after the close of World War II.

The modernization program on the Nickel Plate, as on other roads all over the country, included the installation of Centralized Traffic Control at various locations. Installations were made between Arcadia, Ohio, and New Haven, Indiana, a distance of 77.3 miles; also between Frankfort and Muncie, Indiana—62 miles. An installation between St. Marys, Ohio, and Muncie was authorized in 1948. Upon its completion continuous double-track or centralized traffic control operation was provided over all main-line trackage in the heavy density territories between Chicago and Buffalo, and between Frankfort, Indiana, and the junction with the Chicago-Buffalo route at Arcadia, Ohio.

This portion of the Nickel Plate—representing nearly half of the total mileage operated—is the way of the red ball trains. Here the 60-mile-per-hour manifests roll.

At three locations bridges were strengthened or renewed to eliminate speed restrictions or increase tonnage rarings, and a reduction of curvature was made at Brocton, New York. The 1948 track program further included the replacing of light rail with 132-pound rail in 172 miles of track, and the placing of nearly half a million new treated ties.

In September, 1948, an interlocking plant with the Chicago, Indianapolis & St. Louis was placed in service at Linden, Indiana. The construction of a new interlocking plant at the crossing with the Baltimore & Ohio, the Chesapeake & Ohio and the New York Central at Fostoria, Ohio, eliminated the last non-interlocking crossing in high-speed territory between Chicago and Buffalo.

1948 saw the completion of a modern fireproof general storehouse, costing $265,000, at Lima, Ohio; also a new engine terminal and office building at Bellevue, Ohio, was finished. Other new construction during that year included a new boilerhouse and eight-stall enginehouse at Chicago, with facilities for the servicing of six steam road engines and two Diesel switching locomotives, a new coal dock, Diesel oil storage and fueling and cinder-handling facilities.

Modern communications aid in speeding the fast freights of the Nickel Plate, and we find that wizard of words, the teletype, in service at all principal points on the Nickel Plate's main line between Buffalo and Chicago, as well as between Arcadia, Ohio, and Frankfort, Indiana.

A standing manifest train has as few friends as a stopped limited between stations. Today's design of living calls for speed in travel, communication, and freight service. The railroads of yesterday did well enough in a horse-and-buggy era, but the modern railroad is in competition with the truck and automobile, the airplane and the waterways, with the result that "speed" is the watchword of the rails.

It was not so long ago that 60 miles an hour for a box car would have been disastrous, but now it has to travel in fast company. This speeding freight car, despite a great increase in the unit cost of doing business, has aided in putting the Nickel Plate in a relatively better position than the road enjoyed in the boom year of 1929. Through the economy of fast operation the Nickel Plate was able to make drastic debt reductions, and more than halved interest over the ten-year period between December 31, 1937, and December 31, 1947.

The Nickel Plate is a fine example of what can be accomplished by the wise investment of capital in modern fast freight movement and facilities, and will continue to be a real "Railroad of Today" under the able guidance of its new president, Lynn L. White, a crack operator and first-class, all-around railroad man.

CHAPTER XVII

NASHVILLE, CHATTANOOGA &
ST. LOUIS

The Progressive "Dixie Line"

Men with vision and the courage to make things come true direct the destiny of the Nashville, Chattanooga & St. Louis Railway, one of the greatest railroads in the country.

The big railroads form the transportation backbone of America, both in peace and wartime. They are of vital economic importance to the health and well-being of the Nation. Just as important, however, are the smaller railroads in the area in which they serve. These roads are important not only locally, but they act as essential connecting links in the vast American rail network. How well these roads are operated and maintained depends on their leadership.

The track mileage of the NC&StL Railway is not great—about 1,100 miles—but more than simple track mileage is involved in this midland Tennessee railroad's approach to greatness. The heart and the spirit of those early Tennessee pioneers is reflected today in the substantial and comprehensive development of the railroad by those who came after.

Originally known as the Nashville & Chattanooga Railroad, the first train was run for a distance of ten miles on April 13, 1851, some five months after the charter was granted. In July, 1854, the line was extended to Chattanooga. By then, other lines had been constructed, and through-freight and passenger service was inaugurated between Nashville, Charleston, South Carolina, Savannah, Georgia, and other Southeastern points.

The Nashville & Chattanooga road was conceived for the purpose of providing an outlet for agricultural products from middle Tennessee to the Atlantic coast. At the time of its conception and construction there were only a few miles of railroad in the country at points contiguous to the Atlantic Seaboard and nothing of the kind in the territory around St. Louis and Chicago. Thus the builders had an eye to the eventual handling of traffic destined for the West, the Northwest and the rapidly developing Southeast.

The first survey of the line was made by John Edgar Thompson, then chief engineer of the Georgia Railroad, who traveled by horseback through the wilderness between Chattanooga and Nashville.

From the beginning the Nashville, Chattanooga & St. Louis Railway has been blessed with wise administration and cautious, energetic and progressive management. Through peace, depression, and wars it has continued to keep abreast of the times in physical development and operating facilities, fulfilling its obligations to those whom its serves. The destiny of the road has been almost wholly in the hands of Tennesseans.

The railroad has never been through any kind of reorganization. It has never failed to meet a just obligation. In common with all roads, the NC&StL Railway suffered under-maintenance of its physical properties during the hard depression years, and it required time and heavy expenditures to bring the road back to anything like a satisfactory condition of plant and equipment.

It was during the years 1941 to 1947 that the Nashville, Chattanooga & St. Louis saw its greatest development and progress. The means and the opportunity were offered and promptly seized upon by men up front. It was conceived that complete modernization of the physical properties and facilities had to be accomplished if the road hoped to maintain its tradition as one of the fine roads of the South.

In a strict adherence to the policy of moving forward, and with the encouragement of modestly increasing earnings, tentative plans were laid down. War seemed imminent in the years through 1941, and wise heads anticipated possible future requirements if America were involved, and began active preparations for the emergency. At the time of Pearl Harbor, the Nashville,

Chattanooga & St. Louis Railway was prepared to play its part in the economic affairs of the Nation fairly well.

Every demand created by the war was satisfactorily met. They were impressive demands, demands that at times strained the road's facilities but never threatened its stability. The rehabilitation, reconstruction and improvement program was inaugurated in 1941 with the purchase of new motive power and freight equipment. Numerous road improvement projects were in full swing by 1944. The trend was toward high-speed trains, both freight and passenger, and speed demands track tailoring all up and down the line.

In January of 1945, the Board of Directors authorized a five-year program for the calendar years 1945 to 1949, inclusive, for grade and curve reduction of the main line from Atlanta, Georgia, to Memphis, Tennessee. Amazingly, this expansive track program was completed in December, 1947, only two and one-half years after the inauguration of construction work. The overall cost was $4,940,425, the major portion of which was chargeable to Additions and Betterments, and financed from current funds of the Railway.

An instance of the substantial benefits resulting from this line improvement was the increased locomotive rating between Bruceton and Nashville, Tennessee, from 1,500 to 1,900 tons.

Several important adjustments had been made in the roadway prior to the inauguration of the general program of grade and alignment improvements adopted in January, 1945. Not including these, it is interesting to sum up the results of three of the major projects:

	General Program	Etowah Bridge	Alatoona Dam & Reservoir	Total
New modern railroad constructed (miles)	74.80	1.93	4.09	80.82
Saving in distance (miles)	2.72	.67	1.65	5.04
Number of curves entirely eliminated	67	2	22	91
Total degrees of curvature eliminated	2,617	212	727	3,556
Number of curves reduced to 2 deg. or less	126	4	5	135

157

In close relation to grade and curve-reduction work, the work of restoration of cuts and embankments was begun. Upon the completion of these two fundamental projects the road had a completely finished roadway sub-structure, well drained, with widened embankments, with no immediate need of any major grade or alignment revision. A superstructure of ballast, creosoted ties, and heavy rail not only met the requirements of current and increasing traffic, but in the future it will be operated far more efficiently and maintained more economically.

Providing an up-to-date and adequate roadway was, of course, essential. Next in importance was the means for prompt, efficient, and economical handling of traffic.

Even before plans for grade and curve reduction had been fully completed, it was decided to install Centralized Traffic Control. The heaviest train movement on the NC&StL is between Atlanta and Junta, Georgia, because of the joint use of that portion of the Atlantic Division by the Louisville and Nashville Railroad, and it was decided to install C.T.C., the modern system of dispatching trains.

This first segment of C.T.C. was completed between Atlanta and Junta in August, 1943. The results were so gratifying that steps were taken immediately for the installation of C.T.C. all the way from Atlanta, Georgia, to Bruceton, Tennessee, with the exception of the 38 miles of double-track between Chattanooga, Tennessee, and Stevenson, Alabama. The final work was completed in June, 1947, giving the Nashville, Chattanooga & St. Louis Railway Centralized Traffic Control on all single-track over a distance of 384 miles.

The cost of the installation was approximately $1,750,000.

With C.T.C. and the improved track conditions fast freights on the NC&StL saved an average of at least four hours between Bruceton and Atlanta as compared with the old train order operation. C.T.C. further added to the safety of train movements. By thus modernizing its plant the road was in a position to render the finest, fastest, and most dependable service in its history, a service comparable with the best in the country.

Bridge Improvements and Replacements

In connection with the general major improvement plans, special study and attention was given to the strengthening, replacement, and construction of new bridges, some of which are listed herewith.

The Chattahoochee River Bridge, seven and one half miles north of Atlanta, Georgia—Deck trusses replaced with deck plate girders and stone masonry piers encased with concrete. Work completed October 6, 1944. Cost: $375,261.

Etowah River Bridge, 45 miles north of Atlanta, Georgia—New deck plate girder bridge on concrete piers, replacing old bridge. Relocation of line eliminating .67 mile of main track and 212 degrees of curvature. Maximum degree of curvature now is 2 degrees, as compared with 5¾ degrees on the old line. This bridge was placed in service December 5, 1944, at an expenditure of $775,259.

Bridge No. 123.1 over the Tennessee River at Bridgeport, Alabama, 28 miles north of Chattanooga, was strengthened, the draw span increased to double its former capacity and its operating machinery rehabilitated. The cost was approximately $123,094.

Draw Bridge at Johnsonville, Tennessee, over Tennessee River, 80 miles west of Nashville.

Contract with the Tennessee Valley Authority was entered into on January 5, 1943, for the relocation of that part of the Nashville Division between Mile-Posts 74.4 and 84.5. This relocation was necessitated by the construction of Gilbertsville Dam on the Tennessee River near Gilbertsville, Kentucky, which raised the water level in the Tennessee River and created a lake across West Tennessee practically from the Kentucky to the Mississippi State lines, submerging approximately 256,000 acres, and having a shore line of about 1,580 miles.

The new bridge over the Tennessee River is 1,737 feet in length and consists of two deck plate girder spans and six through truss spans, one of which is a movable span of vertical lift type 360 feet long. The new line is 10.74 miles long, compared with 10.06 miles of the old line, an increase of .68 of a mile of track.

This bridge is the most modern structure of its class in the Southeast. The entire cost of approximately $2,500,000 was borne by the Tennessee Valley authority.

The new line was opened for traffic and the old line abandoned on December 17, 1945.

Beside these major bridge projects, special attention was given to raising and reconstruction wherever necessary, renewing decks, concreting piers and abutments, and to the strengthening of all bridge structures to enable them to carry the heaviest traffic.

Plant and Rolling Stock Improvements

The improvements of buildings on the Nashville, Chattanooga & St. Louis included the enlargement of the shops at Nashville, the construction of new storehouse units, and the erection of quarters for the servicing of Diesels. The extension, remodeling and construction of new freight and passenger buildings at various points on the road kept pace with the swift modernization of the other facilities.

Four old 90-foot turntables at Nashville, Bruceton, Chattanooga and Atlanta were replaced by new 110-foot turntables. A reversible escalator, with a 29-foot lift, was installed in the Union Station at Atlanta.

Possibly no railroad in the country ever underwent so complete a housecleaning. The NC&StL left no stone unturned to build its "Railroad of Today." It built from the ground up. It was both an astonishing and remarkable example of what could be accomplished by a resourceful and energetic president and board of directors, once they had established their goal.

Out came old railroad ties and down went new cresoted units, until there was not a single cross-tie or switch-tie in any main or side tracks that was not creosoted.

During the years 1941 to 1947, inclusive, the following new rail was laid:

131 pound	20.85 miles
112 "	284.50 "
110 "	5.58 "
90 "	55.22 "
Total	366.13 miles

The 131-pound rail was laid in 1947. However, very little of this rail was laid before it was decided to abandon that particular section and adopt as the current standard the 132-pound AREA section. This weight rail was selected for main track.

Between 1941 and 1947, inclusive, an average of 165,000 yards of ballast per annum was used in maintaining and strengthening the track. The necessity of modern mechanized roadway facilities has long since been recognized, and the NC&StL included in its program the purchase of new locomotive cranes, grading equipment, motor cars, electric tie tampers, tie adzers and other equipment for the efficient and economical maintenance of the track structure.

The roadway was also substantially improved by the purchase of additional and larger tie plates, rail anchors, gauge rods, etc. Then came the application of the latest appliances to signals and interlocking plants, the substitution of creosoted poles, and cross-arms in all renewals over the entire system. All this was climaxed by the installation of the Centralized Traffic Control system.

During the period of which we write, the Nashville, Chattanooga & St. Louis Railway, "The Dixie Line," purchased the following motive power and freight equipment:

    20—J-3, 4-8-4 Roller Bearing Steam Locomotives
    20—Diesel-Electric Switch Engines
 1,000—Box Cars
 1,250—Hopper and Gondola Cars

The expenditure for this equipment was $11,985,335. Equipment obligations were issued in the amount of $7,843,500; the remainder was financed from current funds in the amount of $4,141,835.

The work of modernizing freight equipment was pushed by the consistent application of "AB" brakes, metal running boards, bottom rods and brake-beam supports, the conversion into all-steel units, the construction of modern bay-window cabooses, and numerous other improvements to the tune of $1,100,000.

Let it be remembered that this is a road that has never been through any sort of reorganization. This is a little road that does things in a big way. It does not hesitate to spend money when and where it is needed. Rather, should we say, the NC&StL makes wise investments, which it guards zealously.

A Streamliner Is Created

It is easy to understand how this Dixie Line road has achieved success. Obstacles do not mean a thing to the NC&StL. This amazing Tennessee railroad simply raises its sights, when the target is a bit difficult, and bangs away.

We heard for a long time of material scarcities and slow deliveries of new equipment. When many concerns, including the railroads, were experiencing difficulties, the NC&StL purchased 22 Pullman cars and reconditioned them to meet service requirements. This passenger equipment as a whole was brought up to meet every operating requirement. The cost ran around $229,206.

The streamlined *City of Memphis* was conceived and born in the Nashville shops, the first time a complete train of this character was ever built in company shops in the South. At a cost of $328,240, a rather considerable saving was effected; not only that, a fine streamliner was turned out while other roads were waiting for car manufacturers.

The *City of Memphis* was given modern trucks, roller bearings and the latest in mechanical features. The interiors received de luxe styling and every modern facility for the comfort and convenience of its passengers was provided.

The *City of Memphis* leaves Memphis at 8:05 A.M., makes a convenient layover at Nashville and completes the return trip to Memphis at 7:40 P.M., making the run of 237 miles each way in five hours flat.

Among the many things we find to marvel at on the Dixie Line is the car ferry between Hobbs Island and Guntersville, Alabama, across the Tennessee River. This is the longest river transfer made by any United States railroad. The distance is 22 miles.

M.P. diesel #7008 with #1 the southbound Texas Eagle just after she went into service in August, 1948. Courtesy Missouri Pacific RR.

Third #3, the California Limited, coming off Horseshoe Curve at Blanchard, N.M., on the Third District of the New Mexico Division with nine cars and engine #3779 of the Santa Fe great 3776 Class 4–8–4 type. Photo by R. H. Kindig.

N. C. & St. L. work train with engine #612 2–8–2 type Class K3 with modern diesel-powered shovel dump cars, Jordan spreader and diesel-powered bulldozer. Modern roadway equipment plays a big part in a "Railroad of Today," like the N. C. & St. L. Courtesy N. C. & St. L. RR.

N. C. & St. L. #576—4—8—4 type, Class J—3 being washed by a modern engine-washing machine at the Nashville Shops at Nashville, Tenn. Courtesy N. C. & St. L. RR.

Nickel Plate's new storehouse at Lima, Ohio, completed in 1948 at a cost of $500,000. Courtesy Nickel Plate RR.

N. C. & St. L. #5 — the City of Memphis — deluxe streamliner operating between Memphis and Nashville running along the Tennessee River at Johnsonville, Tenn., on the Nashville Division. Photo courtesy of N. C. & St. L.

Missouri Pacific #2107—4—8—4 type, solid train of empty reefers and two cars of stock west of Tribune, Kansas, on the Colorado Division. This class was rebuilt from the 1901 2—8—4 type. Courtesy Otto C. Perry.

New lightweight divided coach in service on Missouri Pacific's crack Eagle running through the magnificent Rio Grande Valley between Houston and Brownsville, Texas. Courtesy Missouri Pacific Lines.

Streamlined San Diegan #76 running along the Pacific near Oceanside on the Fourth District of the Los Angeles Division. Courtesy Santa Fe RR.

Type of lounge car in service in center of train on Santa Fe Super Chief. There are three lounge cars on this great train. Taken from cocktail bar. Courtesy Santa Fe RR.

New diner lounge cars in service on Missouri Pacific's Texas and Colorado Eagle. Courtesy Missouri Pacific RR.

N & W Extra 2110 east with a heavy tonnage coal train rounding the 4% curve at Pearisburg, Va., on the Radford Division. Courtesy N & W RR.

Westbound passenger train #37 has just run around a westbound extra in double track CTC territory. Now it meets #92, eastbound manifest at Lockwood, Ky., an example of CTC at its best. C & O Big Sandy Branch installations.

The City of San Francisco's diesel being washed by the new Whiting diesel washer in the Southern Pacific Yards at Oakland, Calif., before returning to Chicago in the evening on train #102—Western Division. Courtesy Southern Pacific RR.

A new 800-horsepower all-steel Diesel tugboat, costing $177,000, handles the traffic formerly moved by two river steamboats, and in much less time. In 1938, the road purchased two big steel barges having a capacity of ten cars each. These new barges, measuring 240 in length, 32 feet in width and eight feet in drawing, effected a considerable saving, both in maintenance and operation, another example of how a thrifty railroad can save money by spending money.

In every department, the Nashville, Chattanooga & St. Louis has brought its operations completely up-to-date, moving forward, year by year, in a constantly efficient manner that is reflected by its streamlined trains and by its streamlined roadway and shops. Certainly no line ever was tailored so completely to meet the demands of the railroads of today as this fine road of the South.

Let us, for a moment, look at the shops. The kind of service you get for your family automobile depends to a large extent on the repair facilities available at your dealer's plant. The servicing of motive power and rolling stock is equally important to a railroad and its patrons.

In the way of shop machinery and tools, the following quotation from the annual report for the year 1946 is typical of the progress of the NS&StL program throughout the period of modernization, which, to any necessary extent, will continue:

In continuing the program of replacing old shop machinery and equipment with more modern units, the following installations were made:

One Cincinnati all-steel press brake; one 90-inch driving wheel lathe; two 750-cubic foot electric air compressors; one vertical spindle grinder; one semi-automatic locomotive washing machine; one 15-ton overhead crane in erecting shop; six low-lift trucks; one high-lift fork-type truck; one 54-unit car wheel boring mill; and one 80-foot coach repair and inspection pit.

The main shops at Nashville, as well as the outlying shops at Atlanta, Chattanooga and Bruceton where the same procedure was involved, are, as a result, adequately equipped with modern machinery to take care efficiently and economically of the repair, maintenance, and reconstruction of all classes of motive power and freight and passenger equipment.

NS&StL steam locomotives were modernized by the application of stokers and feed-water heaters and other appliances. The main line steam power is some of the finest to be found anywhere, both in trim and sparkling appearance, and in operation.

During the period which we have reviewed, 57.30 miles of unprofitable branch lines were abandoned. On the NS&StL every foot of track is expected to pay its way.

The road is a "bridge line," with traffic moving from points north of the Ohio and west of the Mississippi to points in the Southeast. To a considerable extent the same applies in the reverse direction. This has been true in a great measure throughout the life of the Nashville, Chattanooga & St. Louis system.

To keep this "life blood" flowing in measurable volume over the tracks of the NC&StL calls for intense solicitations for both freight and passengers, and effective traffic organizations are maintained in Chicago, St. Louis, Kansas City and at other strategic points throughout the entire Southeast. It is essential for a live railroad to keep on its toes constantly, and energetic, alert, and diligent attention has been devoted to sustaining and increasing the flow of business by up-and-coming traffic representatives.

In the case of the NS&StL, these representatives have something worthwhile to sell, and they are telling the world about it. The result has indeed been gratifying.

Industrial Development

Having a full realization of the importance of encouraging industrial development along its lines, the Nashville, Chattanooga & St. Louis Railway has not only co-operated closely with existing industries along its lines but also has encouraged the establishment of new plants with a view of developing a self-sustaining freight business and being less dependent on the volume of through and competitive traffic.

The potentialities of this policy are clearly illustrated in the following instances: during the latter part of 1946, industrial tracks, with appropriate switching sidings constructed at the expense of the NC&StL, were completed in order that the road might better serve four imporant plants—the Combustion Engineering Company and the Wheland Company, both located at Chattanooga; the Nashville Corporation, at Nashville, and the Murray Manufacturing Company, located at Murray, Kentucky.

During the calendar year 1947, 5,721 carloads of freight were handled to and from these plants, as compared with 2,685 carloads for the year 1946, an increase of over 100 per cent.

Sites for industrial and manufacturing concerns, warehouses, etc. along the NC&StL are scarce and often unavailable. The need for providing such sites to increase local traffic is in line with the policy of the road. There was, for example, the situation in the Atlanta area, which had become increasingly acute. In April, 1947, the NC&StL availed itself of the opportunity to acquire over 234 acres which were conveniently located to its yard facilities. The cost was around $74,000. Development of the tract as a potential industrial center of importance got under way, with every indication that in the long run it would be remunerative to a high degree.

The same thing happened at Jackson, Tennessee, with the acquisition of a 32-acre tract early in 1948 for $35,000. This does not mean that the Nashville, Chattanooga & St. Louis Railway is looking to clean up in real estate. It is simply an indication of a far-sighted policy whereby the road is cannily laying the foundation for a backlog of future freight business.

The industries which the NC&StL has been instrumental in locating adjacent to its tracks in the past are today furnishing a substantial and constantly increasing volume of local traffic.

The NC&StL is a one-third owner of the Paducah & Illinois Railroad, consisting of 14.94 miles of railroad and a double-track bridge across the Ohio between Paducah, Kentucky, and Metropolis, Illinois. This segment of line is owned jointly with the CB&O and the Illinois Central.

One of the marvels of the Nashville, Chattanooga & St. Louis road is the famous Cumberland Mountain tunnel, blasted through solid limestone back around 1850. Unlike most tunnels of that time, built to accommodate the small locomotives of the day, the Cumberland Mountain tunnel is still big enough for modern motive power.

For a period of two and a half years, beginning in 1942, The NC&StL conducted a school of railroading called the "Employes Educational Service." This was under the direct leadership of Professor Roy L. Garis, of Vanderbilt University, who devoted his entire time to this work.

The service was inaugurated with the subject "The Development of Transportation in the Southeast prior to 1845." As the instructions and studies progressed, 18 different textbooks or pamphlets were printed for use of employees. Every phase of railroading in general and every department activity of the NC&StL Railway in particular, no matter how small, were covered. The history of various periods of the road in the form of separate lessons and textbooks was written and printed. Classes were conducted and oral and written examinations were held. The papers submitted were carefully judged and reports made to the individuals showing their ratings.

Generally it was conceded that a great deal of good had been accomplished. Certainly any railroad employee with a knowledge of the background and history of the road on which he or she works will be better fitted to serve in any public relations capacity.

In the opening chapter, we spoke of the Train Passenger Agent, Mr. Jones. His complete knowledge, not only of the train and the division but of the background of the road, and his willingness to draw on that knowledge, both by volunteering information and by fully answering questions, made him an invaluable asset.

Nine More Diesels

In closing this chapter, we would like to quote from the editorial page of the *Nashville Banner* of October 27, 1948:

NINE MORE DIESELS

Railroad progress is aptly described in the term "Dieselize," and the word fits the accomplishment of the NC&StL, rapidly materializing under the leadership of President W. S. Hackworth, and emphasized again by the announcement that nine MORE Diesel power units will be purchased, this time for all passenger and freight trains on main line runs.

The board of directors yesterday approved that recommendation, for a total of 30 Diesel units now in operation on NC&StL tracks or on order. It represents an investment of nearly $5,000,000 for these engines; in addition approximately $4,000,000 is being spent for all-steel, open-top freight cars to further improve the line's rolling stock.

Progress costs money. Improvement and modernization along these lines are undertaken for progress in the interest of greater public service.

Men possessed of vision and with confidence in an area's future manifest the enterprise that built this railroad and guided it successfully through the years. On that roster of great railroad leadership the name of W. S. Hackworth belongs. Under his guidance, the NC&StL is magnificently discharging its obligations of service, and making the investments which vision underwrites to improve that service.

The "Banner" is 100 per cent correct and states it mildly. President Hackworth is tops in every way and knows the game from the Head End to the Rear End as well as any railroader I ever knew.

CHAPTER XVIII

THE SOUTHERN PACIFIC

Diesels

Most of the postwar Diesel locomotives on the Southern Pacific augmented rather than replaced steam power. There has, however, been a notable slackening of new steam locomotive purchases since 1943. Because of their vast numbers, steam locomotives will undoubtedly predominate on the S.P. for some years to come. You just cannot replace around two thousand locomotives overnight.

In 1939 the Southern Pacific received its first Diesel switch engine and its performance was so impressive that in the next few years the road had built up one of the largest Diesel switching fleets in the country. Shortly after the end of World War II, the S.P. began equipping some of its Diesel switchers with radio as a means of further expanding their operating usefulness in certain metropolitan industrial areas.

It was in 1936 that the Southern Pacific's first Diesel power appeared on the streamlined *City of San Francisco*, which is jointly operated with the Union Pacific and the Chicago & North Western along the Overland Route between San Francisco and Chicago. This train began making five round trips a month in the summer of 1936 and became a daily service train in the autumn of 1947.

The Southern Pacific's first solely owned mainline Diesels were 6,000-horsepower freight and 6,000-horsepower passenger locomotives received from the Electro-Motive Division of General Motors in 1947. These were followed in 1948 by 6,000-horsepower passenger Diesels built by American Locomotive

Company. Additional Diesels for freight service were purchased from Electro-Motive in 1948.

The first definite replacement of steam by Diesel power on a top passenger train of the S.P. came in 1947 on the *Golden State*, which became a full streamliner early in 1948 on its run between Los Angeles and Chicago, via the Southern Pacific-Rock Island lines.

Except for the *City of San Francisco*, most of the early Diesel mainline operations were confined to the Southwest. Principal servicing shops were built at Los Angeles, and on-line fueling facilities were provided at Tucson and other points. Diesels invaded the Shasta Route between San Francisco and Portland in 1948, using the shopping facilities that had been established in Oakland for the *City of San Francisco*.

The Shasta Route Diesels, "broken in" on the *Cascade* in 1948, served their apprenticeship for a fully streamlined Cascade when the new cars were available. At that time this power was also scheduled for the new coach train called the *Shasta Daylight*. It was hoped the cars for this train would be coming from the builders in 1949. The Southern Pacific had optimistically announced plans for this train in January, 1946, but they were not to be had.

In the fall of 1948, the Southern Pacific announced plans to Dieselize the famous *Sunset Limited*, making it a full streamliner and improving its already fast schedule between Los Angeles and New Orleans. This new train probably will be running early in 1950.

In the summer of 1948, people living along the S.P.'s Coast Lines saw Diesels beginning to appear occasionally on the famous *Lark* and the *Noon Daylights*. This was done to obtain full utilization of this modern power. Diesels are potentially available 24 hours a day, and the Southern Pacific saw no reason for allowing them to remain idle in Los Angeles when they could be put to use. It was pointed out, however, that this should not be taken as evidence that the "Daylight" type steam locomotives were not doing a good job. They always have been the finest type of steam power anywhere.

In the vast Southwest, where it always has been a problem to supply good water for steam locomotives, the Diesels are particularly valuable. More and more, these long black freight Diesels, with their colorful aluminum front-ends and their red and orange color bands, will be seen in the desert country.

Colors of the passenger Diesels are in two distinct schemes. Red and silver are used on the locomotives for the Golden State and red and orange have been adapted for use on the Shasta Route.

In 1948, the Southern Pacific also began to experiment with a new type of Diesel built by Baldwin. These were designed for use either in mainline or switch yard operations. In addition to the first 1,500-horsepower locomotive of this type to see service on the Espee, 14 more were on order during the latter part of 1948.

During the first three years after V-J Day the Southern Pacific had received or ordered more than $217,000,000 worth of new rolling equipment. This included 195 Diesel locomotives and 20,715 freight and passenger cars. There were also 8,000 new refrigerator cars for the Pacific Fruit Express, which the S.P. owns jointly with the Union Pacific.

Of the new equipment for passenger service there were 17 new Diesels, a third interest in a new locomotive for the *City of San Francisco*, and 185 new passenger cars for five completely new *Sunset Limited* trains, two new *Cascades* and two *Shasta Daylights*. Also included were new cars for other trains in the S.P.'s great passenger train fleet.

The builders maintained deliveries of the new passenger locomotives fairly close to announced schedules, and at the end of 1948 eight were in service. The *Sunset Limited* had nine scheduled for power equipment in 1949.

The delivery of new passenger cars was something else again. They didn't come through, and in the fall of 1948 the S.P. was still waiting. Many people have blamed the railroads, but for a long time getting new railroad passenger cars was like getting new automobiles—there just were not enough to go around.

The end of 1948 saw about half of the 20,400 freight cars and the 130 bay-window cabooses, which had been ordered, in service. At that time, 20 of the new mainline freight Diesels were pulling trains. Another 50 were on order—eight for delivery in 1949. Augmenting the S.P.'s then large fleet of Diesel switchers were 33 that had been placed in service since the end of World War II. Sixty more were on the books for 1949.

Two additional road switchers joined the fleet of Southern Pacific locomotives at the close of 1948 and 12 more were to follow in the ensuing months.

Of the 8,000 new refrigerator cars ordered after V-J Day, 5,000 were carrying perishables by 1948. The remaining 3,000 were building in Pacific Fruit Express car shops in 1949. Thus it can be seen that in spite of material shortages and labor difficulties, both part of every reconstruction period, the S.P., in line with other railroads of the country, were steadily patching up their fences.

Improved Freight Handling

The postwar activities of the Southern Pacific included a campaign directed toward reducing loss and damage claims, which is part of a campaign being conducted by other railroads in a search for ways and means of eliminating a loss that nationally reached staggering proportions.

Using 1939 statistics as a base, the Interstate Commerce Commission reported in 1948 that while the revenue ton miles on the railroads had about doubled in 1947, loss and damage payments increased nearly six times. The situation on the Southern Pacific was relatively the same as that on other lines.

Because at least half of the claim payments are chargeable to container failures, the Southern Pacific directed special attention to this field. The road enlisted the aid of "container engineers" in its Freight Protection Department. It further devised a container of its own for the mass handling of less-than-carload merchandise items.

The Freight Protection and Station Service Department of the

S.P. is affiliated with the Operating Department, and closely allied to the Freight Department, and it reaches out to exert its good influence in almost every angle of railroading. Under the manager of this Freight Protection and Station Service Department there is a road staff consisting of 11 container and packaging experts. These men work closely with all of the thousands of loaders, train crews, station agents and truckers—yes, and even with the stowers, waybill clerks, checkers, inspectors and railroad police—in seeing that your freight shipment gets to its proper destination efficiently and safely.

From the moment a shipment is received by the Southern Pacific until it is delivered to the consignee, the S.P. is its custodian as well as its mover. The Southern Pacific, in conjunction with other railroads, conducts a continuous program of education among the personnel, training them not only in methods of proper freight handling, but also in the necessity of careful handling of goods entrusted to them. On S.P. bulletin boards in six western states there are reminders to employees to treat each and every shipment as though it were their own.

In addition to the education of manpower, the Southern Pacific introduced mechanical devices to reduce some of the handling and rehandling of shipments. The road in 1948 designed and placed in service a number of special containers built of metal and plywood, and placed on skids for mechanized handling.

For more than a year, scores of these containers were tested and they gained a 100 per cent record for protection against damage to goods loaded. This elimination of damage was due in part to the reduced handling of small items in the less-than-carload merchandise traffic, and partly to the extra overall protection of the container itself. The S.P. found that use of the containers speeded the movement of shipments at both origin and destination. Through the employment of these containers it was possible to load and unload merchandise in about one-sixth the time that was formerly required. The new containers were a natural outgrowth of increased mechanization in merchandise handling.

The S.P. had considerable mechanized freight handling equipment in use before World War II; it added to it during the war years, and after V-J Day the mechanization program was given new stimulus by the restoration of the Southern Pacific's famous "Overnight" merchandise trains. These trains are so fast that speed in handling merchandise to and from them, to prevent delay, was increasingly important. A great deal of this work is done with tractor and trailer trains, mobile cranes and forklift trucks.

Peacetime High for Freight

At the close of 1948, the S.P.'s able president A. T. Mercier, announced that the volume of freight service rendered by the Southern Pacific was the greatest of any peacetime year.

During 1948, the Espee rolled up the astonishing volume of 37 billion revenue net ton miles. To break this down into figures a little more understandable, this was the equivalent of trans-porting more than 4,000 tons of freight around the equator every day in the year.

It was through large capital expenditures for plant improve-ment, including further Dieselation of motive power that the company was able to handle this record peacetime traffic with dispatch. With the acquisition of a large number of new freight cars and the expeditious movement of trains, together with the help of shippers and receivers of freight in speeding the loading and unloading of shipments, freight car shortages during periods of peak loading requirements were less in 1948 than in 1947. At this writing, the S.P. reports that the outlook for car supply is brighter than it has been for some time.

President Mercier, in reporting these highlights of Southern Pacific operations in 1948, stressed the need for rate increases to offset the higher wage and material costs and to permit the rail industry to go forward with improvement programs for the bene-fit of both the shipping and the traveling public.

CHAPTER XIX

NORFOLK & WESTERN

Portsmouth-Cincinnati C.T.C.

Heavy traffic and grades combined to provide a serious operating problem on 96 miles of single-track on the Norfolk and Western between Portsmouth and Clare (Cincinnati, Ohio). This track carries at times as many as 30 trains daily and serves as the entry to Cincinnati for the entire Norfolk and Western. In 1926 the line was equipped with absolute permissive automatic block signals. Train movements were authorized by timetable and train orders, with automatic block protection, but there came a time when something more was needed to move the traffic.

The answer, of course, was C.T.C.—centralized traffic control.

Much has been written about C.T.C., some of which was intended to let the lay reader in on the secret of "push-button" railroading. In another chapter we wrote of C.T.C. (centralized traffic control) and Coded Track Circuits, but this may not be too clear to those unfamiliar with the present train dispatching methods under centralized traffic control.

Let us assume that you have installed a rather large miniature railway system, with several trains in operation in both directions on a single-track, which has sidings at intervals. Before you, there is a panel with a row of small levers. These levers operate the signals and switches on your miniature railway. Your trains, let us say, are automatically controlled and will proceed only when the lights are green, coming to a stop at each red signal and waiting until it shows green, or clear.

Your task is to operate the control panel levers so the trains may meet and pass with as little delay as possible. The miniature railway is so arranged that it is impossible to operate the signals and switches so as to set up dangerous conflicting movements.

Because these miniature trains are constantly under your eye it is a simple matter for you to dispatch them. Now let us expand our railway to full-size operation on a regular division, with Clare Yard (Cincinnati) to the west and Vera, just outside Portsmouth, 96 miles away to the east. Instead of actual vision you now have before you a track model along the top of your three-sided control panel. Lights on this track model, winking on and off, indicate the position of the trains. You make your moves exactly as though you were operating your miniature railway, making meets, running faster trains around the slower ones and, in general, keeping traffic moving without unnecessary delay.

The Vera-Clare line handles not only considerable local business but also a large volume of through passenger and manifest freight traffic in both directions, as well as solid trains of coal westbound.

Four passenger trains are scheduled in each direction daily, including one local and three through trains—the Pocahontas, the Cavalier and the new Powhatan Arrow. The Powhatan Arrow is the fast all-coach train, operating in both directions between Norfolk, Virginia, and Cincinnati. Three scheduled manifest trains are operated eastbound and two westbound daily. Frequently these trains are run in more than one section. Their tonnage is held down to a point where they can maintain their schedules. A local freight operates each way between Portsmouth and Sardinia, 58 miles west of Portsmouth.

Westbound coal trains move at fairly low speeds, and this traffic runs from four to six heavy trains daily. The total number of trains in operation, counting extras, may range up to 28, or more. Because of the variations in the speeds of the different classes of trains, as well as the necessity of giving certain trains preference, difficulty was experienced in keeping traffic moving effectively on this hilly single-track.

Today, with C.T.C., the dispatcher can cope with circumstances that formerly caused him to sprout gray hairs. The new C.T.C. control includes power switch machines at the ends of sidings and the ends of the second track between Mineral Springs and Plum Run, and these switches as well as the signals at these locations are under control of the dispatcher at Portsmouth. Accordingly trains enter or leave sidings without stopping and all train movements are authorized by signals instead of train orders and timetable.

The time waiting in sidings has been reduced, for with C.T.C. a dispatcher is provided with a means of quickly advancing trains by signal indication when other trains have been unexpectedly delayed. A Norfolk and Western dispatcher has said that the C.T.C. signals and power switches save about 20 minutes when a freight train is making a move out of one siding and heading into the next one. This time saved is often the factor which permits the dispatcher to advance an opposing train one or more sidings when it would otherwise be delayed from 20 to 30 minutes.

This Portsmouth-Cincinnati main line of the Norfolk and Western runs through hilly country 10 to 15 miles north of the Ohio River. Leaving Portsmouth, which is on the Ohio, the line follows up the Scioto River for about nine miles to a point just east of McDermott. From here the line follows the valley of Scioto Brush Creek for about 18 miles; then it crosses several ridges and intervening streams—the Ohio Brush Creek at Lawshe, White Oak Creek at White Oak, and the East Fork of the Little Miami at Williamsburg.

From Batavia to Clare the line follows generally down the valley of the East Fork of the Little Miami River to the Miami River, which enters the Ohio near Clare. The maximum grade westbound is approximately 1.4 per cent for four miles between Lawshe and Seaman. At one time a 1.11 per cent grade extended westbound from Mineral Springs to Beaver Pond, 1.5 miles, but in 1948 a new line was built from Mineral Springs to Plum Run, 4.7 miles, on a maximum of 0.52 per cent grade and 2 degree curvature. The old Beaver Pond line was retained in service and equipped with C.T.C. to serve as a second main track, thus providing two tracks, each equipped with C.T.C. for train movement in both directions.

Norfolk and Western Y5 or Y6 compound Mallets handle 3,100 tons westbound and 2,900 tons eastbound. By "doubling the hill" westbound between Lawshe and Seaman this class locomotive can handle 6,200 tons.

By "doubling the hill" we mean that a train, finding a grade too steep to negotiate with it full train, leaves half of its train at the foot of the hill, returning for it after the front half has been pulled to the top. We will come back to this matter in a little while, for it is a most unusual operation neatly handled by C.T.C.

During their improvement program, the Norfolk and Western lengthened many of their sidings on this line. The locations and capacities of these sidings are shown in the accompanying table, which is based on a car-length of 45 feet, with 300 feet of track allowed for locomotive, caboose and tolerance at the ends.

Two new sidings were constructed at Mt. Zion, each about 6,000 feet long. Mt. Zion is just west of Seaman, which is the top of the 4 miles of 1.4 westward grade from Lawshe up to Seaman.

SIDING CAPACITIES—VERA TO CLARE

(Reading East to West)

Book	144	Cars
Brookside	144	"
Otway	144	"
Rarden	142	"
Lawshe	143	"
(Seaman)		
Mt. Zion	141	"
Winchester	104	"
Macon	104	"
Sardinia	140	"
White Oak	123	"
Eastwood	143	"
Afton	141	"
Batavia	90	"
Perintown	142	"
Ancor	162	"

At Mt. Zion, one of the new sidings is on the north side of the main track and the other is on the south side.

As an aid to trains which double the Lawshe-Seaman hill, a crossover was installed between the north siding and the main track at a point near the middle of the length of the siding. The switches at the ends of the sidings are power-operated as part of the C.T.C. installation, and the switches for this crossover are hand-operated with electric locks.

Now that we have the picture of this unusual mainline movement we will take up "Operation Mt. Zion."

Operation Mt. Zion

When a westbound tonnage train reaches the foot of the Lawshe-Seaman hill it is cut in two. The locomotive pulls the forward half over the hump at Seaman and into the westward siding at Mt. Zion. Remember, we have a crossover halfway through this 141-car siding. The locomotive leaves the forward half of the train east of this crossover, slips out of the crossover and backs down the hill to Lawshe for the remainder of the train.

Returning to Mt. Zion with the rear half, the train is stopped on the main track east of the crossover. The locomotive cuts off, pulls up and backs through the crossover and onto the first half of the train, which it pulls out of the siding and couples onto the rear half standing on the mainline. The drag is then ready to highball down the grade toward Winchester.

The track of the Mt. Zion siding used in the doubling operation descends westward, and because cars left standing on this siding might start to roll when they are not supposed to, a derail was installed at the west end of the siding. This derail is operated by a switch machine that is controlled by the same lever that controls the switch.

The purpose of the second siding, located on the south side of the main track at Mt. Zion, is to improve the flexibility of train operation when a westbound train is doubling the hill. Also, in numerous instances, the sidings at Mt. Zion are used effectively to advance freight trains from both directions to these sidings for meets with passenger trains. For instance, an eastbound freight could go into the south siding while a westbound drag was doubling the hill. Then, if a passenger train is getting close, the westbound freight can take its full train into the north siding.

When timetable and train orders were used before C.T.C., a lot of time was lost when trains doubled the hill because the dispatcher had no means of knowing about the progress being made from minute to minute. As it is now, the track "occupancy" lamps on the dispatcher's track model show the locations of the trains, and each move is authorized by indications of signals, which are controlled by the dispatcher on a minute-to-minute basis.

When doubling a train it is necessary that an aspect be displayed to authorize a locomotive to back down on portions of its own train which are occupying track circuits that automatically hold the signal at the *Stop* aspect. For example, when the rear half of a train is standing on the side track at Lawshe, the locomotive, backing down eastward, can be authorized to pass the signal by display of the restricted-speed aspect, which is a row of three lamps in the left-hand 45-degree angle.

In order to control this aspect, the dispatcher not only sets the lever, but also flips a small toggle switch below the lever before he pushes the code-starting button. The automatic controls at the field locations include directional stick relays and time-element relays so that the restricted speed aspect can be displayed on the signal only when a train makes a westward move and then returns. Furthermore, a period of four minutes or more must elapse between the first move westward and the return.

Special Aspect at Water Stops

When eastbound trains stop to take water on the main track at Rarden, the rear of the train often extends beyond the switch at the west end of the siding. Hence, if the dispatcher has a westbound train waiting on the siding, or if he anticipates a meet at this point, he sends out a special control that, in addition to setting up the signal for the eastbound, displays a single lamp unit on a five-foot mast at the right of the signal. This special lamp is amber and, when lighted, calls the engineer's attention to the word "Clear." This serves as an indication to the engine-man of the eastbound train that he is not to stop until the rear of his train clears the siding switch. If he wants to take water, he must wait until the other train departs before backing up his train to spot the tender at the water column. Similar "Clear" signs are located at Rarden's east end and at Lawshe.

One reason for the long sidings in a territory where most of the freight trains do not exceed 70 or 75 cars because of adverse grades is to allow track lengths sufficient for a train to enter the siding at the speed for which the turnout was designed, and, after the rear end is in the clear, still have track length in which to stop. Furthermore, long sidings aid in "running meets," or meets which are made without requiring either train to stop.

Turnouts at the ends of the power-operated sidings are No. 15, which are good for speeds up to 25 miles per hour, entering or leaving. Each siding is equipped with a track circuit which enters into the control of the signals and also controls the lamps on the C.T.C. machine which indicate "track occupancy." Controls are so arranged that the signal for entering a siding cannot be cleared if the siding is occupied. Thus when a restricting aspect is displayed the engineman of an approaching train can pull his train into the siding at the speed for which the turnout was de-signed.

Approach-Medium Aspect

As advance information for enginemen to approach a siding at permissible turnout speed, the first signal in approach to each power siding switch is equipped with a second operating signal head. Such a distant signal displays the "Approach-Medium" aspect when the corresponding entering signal displays restricting.

A grade signal aspect is provided on each intermediate signal located on an ascending grade of more than 0.95 per cent. The most restrictive aspect of such a signal is a horizontal row of lights in the top unit, over a row of lights in the lower right-hand quadrant. This aspect authorizes trains to pass this signal without stopping and proceed at restricted speed, prepared to stop short of train or obstruction.

The previous automatic block signals included position-light signals which were retained in service in the new centralized traffic control. At the end of a siding, the main-track station-leaving and the leave-siding signal are both mounted on the platform of a bracket mast.

In this Vera to Clare C.T.C. installation head-on protection for opposing moves between sidings is accomplished by the leave-station signals which are normally at stop. Fewer intermediate signals are required than in the previous normal-clear automatic block, which, in some instances, required more intermediate signals to insure head-on protection. For example, between Lawshe and Seaman, six miles, there were previously five double locations of intermediate signals, as compared with only two now. Also between White Oak and Eastwood, about 4.6 miles, there were formerly four intermediates for each direction, compared with only two now. In the shorter station-to-station blocks, as for example 3.5 miles between Macon and Sardinia, there were two double locations on intermediate signals compared with one now.

Passenger Trains Take Sidings

On the Norfolk and Western line between Portsmouth and Cincinnati, the first train to arrive at a siding for a meet is run into the hole, regardless of class. With C.T.C. this makes sense, for there are numerous instances where the operation of a passenger train through a siding means little or no delay to the first-class train but may save considerable delay for a freight.

The maximum permissible speed for passenger trains varies from 50 to 65 miles per hour, but on some curves the speed is restricted to as low as 35 miles. The Powhatan Arrow, which makes no intermediate stops, makes the 96 miles between Vera and Clare in two hours and eight minutes westbound and one hour and 56 minutes eastbound.

The maximum permissible speed for freight trains is 45 miles per hour and is restricted to about 28 miles on some curves. Manifest trains make the eastbound run, Clare to Vera, in about three hours and ten minutes, and westbound in about three hours and thirty minutes. Westbound coal trains which double the hill, ordinarily make the run in less than six hours.

On the whole, the Norfolk and Western reports that there has not only been a considerable saving in overall time between terminals but also that the average performance is better, especially in minimizing delays which would otherwise result when some train develops trouble such as a hotbox or broken coupling.

CHAPTER XX

ATLANTIC COAST LINE

Recorder Aids Diesel Performance

The Diesel-electric locomotive, like your automobile, is a highly developed piece of machinery and the efficiency of its operation depends to a large extent on the man at the wheel. An inexperienced driver or a careless driver can do much to reduce the operative capabilities that have been engineered into it. This also applies to Diesel-electric motive power, and it is why the man at the controls must be carefully schooled in the handling of this modern powerhouse on wheels.

An incompetent automobile driver can cause needless waste and wear on the parts of the machine which serves him. The correct operation of the Diesel through all of its phases is of major importance in this age of specialized, high-speed travel, with its rising demands for high standards of performance.

This is why the railroads are constantly striving to obtain maximum service from Diesel motive power. The Atlantic Coast Line, under the direction of J. D. Loftis, chief of motive power and equipment, has investigated from the beginning every possibility of preventing trouble before it occurs, with a view to keeping their Diesel-electric locomotives out of the shops and available for hauling revenue trains.

This chapter deals with the development of the Diesel operation recorder on the Atlantic Coast Line and is presented through the courtesy of Mr. Loftis. Certainly, no one is better qualified to report on the findings and conclusions of the road's engineering strategists, in connection with the research and experiments carried on in co-operation with the Valve Pilot Corporation. It would be futile for us to attempt to tell in words other than his own, the story of what J. D. Loftis and his assistants have accomplished in raising the efficiency of one of the largest fleets of Diesel-electric locomotives in the United States.

Mr. Loftis writes:

. . . It has been apparent since the delivery of the first Diesel-electric locomotive that precise locomotive handling on the part of the engineman is necessary to prevent damage to both electrical and mechanical equipment. Improved maintenance methods and routine checks by shop forces have reduced failures, but it was realized from the first that further savings could be effected by improving operating techniques while on the line. The overheating, for instance, of traction motors for a short time, due to overloads, might show no immediate damage, but constant overheating of such equipment, through poor or careless operation, is bound to materially shorten the life of the traction motor.

Much time and effort was devoted to the instruction of crews in the "whys and wherefores" of correct operation, but it was obviously impossible to provide a road foreman or electrical supervisor for every trip with every engineman. Speed recorders have been used on all road Diesels from the time they were placed in operation. These have played an important part in assuring proper operation, but speed in itself, within limits, is not harmful to the component parts of a locomotive if the throttle and transition lever manipulations are coordinated with speed and load conditions. The Atlantic Coast Line road passenger locomotives have an automatic transition device, but on road freight locomotives the transition changes are completely manual and a responsibility of the engineman.

It was felt that some sort of recorder should be provided for Diesels to (1) determine whether or not the operating methods materially contributed to traction-motor failures and high maintenance costs, (2) determine if the road crews were handling Diesel motive power in a manner which would produce the best operating results, and (3) determine conditions of operation that could possibly cause electrical and mechanical failures.

Accordingly, negotiations were conducted between the chief of motive power and equipment of the A. C. L. and the Valve Pilot Corporation which resulted in an agreement to develop and test a recorder of this type. The road, during the tests, was to render full co-operation in the development work and further assist in making an analysis of the data obtained. After considering electrical, hydraulic, pneumatic and mechanical methods of producing the desired record it was decided that a mechanical linkage would provide the most accurate, trouble-free results.

It was decided also that a record of the throttle position and reverse lever correlated to speed for passenger locomotives having automatic transition, and a record of the transition position correlated to speed for freight locomotives having manual transition, would provide a suitable record and would accomplish the control desired. To obtain this record from the passenger Diesel with automatic transition, a sprocket and cable connection was made directly to the throttle shaft and the reverse handle of the control stand in such a manner that every movement of each handle would be recorded on the tape in relation to the speed line. The throttle record showed eight equal steps above the center line of the tape for the forward movements and below the center line for reverse movements.

An Electro-Motive 2,000 horsepower passenger locomotive, A. C. L. No. 532, with automatic transition, was assigned to the test. Test equipment was installed and the 532 was returned to service. Little supervision was required, except to remove and analyze the tape after each run. It was found that the recorded speed with the recorded throttle and reverse lever movements provided an excellent and inexpensive method of supervision as an aid to road foremen of engines and other supervisory officers.

The tape records accurately indicated whether or not throttle reductions were made for railroad crossings in accordance with instructions to prevent damage to traction-motor commutators and brushes, and also whether or not the throttle was reduced for transition changes. Slipping of wheels was also recorded on some of the runs, and this permitted corrective action to be taken. In a few instances where the schedule was not maintained it was found that the operator had done everything possible to maintain the schedule but had been unable to reach maximum operating speed, which indicated too much tonnage or that the locomotive was not developing its full rated power. Conversely, where the locomotive was found to be operated with reduced or drifting throttle for a considerable portion of the run, it could be determined that more tonnage could be handled or that less horsepower could be furnished for the run.

The railroad also assigned locomotive No. 333, an Electro-Motive freight-type of 2,700 horsepower, A and B units, with manual transition, for another test run. A speed recorder was applied to this locomotive and was mechanically connected to the transition shaft in such a manner as to record the transition position in relation to the speed and to make the transition record on the tape at the miles per hour appropriate to the first, second, third and fourth transition, respectively.

After the test of locomotive No. 333 had been in effect for some time and after several test runs in freight service on the main line, the tape records were collected and carefully studied. From these it appeared that while the record of transition was new and useful of itself, to enjoy full advantage of the recording equipment on locomotives with manual transition a record of throttle and reverse lever similar to the one produced on locomotive No. 532 should be produced on locomotive No. 333 in addition to the transition record.

The change involved the addition of another recording pencil and certain major changes in the speed recorder itself. When this was done the new instrument made a complete record of speed, throttle, reverse lever and transition, information necessary for accurate and detailed analysis of the operation, which before had been unavailable on Diesel No. 333. With these data available, when the speed line crossed the transition line with the throttle on the eighth notch, an overload or late transition, depending on whether the speed was increasing or decreasing, was readily apparent. As a protection to the traction motors an overspeed switch set for 83 miles per hour, the maximum permissible speed on this particular locomotive, was installed in the instrument.

The Story the Tapes Told

After several weeks of operation, the tapes were again collected and studied and the plain dial on the instrument was changed for one marked with transition points at the speeds at which the transition should be made in accordance with the builder's emergency instructions.

Several hundred readings were made comparing the transition points on the speed dial with the indication on the transition meter. It was found that the indications were identical and, due to the inherent accuracy and reliability of the mechanical speed recorder, transitions could be made accurately using the speed as a guide. This is important, as a sluggish or inaccurate speed indication would cause transitions to be made well outside of the safe current limits of the transition motors and would only increase the difficulties which the railroad was seeking to cure.

It was found after about 75,000 miles experience that the error was less than two miles per hour and was caused by locomotive wheel wear. This wear was then compensated for by a minor gear change in the drive mechanism for which provision had been made.

Marked Dial Helpful

The dial marked with the transition points met with immediate favor among the operators, the consensus being that transition changes in accordance with miles per hour was an indication which was understood and which made sense to them. In addition, while accelerating and operating, it is necessary to frequently consult the speed indicator. The transition position as marked on the dial was always apparent and noticeable, making it easy to observe the changing transition while attending road conditions.

No instructions were issued to the enginemen in the use of the marked dial but the second group of tapes from the instrument, made while the marked dial was in use, produced many records which indicated improved operation. When it later became desirable in the conduct of the test to return to the unmarked dial temporarily, every operator who had used the marked dial complained about not having it and the overrunning of transition points increased noticeably.

The first group of tapes from the instrument, made while the unmarked dial was used, showed many careless transition changes and, in a few cases, serious overloads due to decreasing the speed with a full throttle below the point at which a reverse transition should have been made. Frequent instances of a late forward transition were noticed, particularly while accelerating out of a big yard. When the road foreman checked with the operators involved, it was found they had misunderstood the original instructions and were not aware of the damage which might result to the electrical equipment by sub-standard operation.

The locomotive was assigned for a time on a division where Diesels seldom had been used before. The difference between the trained operators and the inexperienced operators was immediately apparent from the records. Wheel slips were frequently recorded on this tape. The obvious increase led to further investigations to determine the cause. It was found that during the periods of these runs that it had rained constantly, the profile was steeper than on any other division, tonnage of train was at the maximum for this locomotive, and 80-pound rail was standard on that part of the road. Any one of these factors of itself could have caused slipping, but the combination produced an excessive number of slips.

Since Diesel road locomotives are in pool service on the Atlantic Coast Line, and a portion of the main line is equipped with automatic control, an additional feature was incorporated to register restrictive signal indications that may have been encountered on runs within train-control territory.

The Atlantic Coast Line has confidence in the value of such a recording device as has been described and all future Diesel-electric road locomotives will be equipped with this or a similar type of recorder.

Conclusions

1. The Diesel operation recorder supplies to the supervisory officers a mile-by-mile report of the handling of the Diesel locomotive by recording autographically the use of the throttle, transition and the reverse levers. The degree of efficiency obtained from the locomotive is dependent to a large extent on the manner in which controls are manipulated.

2. The record of the various positions of the throttle in combination with the reverse lever offers a ready means of analyzing the handling of the locomotive in both forward and backward direction, particularly when switching is done.

3. The dial of the instrument provides a visual guide to the engineman for the selection of the transition point appropriate to the speed, and the corresponding record certifies whether instructions in this regard are followed.

4. In instances in which the engineman does not properly follow instructions, the record alerts the road foreman to a need for further instruction of the engineman. If the deviation from standard is

caused by some emergency on the road, the record gives the engine-man the means to show exactly what he did and why when faced with the emergency.

5. Increased and better-directed supervision, resulting from the analysis of the records, will raise the standard of both man perform-ance and locomotive performance.

6. The record will enable supervisors to trace faults of locomotive operation which are beyond the control of the engineman. This naturally calls attention to the mechanical condition of the loco-motive responsible for the operational fault.

7. The record readily identifies overloads due to operation in an incorrect transition at low speed or due to long operation in short-time rating of the traction motors, and proper methods to prevent a repetition can be put into effect.

8. The record of high-speed operation under power over railroad crossings with possible damage to commutators and brushes is brought to light, and necessary corrective measures can be taken to prevent their recurrence.

9. Excessive or dangerous wheel slips become immediately ap-parent, and efforts to prevent or put them under prompt control can be made effective.

10. An analysis of the autographic record of the actual performance makes it possible to accurately check tonnage ratings and schedules and make any necessary adjustments which an analysis of the record indicates.

11. Correcting late transitions raises the efficiency of the loco-motive with a consequent decrease in fuel consumption per thousand gross ton-miles.

12. By the use and careful analysis of each record, a uniformly high standard of operation on the road becomes at once attainable.

13. To be most effective, the records must be collected and analyzed as soon as possible after each engine crew has completed its respective run.

The Atlantic Coast Line's great fleet of E.M.C. Diesels are turning in a fine job and the road is constantly improving its freight and passenger service, while waiting the delivery of its new lightweight streamlined passenger cars.

CHAPTER XXI

SANTA FE DIESEL OPERATION

Transcontinental Service—Diesel Instruction

The Atchison, Topeka and Santa Fe Railway System continues to pile up astronomical Diesel mileage over a right-of-way where trains experience a wide variation of climate and elevation, and through the years this has proved to be the finest sort of testing ground for Diesel-electric motive power.

In October, 1935, a Diesel passenger locomotive, built by the Electro-Motive Corporation, made a test run on the head end of the Santa Fe's *Super Chief* between Chicago and Los Angeles. The run was made in 39 hours and 34 minutes, and the Diesel was on its way. The "Iron Horse" continued to snort and prance on the Santa Fe, and will for some time to come, but it is riding into the sunset.

In 1941, Diesel-electric freight locomotive No. 100 coupled onto 60 loaded freight cars in the yards at Argentine, Kansas, and started its 5,400 horses galloping toward Los Angeles, 1,782 miles away. Some 53 hours after the departure from Argentine, No. 100 was wheeling its 3,150 tons of assorted freight into Los Angeles, California. This also was a test run, and once more the Diesel proved itself to be a long-distance champion.

Prior to 1914, 15 steam locomotives were required to handle one transcontinental passenger train between Chicago and Los Angles, a distance of 2,227 miles. The crack California Limited at that time was operating on a 72-hour schedule.

Improvements through the years produced a steam locomotive capable of pulling the California Limited on a schedule of less than 48 hours between Chicago and Los Angeles, and with but one engine change. Long-distance freight haulers came into the picture, with freight locomotives covering as much as 800 miles and more without change. The Santa Fe Operating Department performed wonders, as indicated by their stepping up of traffic movement, particularly during the war years. Steam power was doing most of the work, but each year saw more and more Diesels in service.

The beginning of 1947 saw the Santa Fe with 103 road Diesels in operation and more on order. A fleet of 53 Diesel-electric 5,400-horsepower locomotives was assigned to freight service between San Bernardino, Barstow and Bakersfield, California, and Belen, New Mexico, a distance of about 870 miles.

Each of the passenger trains in transcontinental service requires six sets of equipment, while the train in Texas service requires four sets of equipment. 6,000-horsepower Diesel-electric units handle the transcontinental passenger runs; also the *Fast Mail.* A 4,000-horsepower Diesel handles the Texas Chief between Chicago and Galveston.

The Santa Fe operates two Diesel-powered streamlined trains between Chicago and Oklahoma; two between Los Angeles and San Diego; two between Bakersfield and Oakland, California; and one between Kansas City and Tulsa, Oklahoma. These are trains in addition to the Transcontinental trains. They are in daily service, with Diesel power of 1,800, 2,000 and 3,600-horsepower.

The Santa Fe started out with a Diesel switcher in 1935. Its first Diesel road locomotive went into service in 1936. As of January 1, 1949, the total locomotive mileage indicated about 38% Diesel. This figure is based on total locomotive miles and not on gross ton-miles. While the figure represents 38% of locomotive miles, we are told that it is feasible to assume that considerably more than 38% of the business or gross ton-miles are handled with Diesel power. Looking at the passenger total locomotive miles percentagewise, better than 60% of the total passenger miles are made with Diesels.

Due to improvements in motive power, roadway and track conditions, C.T.C. and other modern methods of dispatching trains, the on-time records indicate that for six months—April-September, 1948—the *Super Chief* was on time 84%, the *Chief* 93%, the *Grand Canyon* 58%, and the *Fast Mail*, Nos. 7 and 8, were on time, 68%. This represented a total overall operation of 76% on time.

This record includes every delay of five minutes or more in arrival at the final terminal. The figures are remarkable. You must remember that they include delays resulting from floods, derailments, and those many and various "acts of God" that are so much part of railroading over a great transcontinental railway system.

It was but natural that many difficulties should be encountered in the Diesel program on the Santa Fe, with its burning desert temperatures, its high mountain passes and the heavy grades encountered, ranging all of the way from mighty Raton, New Mexico, to the steep and difficult mountains of the Tehachapis in California. An accumulative study of 11 months, February through December, 1948, showed more than 1/5th of a million miles per locomotive failure. That figure substantiates generally a progressive increase over the years in miles per engine failure. With the constant improvements in construction, and with the experience gained, the Santa Fe anticipates betterment of the figures presented.

Another item to be taken into consideration in connection with the Diesels is the tremendous value of the dynamic brake which, together with the Diesel, has contributed a great deal to the economy of operation. No accurate study has been made of the ultimate value of the dynamic brake and the saving accomplished through its use, but it runs into the millions of dollars to this carrier.

At the present time, the railroads are confronted with a braking problem that the dynamic brake may help to solve. In the opinion of many railroad men, engineers have gone about as far as they can with the air-brake, as it concerns the control of the high-speed trains of today, due to thermal checks in wheels where brake shoes have contacted them and various other difficulties resulting from heavy brake operation. The dynamic brake has been improved and will be improved further, and if the motors are used as a braking power instead of the brake shoes, thus eliminating wheel heat, the wheel difficulties experienced will be vastly reduced.

Every motorist in mountain country knows the trouble resulting from contact braking and the advantages and safety of coming down the grade on compression, which might be compared to the dynamic brake.

Diesel Instruction Car

The Santa Fe uses a 78-foot Diesel instruction car, equipped with the FT type locomotive electrical equipment, which is the most universal in the road's applications. This equipment is so arranged that the same relative position is maintained as found in a locomotive cab, with the advantage of all covers being removed and the equipment being easily available for instruction purposes.

In the car is a cut-away engine of the EMD-567 type. This model shows two cylinders in cut-away portions. The model is motorized to indicate exactly the sequence of events and the functions of the parts can be observed. At the rear of the car, a DRK steam generator is installed. A slide projector and a sound movie projector also are used in connection with the equipment.

The Santa Fe instruction program was begun in the fall of 1947, and at the end of 15 months it had been attended by 10,120 persons. The students consist of machinist and electrical apprentices, machinists and electricians, steam generator mechanics, engineers, firemen, and all supervisors. Four classes constitute a course of instruction. Thirty-four terminals are covered each year. The length of time the classes are held at each point is determined, of course, by the number of men involved at each terminal.

The *first class* consists of mechanical instruction—tracing out water, lube oil and the fuel systems of the Diesel engine from prepared charts. Using the motorized cut-away model, the instructor traces out these systems, giving a full explanation of a two-stroke-cycle engine, including the principle and operation of the over-speed trip, the governor, etc.

The *second class* consists of electrical instruction where basic principles are discussed. Using two films, entitled: "Current and Electromotive Force" and "Series and Parallel Circuits," a great deal is presented which would take days to explain in normal word classes. Then, the actual working of the electrical equipment is taken up—creating transition in sequence as it occurs, while observing the functioning of the different relays and contractors.

The *third class* is a steam generator class. As several types of steam generators are in use, slide films are shown first, with a narrative about these types of generators. While the class is grouped around the steam generator a simplified description of the operation of the generator is given, by tracing out the passage of water, steam, air, and fuel on the generator itself. The men are then allowed to perform the functions of filling and starting the steam generator, and turning the steam into the trainline as well as stopping it. Models of the different controls are available for a more complete explanation of the operation.

The *fourth class* is a miscellaneous class in which several items are discussed that seem to be stumbling blocks, such as a description of the operation of the throttle or governor control, or new equipment which differs from previous equipment. Also in this class a motion picture film is shown, giving a clearer conception of everything that goes into proper maintenance and operation.

At its regular maintenance terminals for Diesels, the Santa Fe holds extra classes giving much more detailed information. There the basic circuits of the general electric control and power circuits are discussed thoroughly.

Other classes planned at this writing will consist of a governor class, with an actual working governor connected to an actual load control; another steam generator class, which is very important in regard to the road men; and another miscellaneous class which was very successful in previous instructions.

194

S.P. #373 San Francisco Overnight hauled by engine 4437 Class GS—4, 4—8—4 Type at San Bruno, Cal., on Coast Division. Notice the high-speed freight cars all identical used in this fine fast service. Photo courtesy Southern Pacific RR.

ACL diesel #522 with #87, the southbound Florida Special, climbing Franconia Hill, Va., running over the R. F. & P. RR. Photo by Bruce D. Fales.

Corner of luxurious compartment in service on modern lightweight trains today. Courtesy Rock Island Lines.

Rear end of rear-end lounge facilities in parlor observation cars. Notice parlor chairs in foreground as used on S. P. Daylights. Courtesy Southern Pacific RR.

View of the outside elevator baggage lift in use on Southern Pacific Daylight. The elevator on left car is closed and in the small compartment at the left door is the operating handle for the lift. Courtesy Southern Pacific RR.

One man controls the three pneumatic car retarders and twenty electro-pneumatic switches at the Portsmouth, Ohio, Time Freight Yard on the N&W. This eighteen-track yard provides an excellent example of how car retarders cut classification time and handle more cars in small as well as large yards.

Coal coming through the retarders on N&W's magnificent hump yard at Portsmouth, Ky. The main line is in the left foreground. Scioto Division. Courtesy N&W RR.

Modern up-to-date yard office at Hagerstown, Md., showing the operator, teletype machine, and yardmaster at the typewriter and Electro Motive switching diesel outside. Courtesy Western Maryland RR.

S.P. #3, the new Golden State, nearing Indio, Calif., headed for Los Angeles running over the Division of that name. Courtesy Southern Pacific RR.

Standing beside cut-away section of a 2-cycle diesel engine on Santa Fe diesel instruction car, Supervisor Rogers explains problem to a machinist from the Chicago diesel shops. Courtesy Santa Fe Railroad.

Santa Fe Extra 5025 east 2—10—4 type coming down Curtis Hill between Belva and Heman, Okla., with 107 cars, 20 miles an hour, slowing down to go into the Heman siding to meet Extra 2903 west. Photo by Preston George.

EMC 5400 h.p. Santa Fe diesel #111 with eastward GFX train — solid green fruit near Rio Puerco, N.M., with seventy cars at sundown on the First District of the Albuquerque Division. Photo by Preston George.

U.P. #3 the westbound Utahn with engines 830 and 803 coupled the second and first of the U.P. great 4—8—4 class climbing Sherman Hill near Sherman, Wyoming, with eighteen cars running 50 miles an hour. Photo by R. H. Kindig.

U.P. #102 the eastbound City of San Francisco running over the Nebraska Division east of Cheyenne, Wyoming, hauled by 3-unit Electro Motive passenger diesel. Photo by R. H. Kindig.

In each of the miscellaneous classes, items of safety are included and a film, showing the use of fire extinguishers, is presented.

Thus the Santa Fe attacks and conquers the matter of educating its forces in the art of skilled Diesel operation and maintenance.

CHAPTER XXII

THE CENTRAL'S POSTWAR
PROGRAM

$233 Million Spent

During World War II the railroads of the country performed the greatest job of land transport in the history of the world. They emerged from the fray battle-scarred and with a lot of worn-out equipment, and were promptly confronted with the task of transporting, in a few short months, the returning soldiers —great armies that it had taken two or three years to send overseas. This job had to be done regardless of worn-out motive power and rolling stock, and it had to be done quickly.

All during the war, and for a period afterward, it was impossible to obtain replacement in any sizable volume, with the result that older locomotives and cars were repaired and kept in service long after it would have been more economical to replace them. This resulted in higher operating costs. To reduce these costs, and at the same time maintain its high operating standards, the New York Central inaugurated the largest postwar improvement program in the country. It planned to spend 233 million dollars on new motive power, rolling stock, additions and betterments to the Central's roadway and structures. The program included expenditures from 1945 through 1947, and also for equipment scheduled for delivery in 1948 and 1949.

The New York Central's modernization program provided nearly $69 millions for new freight cars alone. About half of these had been delivered at the end of 1947. Sixty-two million dollars went into new post-war passenger cars, and $45 million were expended for new Diesel-electric freight and passenger loco-motives, deliveries of which extended on into 1949.

Approximately $50 million were devoted to rebuilding track and railway structures. Six million dollars went into the purchase of the Niagara-type steam locomotives.

However, the Central was not dressing up in its best bib and tucker just for fun; it was going after business. To encourage cus-tomer utilization of the passenger train service, the road inaugu-rated certain new travel promotion aids, including a "rail-auto" plan, a "travel-load" plan and a "travel-service" bureau. The rail-auto plan provides business men and pleasure travelers with both forms of transportation. The traveler reaches his destination, for instance, by train, and then makes his local calls by automobile —rented from garages in leading cities and reserved in advance through the assistance of Central ticket agents.

The travel-loan plan permits installment buying of tickets and other rail-travel expenses, and was established in co-operation with local banks. You simply arrange for tickets and reservations just as though you were paying cash. Repayments are made to the bank in 12 monthly installments. All you need is the same credit rating required for any merchandise purchase.

Having once established your credit you can travel on more than 30 leading railroads which jointly established the plan. This plan is a great boon to many firms as well as to the person suddenly confronted with the necessity of making a trip because some emergency has arisen.

The biggest travel salesmen on the Central are the new trains themselves. You have only to see these trains to want to ride them. Although the carpet is rolled out for the Century only, any one of the Central's new trains represents the last word in travel comfort and convenience in its class. Number 1 of the all-new parade was the all-coach "Pacemaker," which made its bow in February, 1948. Before the year was over the speed queens of the Central included the new Twentieth Century, the Commodore Vanderbilt, the Detroiter, the New England States, the Ohio State Limited, and others.

Through the Central postwar improvement program, Diesel

motive power was available for these trains early in 1947; it also was assigned to such trains as the Wolverine, the Knickerbocker, the Lake Shore Limited, Empire State Express, Southwestern Line, and many more. A brand new James Whitcomb Riley, one of the Central's postwar fleet of 28 streamliners, waltzed down the rails in April, 1948, with 11 gleaming stainless steel cars behind—the last word in Diesels.

As more and more of the 720 postwar passenger cars became available they were placed in service in support of this vast postwar program, the most ambitious ever attempted. The spring of 1948 saw 29 Diesel-electric locomotives pulling long-distance passenger trains. Many sleepers ordered in 1945 were finally coming through in 1948. Gradually the $83,000,000 passenger equipment came within sight of its goal, but this was only part of the program.

Over 18,000 new freight cars began to roll down the rails of the Central. These included 1,000 new, ultra-modern refrigerator cars for perishable foodstuffs—fresh, processed, and frozen. These cars were the aristocrats in freight service, built to rigid specifications and equipped with modern, high-speed, easy-riding trucks. They were placed in service through a Central subsidiary, the Merchant Despatch Transportation Corporation.

These new MDT reefers were painted distinctively with white sides, and a bottom striping of red, white, and blue. The ends and roofs were painted red-brown, and the grab-irons and underrigging were painted black. They were designed with complete facilities for forced circulation of air around the lading, and the equipment included powerful fans driven by axle-belts, driving the air, either heated or refrigerated, as desired, through channels provided.

An outgrowth of the postwar plan on the Central was the Pacemaker hotshots of the freight service, with authorized speeds of 65 miles per hour with 75 cars or less. An initial pool of 525 cars was made available for Pacemaker Freight Service. The Pacemaker freight service represents another milestone in the postwar parade. It is a striking train, with the upper half of its cars painted a vermilion red and the lower half a dark gray.

A unique Freight Train Timetable, presenting the new post-war schedules of the fast, regularly scheduled "symbol" freight trains on its line was issued by the Central. It was prepared as a handy guide for both carload and less-than-carload shippers. It is an attractively designed 24-page pamphlet that gives the schedules of more than 100 daily fast freight trains on the 11,000 miles of line, including the New York Central Main Line, Michigan Central, Big Four, Boston & Albany, and Pittsburgh & Lake Erie territories.

This new freight timetable contains information about the arrival and departure at terminals and intermediate points, and the make-up and connections of the symbol trains. It does not include extra symbol trains or the many scores of local freights. A special table features the overnight New York-Buffalo solid Pacemaker and its connections with other cities. There is also a map of the New York Central System, a full list of all New York Central traffic representatives and special service announcements.

Included in the Central's postwar modernization program was a movement to bring the suburban service up-to-date. This involved an expenditure of some $3,000,000 for new commutation cars with electric power, air-conditioning, fluorescent lighting, automatic temperature control, and advanced features to provide smoother riding.

The Central's postwar planners are fully aware that a new railroad era is unfolding. This is the "Railroad of Today" and as modern as milady's new "push-button" kitchen. New and modern facilities had to be incorporated all down the line to keep pace with the beautiful new trains—new Diesel maintenance shops, new signaling, new methods of communication, new dock and station facilities. Streamlined trains demanded streamlined track. A river curve interfered with the Central's busy four-track main line, and the main bed of the Mohawk River was shifted bodily to make the new Gulf Cutoff, to the tune of $2,500,000.

Modernization reached into the freight yard and out to the tugboat fleet in the form of two-way radio communication systems. New passenger stations were built and new track layouts provided. The Central was shooting the works, with its Pacemaker trains a symbol of railroad progress.

On October 2, 1947, "Railroad Day in Toledo," work was begun on the new Union Station, a strictly modern structure featuring the liberal use of glass, at a cost of $3,500,000.

In August, 1948, President Gustav Metzman, of the New York Central, announced that work would begin early in 1949 on a new station for passengers at Harmon, New York, with a provision for future needs. Harmon is an important station on the Central because all Central main line trains stop here to change locomotives. It also serves many residents of Westchester and Putnam Counties, New York, and western Connecticut who board trains at Harmon for upstate and midwestern cities instead of using New York City as the terminus.

Also at Harmon the Central has located modern Diesel-electric shops for the care and maintenance of both freight and passenger Diesel engines. Other shops were located at Collinwood, Ohio. At both locations existing electric shop facilities were expanded to provide complete servicing of Diesel motive power.

Expansion at Harmon and Collinwood involved an expenditure of one million dollars. At Harmon, the electric shop was equipped with two working platforms and large fuel oil and lubricating oil tanks were erected. The shop handles running repairs and general overhaul of Diesel passenger locomotives, beside overhaul of Diesel switchers on lines east of Buffalo and on the Boston & Albany.

At Collinwood, Ohio, additions included shops for running services to Diesel road freight locomotives and for the overhaul of these engines and all Diesel switch engines on lines west of Buffalo.

At Niles, Michigan, a former steam locomotive repair shop was equipped to handle general repairs and overhauling of Diesel switchers operating in the Chicago district and on the Michigan Central. At Buffalo, New York, Bellefontaine, Ohio, and Matoon, Illinois, permanent fueling stations for Diesel-electric road passenger engines were installed.

The Dieselization program also included the equipment of a

Diesel-electric training car which is employed at engine terminals on the system to instruct enginemen and firemen in the proper operation and repair of this type of motive power. The great coal docks on Lake Erie at the port of Toledo represent another postwar project. They were constructed jointly by the New York Central and the Baltimore & Ohio Railroads at a cost of $18,-500,000. Operated by the Lakefront Dock & Railroad Terminal for the Central and the B.&O., these docks have adjacent yard facilities for 5,400 cars.

The new docks, located on Maumee Bay, have a capacity for handling 20 million tons of coal and four and one-half million tons of ore per year.

Greater efficiency in freight car classification work on the New York Central has been accomplished through the installation of two-way FM radio communication in two additional freight yards, the DeWitt Yard at East Syracuse, New York, and the Gardenville Yard at Buffalo. DeWitt is the business classification yard on the Central, in fact, it is one of the busiest in the country, handling as many as 5,500 cars per day. Both its east and westbound "humps" are equipped with fixed radio stations and seven attendant Diesels have been equipped with receiving and transmitting apparatus. Gardenville Yard, with a "hump" for westbound classification only, has FM radio communication with four Diesel switch locomotives.

Eleven of the Central fleet of 24 tugs in New York Harbor were equipped with radio after the war. The dispatcher's office at Weehawken, New Jersey, was similarly equipped, with its transmitting and receiving antenna located on top of the Central's grain elevator at Weehawken, 218 feet above the water. Before radio installations were made, the dispatcher had to shout orders to tugs in the vicinity of his office through a megaphone, a method far from effective during windy weather. Land telephone communication, which frequently caused delay, was formerly used when tug crews wanted to call the dispatcher from distant piers. In emergencies involving fires and harbor accidents instant radio contact is invaluable; it permits the immediate mustering of fire or rescue boats.

The New York Central's postwar planning included not only new trains and equipment, but also modern track machines to keep pace with the increased railroad tempo. New power ballasters were perfected to speed maintenance and to eliminate heavy manual work in roadbed rebuilding.

Power ballasters are self-driven rail cars with three-ton ballast-tamping hammers. Track power jacks are also used with tamping machines, making possible greater efficiency. When operating with a full crew, a single machine can tamp the ballast under 400 feet of track per hour worked, or approximately three times the amount accomplished by a gang working with hand-operated air or electric tamping tools.

Each machine weighs 15 tons and is powered with a gasoline engine for movement over the rails. Wheels are also provided for lateral movement to remove the machine from the rails. A power ballaster employs a gang of six men—a foreman, a machine operator, and four laborers to throw ballast under the hammers.

Twenty-eight tamping hammers pound the ballast, 14 on each side of the tie. The tamping is completed with six blows in 16 seconds.

Safety is the first watchword in all railroad operations, taking precedence over the two other objectives in service to the public, comfort and speed.

Recent years have seen long forward strides in signaling systems and automatic train control. The value of these installations was proven during World War II when the railroads hauled the greatest volume of freight and passenger traffic in all their history, and remarkably few train accidents occurred.

Aside from the employment of radio in connection with the big freight yards and the handling of the Central's fleet of tugboats, the System included in its postwar program exhaustive experimentation in the field of message transmission as applied to moving trains with a view to the eventual application of radio equipment to locomotives, cabooses, towers and stations on a large scale.

Safety was engineered into all types of the 720 cars delivered to the New York Central, the largest order ever placed for new passenger equipment in railroad history, through careful attention to their construction. All glass used was non-shattering safety glass. Arm rests and chair upholstery was given a base of heavy padding. Water fountains, cup containers and all appurtenances that might cause injury were recessed. Even door-knobs were streamlined or eliminated.

Grade crossings were given increased protection in the vast postwar program in an effort to reduce further the threat of these danger spots.

Safety at high speed is always in the minds of the railroad's engineering forces. Many times the safety factor is no stronger than the human element with which it is so closely linked. Signaling and automatic train control are vastly important to the security of the rushing train but of even greater importance is the judgment and the alertness of the man at the controls, particularly when going into a curve. A curve is, and always has been, the enemy of high speed, and serious wrecks have occurred when the engine runner failed to obey slow orders on a curving track.

The New York Central had a 7-degree, 24-minute curve on its four-track main line near Little Falls, New York. The reason that it had never been eliminated was that a river stood in the way— the Mohawk River. So the Central did a little job of track tailoring and carved a new river channel out of solid rock at a cost of some $2,500,000.

River Takes Siding on the Central

In November, 1947, the New York Central completed the line change that eliminated the famous Gulf Curve at Little Falls. In addition to lifting a speed restriction of long standing, this line change also reduced the gradient for westward traffic and provided for the realignment of a compound curve into a simple curve of lesser degree immediately east of Gulf Curve.

Originally when built in 1836, the then single-track line was part of the old Utica and Schenectady Railroad, and at Gulf

Curve it followed the north, or outside, bank of a sharp "elbow" in the Mohawk River. Subsequently, a barge canal was constructed on the south side of the river, which severed a point of land from the mainland, forming an artificial island in the river bend, known as Moss Island. On each side of Little Falls, which is 74 miles west of Albany, the line follows the valley of the Mohawk River which, in the vicinity of Little Falls, lies in a deep rock cut.

As the speed of trains was stepped up, the size of equipment grew and the volume of traffic increased, the trackage of the railroad was improved, both in the number of tracks and the standards of construction, to keep pace with these increased demands. There was little that could be done, however, to ease the curve at this location in the river valley, and a speed restriction was necessary which was a veritable "thorn in the side" of operation for many years. This curve could only be reduced by moving it south over the existing channel and flattening it to bring the curvature within the limits for high-speed territory, which meant placing the line some 340 feet south of the apex of the old curve where it would rest on the north point of Moss Island.

In more recent years, with the new methods and equipment available, the means for doing the job economically was provided. And the work was scheduled for 1940, but was held in abeyance until the close of World War II.

The plans called for the excavation of a new river channel across Moss Island, 600 feet long and 150 feet wide at the bottom, which had to be cut out of solid rock. A 1-degree 30-minute track curve was designed which would rest on the point of Moss Island at the center, on a long embankment, and cross the existing channel at each end on deeper embankments. Two new bridges to carry the new tracks across the state highway and an industrial track were also included in the plans.

Since the removed rock was to be used in facing the new embankments, especially on the new channel side, and for this purpose had to be stockpiled on the mainland because of insufficient room on Moss Island, a construction bridge 180 feet long was built between the island and the mainland.

The natural ground in the Mohawk Valley at this point is composed of a dense, hard gneiss rock which required heavy blasting. Also encountered in the work were numerous potholes formed by the grinding action of entrapped boulders when the river flowed over a waterfall at this point in past ages.

The contractor decided to excavate the channel "in the dry," which meant that actual excavation could not be started until means of damming the ends of the new channel were provided to keep the work area as free of water as humanly possible. The required dams were formed by allowing a narrow rock wall to remain in position at the up-stream, or west, end of the new channel, and by constructing a sheet-pile cofferdam at the down-stream, or east, end, which consisted of seven circular "cells."

Each cell of the cofferdam was 32 feet in diameter and was constructed of shallow-arch steel sheeting. This sheeting was driven around a floating timber template by an air-operated hammer. As each successive cell was driven it was filled with gravel to seal it and to help hold it in place, and to provide a roadway for "walking" the crane supporting the air-hammer forward to permit the construction of the next cell.

To seal the ends of the cells, a small auxiliary rectangular cell was placed in a convenient cleft in the rock wall of the river channel at one end, while the opposite end was sealed off with a rock-filled timber crib tailored to fit the bottom of the river.

With the completion of the cofferdam, excavation in the new channel area was begun. Rock was removed by being blasted to pieces small enough to be loaded into trucks with shovels. The rock was so hard that the average drilling rate was only about 13 feet per hour, and bits were dulled at an average of 15 inches, and in some cases only two inches. To keep a supply of sharp bits on hand, a blacksmith shop was set up with three heating furnaces and a quenching tank and two sharpeners. The density and the hardness of the rock was such that the blacksmith shop had to turn out 500 to 600 drills a day most of the time.

Twice during the work high water flooded the channel. When excavation in the channel between the cofferdam and the natural rock dike was completed, the work of removing the cofferdam and dike was begun simultaneously. The gravel was dug from the cofferdam cells and the steel sheeting pulled. The new channel was flooded in May of 1947.

While completing the work on the new channel, construction of the new line embankment was started; also the building of the two new bridges went ahead. One bridge carried the four new tracks over the state highway and the second bridge carried the four main tracks over an industrial branch track.

The new line is approximately 3,000 feet long, but the additional realignment at the east end extended the project over a total length of 6,300 feet. The cost was about two million and one half dollars. Thus a new river channel, blasted out of solid rock, turned the course of the Mohawk River and allowed the removal of the speed restriction that had slowed the flight of the charging trains on the New York Central main line.

Service with a Smile

Courtesy costs nothing and it pays dividends in jobs for the worker and in business for the railroad. In the chapter on the new Century we spoke of the "Good Will Department." *Good will* is John Q. Public's opinion of a business, its people, its products and its services. Good will is the same as money in the bank. The New York Central, and every other railroad, knows that and today, more than ever before, "Company Manners" are being stressed as important cogs in the railroad business, as important as new motive power, new cars, and straightening out curves.

The Central's personnel and public relations department has issued a booklet called "A Course in Public Relations." It is for its employees, but it contains a lot of good reading for anyone. There are things in it most of us could use even in doing nothing more than walking to the corner store, or driving across town as —politeness, for instance.

"Customer satisfaction," says the booklet, "today involves more than moving the passenger or his goods from place to place." It goes on: "Passengers are not human baggage. They are individuals with specific rights and liberties. . . . Employee attitudes which interfere with the rights, enjoyments, comfort or esteem of our customers are certain to make enemies. . . . Rudeness is the unforgivable sin in any contact with the public."

In the opening chapter of this book we emphasized that little touch that "makes the whole world kind." Nothing so flatters a person as to be addressed by name. You are immediately made to feel that you are a person of importance and you warm up to the one who has addressed you and to the company for whom he works. You inwardly resolve to give these folks more of your business.

"You are Mr. John Smith." The neat young man in uniform gives you a smile. "I am the Train Passenger Agent, John Jones. If I can be of service to you at any time during your trip, please feel free to call on me."

John Jones has just sold you the railroad. He not only has sold you that particular railroad but he has sold it to a lot of your friends. For, certainly, you are not going to pass up the opportunity to tell your friends of your train trip and of being given personal attention by the astonishing Mr. Jones.

John Jones is a priceless pearl to the railroad. He not only is making money for the company, he is writing job insurance for himself, promotion insurance. The Twentieth Century Limited has among its personnel two gentlemen named Tommy O'Grady and Tommy Walsh—the "Tommies of the Central." They are listed as stewards—maestros of the dining car—but they come nearer being prime ministers. Prime ministers of Good Will.

Tommy O'Grady and Tommy Walsh probably know more celebrities than the President of the United States. A lot of people in the top travel brackets like to ride the Century just to meet these famous Tommies, and there you have a course in public relations that pays off at the ticket window.

A great many people do not travel often, and they are consequently easily confused and ill at ease. They have a horror of boarding the wrong train, of getting off at the wrong station, and they ask questions that may seem foolish. On the Central, employees are instructed to give every aid to the worried passenger. A smile and a courteous answer, even to the silliest question, will go far toward making a friend and that friend might one day turn out to be a valuable shipper.

Rudeness is inexcusable and the lack of tact by some minor employee may make the traveler hate the entire railroad. That is why teamwork and good public relations are of inestimable value on the Central, or on any railroad. The train with an "air of hospitality" will always have passengers.

It is surprising how many men and women of the Central were interested in the Public Relations courses when they were offered. In a short time over 50,000 had graduated. One hundred fifty thousand copies of a little booklet called "Company Manners" went to Central railroaders. In addition, 50,000 more copies were requested by shippers, passengers, schools, libraries and people in every walk of life.

A few plain little words are doing a big job of railroading today. They are: *"Please"—"Thank you"—"I'm sorry."*

Intensive training is given dining car employees. One phase of the program includes instruction in sanitation, preparation and handling of food, use of equipment, and practical demonstrations of proper methods of service. Each session culminates in a regular meal served to members of the class by several waiters whose performance is observed by the others. Constructive criticism is made whenever it is found necessary.

In addition to training programs which range from classroom instruction, demonstrations in telephone courtesy, and apprentice training for mechanical crafts, the Central, in 1947, inaugurated an extensive freight station program. The object of this last instruction class is the elimination of the causes of loss and damage to less-than-carload freight, to the benefit of the freight shipper, the receiver and to the railroad itself.

Every major freight station on the New York Central participated in this program which has been extended to smaller stations. At each of 60 key locations a service committee worked with the freight agents in bringing instructions to all of the freight station employees. To extend this and other programs of a similar nature, the Central has built, and is building at this writing, instruction cars. These cars seat 54 persons and are equipped for visual education, such as motion and sound-slide pictures, charts, and diagrams. The cars are staffed with trained instructors in various fields.

Before it was completed, the postwar improvement program of the New York Central System and its affiliated companies reached a cost of approximately $287 millions as compared to the planned $233 millions. In fact, new motive power and cars alone, receive or ordered since early 1945, cost $235 millions.

Aside from the millions invested in the Central's postwar problem, the basic expenses have outdistanced the rates, which have put the railroads in a difficult position. The future of America depends to a large extent on the railroads and they must be maintained on a paying basis. The American people are noted for their fairness and the soundness of their judgment as long as they understand the issues at stake. Hence it becomes obvious to anyone familiar with the railroad industry that the financial health and serviceability of the railroads are dependent on sound and enlightened public policies, and believe me President Gustav Metzman knows how to think them up.

CHAPTER XXIII

JOURNAL BEARINGS FOR HIGH SPEED FREIGHT SERVICE

Roller Bearings

A railroad freight car gets a lot of rough treatment—probably more slam bang knocks than any other piece of rolling equipment on earth. It is kicked around in classification yards; it is jerked out onto the main line and started across country in all weather and at all speeds. Supporting and carrying this freight car is a thing called a "bearing." The bearing is the vital point of contact between a stationary surface and a moving surface.

For a great many years the only kind of bearings known were *friction* bearings. A friction bearing contains no rotating parts; it is merely a cylinder of metal different from that of the shaft or axle which it supports.

Before taking up the modern roller bearing as applied to railroad service, we will turn back the pages briefly. Even before roller bearings had reached a stage of development sufficiently advanced to allow their application to automobiles, manufacturers had been experimenting with their use in connection with railway rolling stock. While these earlier attempts were not very successful they, nevertheless, taught the engineers a good deal about the problems involved. Later on this hard-won knowledge proved valuable.

Back around 1923 the Timken people turned their attention to the railroad field. The earliest installations were on the axles of self-propelled gasoline rail motor cars, many of which were being placed in service at about this time. The experience gained in this type of application was a valuable background for later developments, and also brought roller bearings to the attention of the railroads, which was important.

In 1926 the Milwaukee Road purchased 131 new passenger and Pullman cars for their *Pioneer Limited* and *Olympian* trains. It was decided to apply roller bearings to the entire group of cars. The question of purchasing new and larger locomotives was raised at this time. However, it was found that trains equipped with the roller bearings did not need larger locomotives. The existing locomotives pulled as many as 18 roller bearing cars, while the same engines had trouble in handling 12 cars on friction bearings.

Tests between Minneapolis and Milwaukee indicated that the running resistance of the friction bearing train was 17.1 per cent higher than the roller bearing train at 65 miles per hour.

This was the first large-scale application of roller bearings to passenger cars. The successful performance that followed established roller bearings as an important part of railroad operating economics. The high-speed, streamlined passenger trains on the "Railroads of Today" are practically all equipped with some type of anti-friction bearing. This also applies to the various types of motive power that handles them, whether it be steam or Diesel.

It was in the mid-twenties that we saw the first application of roller bearings to the axles of steam locomotives. The first axles to be given attention were the engine trucks, which had been a considerable source of hot box trouble. Trailing trucks and tender axles followed. To prove the feasibility of roller bearings for steam locomotive driving axles, the Timken company built a 4-8-4 locomotive with roller bearings on all axles.

This was the world's first completely equipped roller bearing steam locomotive and it attracted wide attention. For 18 months it was loaned out to 14 different roads for testing purposes. The result of its performance established the position of the roller bearing in the steam locomotive field. The engine finally went to the Northern Pacific where it is still in service.

With the advent of the Diesel-Electric locomotive and the improved electric locomotives, roller bearings were incorporated from the beginning. Practically all road and road-switching Diesels are equipped with roller bearings.

Experimental roller bearing applications were made to the axles of box and hopper cars as early as 1925 and 1926.

The application of roller bearings to freight cars has lagged behind applications to other types of rolling stock for several reasons, the chief reason being the relatively slower operating speeds of freight trains in the past. Also to be considered was standardization to facilitate car interchange and the initial cost of the roller bearing applications.

Three years after the close of World War II freight train speeds had increased to a point where fast freights were operating on schedules closely approximating those of passenger trains. The ordinary freight car was never built to stand that sort of high-wheeling. A lot of fast freights were made up of cars with special trucks, and the journals, of course, were carefully checked, but the friction bearings often ran hot. It would be unthinkable to use anything as antiquated as a friction bearing on a truck traveling the highway, and it is equally unthinkable to believe that this type of bearing will long survive in the modern high-speed railway age.

Over a period of years, the railroads have found the following 12 important advantages in employing roller bearings on all types of railway equipment:

1. Remove all speed restrictions as far as bearings are concerned and make higher sustained speeds possible.
2. Reduce starting resistance of individual cars 88 per cent.
3. Reduce maintenance costs.
4. Increase life of equipment.
5. Hot box delays eliminated.
6. Fuel economy improved.
7. Increase hauling capacity.
8. Make possible fast, to-time schedules.
9. Reduce claims for damage to lading.
10. Greatly reduce "in shop for repair" time.
11. Increase availability of equipment.

12. No change in tonnage rating is required between summer and winter.

It might be summed up by saying that roller bearings, once installed, mean freedom from trouble which, in turn, means reduced maintenance expense. There are many intangible advantages which, together with the direct advantages, make it possible for the railroads to perform better the job of goods transportation through the medium of the freight car.

Specifications have been worked out by the American Association of Railroads for standard roller bearing truck side frames and axles, the adoption of which will reduce the interchange problems of freight car equipment. The roller bearing side frame recommended provided a jaw-type opening at each end for containing the roller bearing journal boxes.

The tapered roller bearing application consists of two separate bearings of the same bore with suitable spacers between the bearings. The journal box, or housing, has a circular bore and a rectangular outside section to fit the jaw of the side frame. Suitable thrust lugs are provided and the top of the box is crowned to provide contact with the side frame.

Roller Bearing Application

The installation of the tapered roller bearing has been made on a number of roads and others are being placed in service as this is written. The largest single installation of this type was made on 1,000 70-ton hopper cars on the Chesapeake and Ohio Railway.

These big hopper cars were designed for the C&O coal service between the mines and the car-dumpers at the various lake and tide-water terminals. The original plans were to operate these cars, so far as possible, as solid trains. In this way maximum benefits will be derived from the low starting and running resistance and trouble-free operation furnished by roller bearing equipped journals.

These coal trains run up to 165 cars and a hot box can cause a lot of grief, delay, and expense.

The Timken Company has developed a roller bearing freight car application which may be applied to existing cars equipped with truck side frames of the integral box type, which is the type of truck side frame predominating on freight cars now in service.

This roller bearing application is fitted on axles which may be machined from existing friction bearing axles. The assembled bearing and box is applied to the existing side frames after removal of the dust guard ribs at the rear of the friction bearing box. The dust guard ribs may be removed quickly and economically by machining or with an acetylene torch, followed by dressing with a hand grinder.

This type of roller bearing application also consists of two single bearings, but with the inner bearing larger in bore and outside diameter than the outer bearing. The outer races are backed against shoulders in the bore of the box and a simple spacer is used between the inner races. The roller bearing box is so designed that its outside contour has assembly clearance at the internal sides and bottom of the integral box on the standard side frame. An insert at the top of the roller bearing box is crowned to the same dimensions as the standard friction bearing wedge. This installation can be made with very little increase in the dead-weight of the car. The increase in weight on 50-ton cars is around 112 pounds and for the 70-ton cars it is only about 52 pounds per car.

The Union Pacific Railroad made this type of installation on 800 existing livestock cars. The program was initiated with 300 cars, which were allotted for an expedited livestock service between Salt Lake City and Los Angeles.

It is on this kind of fast freight service that we see how roller bearings really put "wings on the wheels." Even before the application of roller bearings, this UP livestock service had earned a wide reputation with its fast-traveling freights. The time required to make the 783-mile run, Salt Lake City to Los Angeles, was from 58 to 60 hours.

Now here is the amazing part of it. With roller bearings, the running time was reduced to less than 30 hours, which eliminated a stop-over at Las Vegas, Nevada, for feeding, watering, and resting livestock.

The demands of livestock shippers for this sort of expedited service resulted in the application of roller bearings to an additional 500 cars. This type of application, designed primarily for the changeover of existing cars, is also adaptable for new cars.

Considerable progress has been made in reducing the initial cost of roller bearing applications for freight cars. This has been accomplished through lower cost fabrication of the boxes. Freight car journal box housings are now being produced as weldments. The housings are die-forged in two halves and welded together, after which they are machined. Housings made by this method weigh less and can be produced to closer tolerances, thereby eliminating machining at some points that would otherwise require it. Other application parts are also made as die forgings and still others as stampings. Since the large volume inherent in the freight car field warrants special machinery for machining boxes and parts, machining costs are greatly reduced.

Servicing Roller Bearings

Roller bearings, without doubt, have proven their reliability, but they still must receive a certain amount of terminal inspection and maintenance. These practices vary somewhat with various types of equipment and service conditions, and from one railroad to another, but usually they follow the same general procedure.

Upon the arrival of cars at established terminals the car inspector touches the roller bearing boxes with his bare hand. The running temperature of a roller bearing varies from 15 degrees to 50 degrees above that of the prevailing atmosphere. This is considered normal, and if you can hold your hand on the box it is in good operating condition.

Lubricant should be renewed at wheel turnings and at wheel

renewal. Experience has shown that a well-bodied mineral oil should be used for the lubrication of the tapered roller bearings under average conditions.

A roller bearing correctly used and properly lubricated will give trouble-free service. However, it sometimes happens that, when wheels are changed or turned and bearing installations removed and re-applied, the assembly is not made in accordance with the specific maintenance instructions. There even have been cases where bearing applications have been placed in service without lubricant in the boxes or housings.

Most roller bearing journal boxes are equipped with heat indicators which detect and indicate abnormal heating. This is a cylindrical metal cartridge located near the top of the journal boxes. These cartridges contain a liquid and are sealed with a fusible metal plug which melts when the temperature inside the journal box exceeds 250 degrees Fahrenheit.

Two types of heat indicators are used. One type sets off an extremely pungent odor when released, and the other emits a dense white smoke for several minutes. These are indications of trouble and the trainmen can take suitable action before damage has been done.

Back around 1945-46 the Akron, Canton and Youngstown Railroad purchased 25 70-ton covered hopper cars equipped with roller bearings. These cars were used for hauling soda ash to Akron and Barberton, Ohio, from points as far west as Texas, operating in regular interchange service on 34 railroads and going through regular hump yard procedure.

More than two years later the A. C. & Y. people reported that the roller bearings on these cars had given a remarkable performance. No maintenance whatever was required and no delays chargeable to these bearings had occurred up to that time. Some time after the purchase of these cars, the railroad selected one car for lubrication tests. At the end of 16 months this car was still operating without the addition of oil in the journal boxes.

The matter of lubricating journal bearings with grease has been under discussion by the railroads. Around 1928 grease was tried out as a lubricant under some early passenger car applications, but it was not considered satisfactory. Modern greases might give satisfactory operation, but oil is a positive lubricant and is less costly than grease. Also, oil is more stable from oxidation and sludging than grease. But it is one thing to set up standards and another thing to maintain them, when they concern the king of hoboes—the wandering railroad freight car.

A new section, however, of the "Wheel and Axle Manual" of the Mechanical Division of the Association of American Railroads contains instructions governing the maintenance, repair and renewal of roller bearing assemblies.

Roller Bearings Are Quality Bearings

The finest of material and the best of workmanship goes into the roller bearing. Each heat of steel is "Earmarked" for the purpose of creating just the correct kind of steel; the hands that shape it are trained to produce a precision article.

Railroad operation deals with life and property and there can be neither gamble, nor guessing when you are operating at speeds up to 100 miles per hour in passenger service, and at correspondingly high speeds in freight service. Over two thousand chemical determinations are made each day to guarantee the production of a steel that will have the correct chemical composition, the right physical and mechanical properties. Also, roller bearings are put through a running-in and inspection process, thus proving their worthiness for the strenuous work to be encountered in railway service.

The energy consumed in hauling a train depends, of course, on the total resistance. This is composed of several factors such as journal friction, rail resistance, air resistance, grade and curve resistance, and that form of resistance caused by vibration and oscillation; all of them may vary considerably under different track, speed, weather, and train conditions.

When determining the reduction of resistance due to the use of roller bearings, it is usual to compare the total resistance of a train with plain bearings and one with roller bearings under similar conditions of train weight and speed. The saving is ordinarily expressed in percentage of the total energy consumed. Considering the resistance caused by the journal friction on a railroad car with friction bearings we find three different periods as follows:

1. Starting period
2. Heating period
3. Period of constant temperature

The starting resistance is of importance, especially on roads with low grades, as it is the deciding factor in determining the size, weight, and rating of the locomotive. Mechanical friction constitutes a large part of train resistance and journal friction is so large a part of mechanical friction that all other elements of mechanical friction may be subordinated to it. Mark this: *Journal friction imposes a dead weight that must be overcome every time a wheel turns.*

Let us take starting, for example. A friction bearing train on a level track will require a draw-bar pull to overcome the resistance on each journal, the brasses of the bearings acting as so many brake shoes until an oil film is produced. With roller bearings, this high resistance is eliminated, for the axle is free to turn when a small amount of power is applied because the action is rolling and does not depend on the presence of this oil film upon which the friction bearing is dependent. The sliding friction is replaced by a rolling motion, which accounts for the difference in starting characteristics.

The application of roller bearings to a freight car axle permits that axle to be loaded to A.A.R. capacity for high speed passenger service. If this was attempted with the plain friction journal a number of hot boxes would soon show up.

Now, you say, how about hump yard operation? The way hump yard grades are figured out, won't roller bearing equipped cars complicate matters? My answer is no. The speed of the car at the time it goes over the hump is governed purely by operating conditions and the characteristics of the hump yard and is, therefore, controllable.

218

In regard to the degree of slope of the track in a hump yard: A survey of a number of hump yards reveals that the degree of slope varies to a considerable extent. Thus, it is apparent that the degree of slope of the track is not figured to such close limits that the increased coasting characteristics of the roller bearing equipped cars would in any way hinder hump yard operations. When you come right down to it, the difference in weight between a lightly-loaded car and a heavily-loaded car might be compared to the difference between a car with roller bearings and one with friction bearings. Too, the shape and mechanical condition of the cars being humped are as important as the grade.

Something else to be considered is the fact that one of the causes of hot boxes on friction bearing equipped cars is the direct result of hump yard operation. The shock of cars coming together momentarily disengages the brass from the axle and the movement of the axle also stirs up waste packing so that strands of waste get between the brass and the axle, causing a "waste grab," which may eventually result in a hot box.

Something that we do not always stop to consider is the fact that the brass friction bearing actually contacts less than one third of the circumference of the axle journal at the top. On the other hand, a roller bearing surrounds the axle journal a 100 per cent and is in contact 360 degrees of the circumference, eliminating any possibility of displacing the bearing from the axle. This, in turn, offers more stable conditions regarding braking and shocks. Further, with roller bearings waste packing is entirely eliminated, the bearing being lubricated by operating directly in a bath of oil or semifluid grease.

Any piece of freight car equipment so constructed that its rolling characteristics will be the same at all temperatures will have eliminated one of the most troublesome variables in the hump yard. Nowhere is this more apparent than in the fact that a more uniform braking or retarding pressure can be established for roller bearing equipped cars.

Emphasizing the quality of roller bearings are the records of roller bearings in high-speed passenger train service. These records indicate that roller bearings have made over 3,600,000 miles in service, a truly astounding performance.

The roller bearing boxes themselves practically never wear out. There is no wear inside the boxes and the outside wearing surfaces are fitted with hardened steel liners, and when pedestal or equalizer surface wear limit occurs it is necessary to renew only these inexpensive wear plates or liners.

Roller Bearings Reduce Lading Damage

Tests have revealed that the maximum resistance of roller bearing equipped cars is lower in winter than in summer, while the constant speed resistance remains the same. Thus we are assured that no matter how low the temperature the resistance of roller bearings will be no higher in winter than in summer; consequently with cars roller bearing equipped there would be no reason to reduce winter tonnage.

Nothing is harder to start than a string of freight cars that has been standing in sub-zero temperatures, a strong argument in itself for roller bearings. The necessary "bunching" of slack for a start on hard pull with those ancient friction bearings is simply courting trouble and can easily mean a pulled drawbar, with the resultant grief and delay that accompany these things.

Lewis K. Sillcox, D.Sc., in his book *Mastering Momentum,* says:

The adoption of roller bearings reduces to a large extent the necessity for the provision of slack and for the present degree of serially starting coupled cars. It is highly desirable that slack in couplings be reduced or eliminated in both passenger and freight service. Without slack there can be no internal collision or impact and the absence of impact removes the cause of much travel discomfort, damage to lading, and stress in the equipment itself.*

Because of the low starting resistance of roller bearing equipped cars, the necessity for taking slack will be eliminated

* L. K. Sillcox, *Mastering Momentum* (New York: Simmons-Boardman Publishing Corp., 1941).

or greatly reduced, permitting closer coupling of cars. The jerks and shocks which cause damage to lading and equipment will thereby be reduced. It will also reduce maintenance of draft gear, couplers, and other parts.

The annual loss to the railroads because of damage to lading reaches a staggering figure. One hundred twenty-two million dollars during 1947. This figure represents over 25 per cent of the final net income earned by the Class I railroads during 1947. In the first six months of 1948 the damage claims were 35 per cent greater than in the corresponding period in 1947.

Tests made with a loaded 70-ton capacity roller bearing equipped freight car and a similarly loaded freight car equipped with friction bearings showed a starting resistance of only 1.5 pounds per ton for the roller bearing equipped car, compared with a starting resistance of 43 pounds per ton for the friction bearing equipped car, or 28.7 times that of the roller bearing equipped car. The temperatures during the tests ranged from 21 to 48 degrees Fahrenheit.

It is hard to imagine an automobile salesman saying to a customer that the car he is selling has the finest possible *friction bearings* all around, and yet, in effect, this is what happens to a considerable extent in the freight car field.

No one as yet has figured out the actual cost caused by a hot box. It is easy enough to isolate the actual material and labor costs, but it is impossible to determine those costs which pyramid from a hot box on an important freight or passenger train, resulting in impairment and delays of scheduled operations.

One mid-western railroad reports 1,315 set outs of system cars and 2,956 set outs of foreign cars because of hot boxes in the first six months of 1948.

In April, 1942, the Union Pacific Railroad Company advised as follows:

The roller bearings applied to the ten 100,000-pound capacity 40'-6" box cars constructed by the Union Pacific Railroad in 1939 for high speed merchandise service have to date operated in various weather conditions and temperatures from in excess of 120 degrees,

Fahrenheit, to under 35 degrees, Fahrenheit, below zero in rain, snow and wind, and have proven satisfactory in all respects.

On July 20, 1934, the Chicago, Milwaukee, St. Paul & Pacific Railroad made the 85-mile run from Chicago to Milwaukee, Wisconsin, in 67 minutes and 35 seconds. The train was equipped with roller bearings. This run established what is said to be a world's record at that time, for sustained steam train speed.

Experience has proven that roller bearings on all types of railroad equipment do meet all of the shortcomings of friction bearings, and not only meet them but go a long way beyond that in reducing the cost of railroad operation.

Friction Bearings 100 Years Old

During World War II roller bearing equipped locomotives and passenger cars demonstrated what can be accomplished in reducing maintenance costs and in increasing availability of operating equipment under difficult wartime operations.

Famous high-speed trains of America using roller bearings under locomotives and cars include:

Santa Fe's *Chiefs, El Capitan*
Milwaukee Road's *Hiawathas*
Rock Island's *Rockets*
Great Northern's *Empire Builder*
Gulf, Mobile and Ohio's *Rebels*
Illinois Central's *Panama Limited*
Missouri Pacific's *Eagles*
New York Central's *20th Century Limited*
Southern Pacific's *Larks*

Gradual development and the trend of "one-speed—high-speed" railroading on roller bearings is visualized through the establishment of freight train schedules commensurate with those provided by many passenger trains. This will mean the re-scheduling of fast freight train schedules.

Immediate installation of roller bearings on all existing freight cars is, of course, not anticipated. For one thing, many cars are too old to warrant the change. But an increasing percentage of new cars placed in service each year will have roller bearings and many freight cars built in recent years will receive roller bearing installations. (See Chapter XXIV.)

It is conceivable that some railroads may be reluctant to go to the expense of installing roller bearings if the cars so equipped are to be used largely on lines other than their own. Roller bearings cost around 15 per cent more than a car equipped with friction bearings, and a return on this additional investment must be provided. Arrangements may be made possibly whereby the owners of roller bearing cars will receive a higher per diem rental for such equipment. And we will undoubtedly see a steady increase in the number of high-speed freight trains operating as fast freight units between large metropolitan centers. The cars of such trains will remain permanently in the service of the railroad owning them and benefits derived from the use of this modern equipment will accrue solely to the owner.

The number of roller bearings in service in the early part of 1949 represent only a small portion of the total number of freight cars in operation on American railroads, but they most certainly indicate a distinct trend, a swing toward complete modernization of the bearings of both passenger and freight trains by the "Railroads of Today."

"One-speed—high-speed railroading" is here. The disadvantages and the high unreliability of friction bearings on the fast-traveling manifest simply cannot be denied even by those who may want to keep in service a bearing design over 100 years old.

In all my extended railroad experience over the U. S. railroads, I have seen only one roller bearing run hot.

CHAPTER XXIV

THE NEW U.P. TRAIL

C.T.C.—Roller Bearing Stock Train

The Union Pacific was quick to seize upon centralized traffic control, the magic train dispatcher, as a means of speeding train movements across the mountains and deserts of its vast Western Empire when traffic congestion threatened single-track train operation during World War II. Aided by the Union Switch and Signal Company, manufacturers of C.T.C. equipment, the road planned its first installation on the Third Subdivision of the California Division between Las Vegas, Nevada, and Yermo, California, a distance of 171 miles.

The project ran across some of the wildest country in the West, but it provided a means of smashing a serious rail bottleneck. Another wartime C.T.C. installation on the Union Pacific was in the rugged eastern Oregon country between Huntington and La Grande, a division point. This project was later extended to Pendleton.

Postwar C.T.C. installations include 207 miles of track between Lynndyl, Utah, and Caliente, Nevada. To handle this district the Union Pacific installed the latest type Union Switch and Signal Company C.T.C. machine at Salt Lake City. This cabinet measures 17½ feet from end to end. Another machine, 15 feet in length, dispatches trains over the 118-mile stretch between Salt Lake City and Lynndyl.

These new machines were the first in the country to include a profile of the territory controlled on the board. The profile arrangement assists the dispatcher by keeping constantly in front of him an indication of the grades in his district. The profile is placed just below the track plan and together they brief the physical characteristics of the territory the board is serving.

The 156 miles west from Lynndyl to Uvada is interesting desert country, with grades ascending at varying degrees, from 0.4 to 1.6 per cent. West of Crestline summit the grade drops to Caliente, Nevada. The territory between Uvada and Caliente is very rough mountain country.

The 124 miles from Caliente to Las Vegas is controlled by a C.T.C. machine at Las Vegas, as is the machine for the Third Subdivision from Las Vegas to Yermo, an installation which was described fully in my book, *Railroads at War*.

The district from Caliente to Las Vegas is one of the toughest in the country, and always reminds me of railroading through a rock pile. It is up and down over and along river beds. The right-of-way through Rainbow Canyon is very interesting and picturesque. There is practically no population at all between Las Vegas and Caliente and the difference in temperature is amazing. This variance of temperature is further marked as the grade climbs to Crestline, 34 miles east of Caliente. In some places this grade is 2.2 per cent.

The entire California Division is scheduled to come under C.T.C. operation. The further speeding of traffic between Salt Lake City and Los Angeles has been accomplished through a postwar Dieselization program which has placed Diesel power on all California Division trains.

The majority of freight trains are handled by 6,000-horsepower motors. These handle about 5,000 tons single, and they make good time over districts that, with steam power, required helpers. For instance, three helpers were formerly used from Caliente east to Crestline, and two on the pull west from Uvada to Crestline. Train movements from Lynndyl to Milford average about 35 every 24 hours, and between Milford and Caliente about 30 every 24 hours.

The Union Pacific has a very interesting operation out of the branch at Lund, Utah, where ore is brought from Iron Mountain on the Cedar City Branch and is hauled to Provo, Utah, for the

Utah and Bingham smelters. One Diesel will handle 11,000 tons between Lund and Milford.

The Cedar City Branch out of Lund is also the gateway to Bryce Canyon, Zion National Park and the north rim of the Grand Canyon. This is a rugged and extremely interesting C.T.C. operation and is handled by the C.T.C. machine in Salt Lake City. There is no finer dispatcher's office in the country than the one at Salt Lake, a glass-enclosed and completely modern one. Another excellent dispatcher's office is located at Pocatello, Idaho, the Union Pacific's great railway hub. Also, here we find the new Pocatello Yard, which has been described in another chapter. This office controls the fine C.T.C. installation from Pocatello to Glens Ferry on the Idaho Division of the mainline.

Pocatello is the gateway to the great state of Idaho, which is almost entirely served by the Union Pacific. Approximately 2,200 persons are employed by the U.P. here, including a number of supervisory officials for the South-Central District of the road, for it is here that the Omaha-Portland transcontinental line intersects with the Los Angeles-Butte, Montana, service. All passenger, mail and freight transfers are made here for points east, west, south and north. It is headquarters for the Idaho Division, that is run by one of the finest superintendents I've ever met. Pocatello is a tourist and vacation center and a gateway to the fabulous Yellowstone National Park, to the incomparable Sun Valley, and the Craters of the Moon National Monument.

Motor Car Signal Men

Two men are vitally important to the efficient functioning of a centralized traffic control installation. One is the dispatcher, the man seated before the control panel of the C.T.C. machine and the other is the signal maintainer, the man out on the line with his motor car.

The first principle of centralized traffic control is safety, absolute "authenticity" of every train movement. This is the guiding principle behind all railway signaling. C.T.C. is simply

226

a vastly expanded interlocking system of signaling and power switch control and so coordinated that it is impossible for the operator to set up a conflicting movement.

With C.T.C. the same safety feature applies. For instance, should it happen that the control levers on the dispatching cabinet were mistakenly or carelessly moved, the signals at all locations affected would be placed in their most restrictive positions, and if these restrictive positions were obeyed there would be no collision or derailment. Traffic simply would come to a halt.

There have been, however, rare occasions when a signal on a C.T.C. installation has shown a "false proceed." A "false proceed" signal may be caused by improper circuit connections, fused or shorted circuits, failure of gravity devices due to rust (and sometimes ice) and sandy or rusty rails. For these reasons it is important that experienced signal men be constantly on guard.

At headquarters in Omaha, Nebraska, a general signal engineer is in charge of installations and maintenance of the Union Pacific's vast signal system there. Assistant signal engineers are in charge of the various districts. Then come division supervisors and their maintenance and construction forces.

Probably one of the toughest districts for signal maintainers is the Huntington-Reith C.T.C. district on the U.P. The day maintenance of control apparatus and power equipment is in charge of a general maintainer at La Grande, Oregon. This position is also covered by a night man. When failures occur, these men direct the field maintainers. A field maintainer at La Grande, working up the grade to Kamela, to the west, goes over his territory on his motor car daily.

This maintainer makes a careful check of all switches, signals, batteries and the various houses full of intricate instruments at the ends of each passing track. Nothing is overlooked in his effort to keep the C.T.C. installation functioning perfectly.

These men take pride in their work, in accomplishing difficult assignments in all kinds of weather. They include the finest type of railroaders and too little has been written of the signal maintainer. The man working out of La Grande faces bitter winter weather in the Blue Mountains as he patrols to Kamela. There are no tops or sides on these motor cars, no protection against storms or bitter cold. Meacham, a few miles beyond Kamela, is the coldest spot in Oregon and temperatures of 50 degrees below zero have been recorded here.

Railroading in the best Union Pacific tradition, the signal maintainer performs faithfully and well his job of helping to keep the trains moving safely and on time.

Rock slides in the canyons of the Blue Mountains have always been a serious maintenance problem. A slide not only may cause damage to the track but it also may start suddenly in front of a train. No amount of patrolling could solve the problem entirely. Slide-detector fences, which were tied in with the automatic block signals, provided a safety feature of great value. When sliding earth broke the wiring on a slide-detector fence it caused the automatic signals to display the same danger indications that would have resulted from track occupancy by a train.

With C.T.C., the slide protection afforded is much the same, but has the advantage that a slide is immediately recorded on the panel of the C.T.C. machine. The dispatcher can then immediately notify the track and signal forces and direct them to the place where the slide has occurred.

The Blue Mountains are a wild heavily-timbered country with many 2.2 per cent grades. The peaks rise sharply and swift mountain streams rush along beside the tracks at many points. For scenic beauty this portion of the Union Pacific equals anything in the West. I have seen 15 elk in one herd from No. 12's engine.

Helper engines are used to the summit from both directions. Returning helpers from the summit interfered with train movements before the installation of C.T.C. Now, however, the dispatcher brings the helpers down without delay to mainline movements.

Not exactly a part of centralized traffic control, but closely associated with it and contributing much to its success in the Blue Mountains, are the motor car indicators. These are essentially the same as the indicators used on the Plains Division of the Santa Fe, which we described in another chapter.

These indicators keep signal and track forces informed concerning the location of trains. Indicators are located at headquarters houses of the men who use track motor cars, and at switches, automatic signals and on sharp curves where view of the track is obstructed.

The indicator is a miniature semaphore signal, housed in a case with a glass front. Its operating mechanism is an electromagnet. A pair of wires on the pole line forms the control circuit which makes frequent connections with the track circuit. Thus the presence of a train is revealed by the position of the semaphore. If the arm is in a horizontal position it indicates that a train is approaching and the motor car must be kept off the track. A 45-degree position indicates a clear track and that there is time for the motor car to reach the next indicator or a safe point ahead.

Hand in hand with the motor car indicators are adequate telephones for maintenance forces to use in reaching the dispatcher. Good, solid set-offs for the motor cars are provided along the line. The runways slope away from the rails, which aids in the motor car removal.

Inspection Cars

The Union Pacific operates some of the finest inspection cars to be found on American railroads. They are called "B" cars because they have Buda motors, and all of them are so numbered. They operate with a clutch and have four speeds; throttle and spark levers are mounted in place of a steering wheel. These cars have large windows forward and to the rear, and a desk for roadmasters and maintenance men to write on if they are looking toward the rear end. Snowplows are on the pilots, and they can accommodate seven people.

This is a typical trip with one of the "B" cars:

Lv. Ketcham, Sun Valley, running as
X B24 East   12:40 P.M.
Pass Hailey   12:55
Pass Bellevue   1:02
Ar. Priest   1:20
Back in on spur for Extra 561 East to clear us.
Pass Richfield   1:55
Ar. Shoshone   2:12
Wait at Shoshone for First No. 18 to leave and follow
    No. 18 to Pocatello.
Lv. Shoshone   3:05
Lv. Minidoka   4:02
Lv. American Falls   4:35
Ar. Pocatello   5:07   Two minutes in back
    of First No. 18, following his yellow block all the way.

These "B" cars will run 60 miles an hour on the mainline with great ease. They ride with amazing smoothness and they are invaluable to Union Pacific men who want a close look at the right-of-way. Passengers riding the U.P. may be assured that the track receives close attention at all times by officials and maintenance forces in these exceptionally able inspection cars—the finest the author has ever ridden.

Sun Valley

The world-famous Sun Valley is located 69 miles north of Shoshone, Idaho, on the Union Pacific mainline, and it is reached by a first-class branch line with good track and excellent roadbed.

This greatest of all United States winter resorts is situated at an elevation of more than 6,000 feet amid the towering peaks of the Sawtooths. Sun Valley is more than a winter resort—it is an all-year vacation land that is attracting world-wide attention. It offers matchless conditions for winter sports; the deep, powdery snow is ideal for skiing; the slopes are treeless. Even in midwinter it is possible to ski stripped to the waist because of the summer-like warmth of the sun.

Skiers are whisked to the tops of the four most popular ski

runs by powered ski lifts. The more inaccessible summits are reached by snow tractors. Tobogganing, dog-sledging, ski-joring, ice skating, riding in reindeer-drawn sleighs, and swimming in the famous outdoor, warm-water pools are other popular sports at Sun Valley in the winter months.

In summer Sun Valley presents a combination of vacation attractions probably found nowhere else on earth. There is dancing and ice skating on open-air plazas, pack trips through little-explored wilderness areas, rodeo contests, some of the finest game fishing in the world, swimming, golf, tennis, skeet and trap shooting, horseback riding, and many other thrilling activities. Life at Sun Valley at all seasons is glamorously gay with the easy informality of the West.

The unusual and abundant variety of big game near Sun Valley makes this region one of the finest hunting grounds in North America in the autumn. There is good duck and pheasant shooting; also dove shooting. There is even an open season for Hungarian partridges, and in 1948 there was a two-day sagehen season in this great outdoor state.

Sun Valley's Challenger Inn, which is open all year, is built in picturesque resemblance to a European mountain village. There is a motion picture theater, shops, a post office, night club, restaurants, game rooms, and an open-air swimming pool. One of the nice things about the Challenger Inn is that it is run for people of more moderate means. A wonderful staff, headed by able E. P. Rogers, Sun Valley's general manager, provides every comfort one could possibly wish for.

Sun Valley Lodge, one of America's finest resort hotels, is open during the winter, early spring, and the mid-summer season.

Sun Valley was established as a vacation center following a report by Count Felix Schaffgotsch, Austrian sportsman. Count Schaffgotsch toured Western America for the Union Pacific in search of a sportsman's paradise. He found it at Sun Valley, Idaho. W. A. Harriman went ahead and developed it.

It is truly one for the book—one for *Railroads of Today*—to see a railroad operating a vacation dreamland like this beautiful mountain valley of the Sawtooths.

Idaho is a land of scenic grandeur; it is rich in natural resources. Many mine products come out of Idaho. The state annually ships some 30,000 carloads of fine potatoes. A large amount of livestock and forest products move to market on the rails of the Union Pacific. Ore is shipped from Butte, Montana, to the great smelters in the Salt Lake City district. Coal in amazing quantities is shipped from the mines of Utah to the northwest. Few railroads in any state have so many branch lines reaching out to serve shippers, passengers, and communities.

A lot of passenger business comes out of cities like Lewiston, Payette, Nampa, Twin Falls, Boise, the state capital, and many others. Fast freights travel the line of the Utah Division extending south from Butte and Idaho Falls. All of this traffic funnels through Pocatello and its great and modern retarder yard.

The Union Pacific serves the greatest of all of our National Parks—Yellowstone. Through-sleepers are operated between Chicago and West Yellowstone's rail gateway, and the Park may be reached conveniently and easily over other routes and various connecting lines from anywhere in the United States.

A lot of pioneer history is wrapped up in Idaho, a lot of scenery—probably more natural scenery outside of the car window or within easy access by rail than any similar area in the world.

Building the West It Helped to Pioneer

The Union Pacific is building for a greater West. The road has done everything possible to eliminate obsolescence. The men at the head of the U.P. realized long ago that they could not meet the cost of new facilities while continuing to maintain lines, terminals, and stations that had outlived their usefulness. Light traffic lines that could not be operated profitably were discontinued and provided with highway service. Perhaps one of the most important postwar considerations, in view of the then existing shortages and the high cost of replacements, was the determination to make better utilization of available equipment. This meant the elimination of all barriers to faster, more continuous train operations. In other words, the Union Pacific was determined to revolutionize operating methods. This began with the introduction of a substantial percentage of Diesel motive power and the reassignment of steam locomotives. Other changes included improvements in roadway and track, the reduction of curvature, the installation of centralized traffic control over long stretches of single-track, concentration of the classification of freight cars, fewer terminals, new and ultramodern hump and retarder yards, and the equipment of such yards with every device that would build greater efficiencey into the plant.

In one year after this modernization program began, the Union Pacific had increased the average tons per train by about 15 per cent, and at the same time increased the average freight tonnage per train-hour by nearly 20 per cent—the latter reflecting both increased tons per train and time consumed, thereby being the highest in the history of the Union Pacific for the month of May, 1948, and perhaps the highest of any other railroad.

Among other technological developments which have aided in the U.P.'s postwar program have been improvements in communication facilities, such as complete telephone installations providing instant communications between all terminal points; the substitution of teletype for the telegraph, thus speeding all types of reports, and the very substantial use of radio, particularly in directing yard switching activities. Various mechanical devices in the clerical departments have been effective in reducing costs in that direction.

In the hope of reducing to a minimum claims for loss and damage to shipments, the Union Pacific people have campaigned constantly and nationally for better packing of shipments, for greater care by employees of the railroad and for container engineers to assist and instruct shippers in packing methods. Officials constantly are instructing employees how to improve switching operations and methods of handling cars and goods at freight terminals to avoid damage.

The Union Pacific's revolutionary modernization program has received the fullest cooperation from labor. The legislative bodies also have been helpful in the passage by Congress of the

Reed-Bullwinkle Bill, a fine contribution to the stability of the railroad industry and the general economic picture.

Roller Bearing Stock Train

For the past ten years there has been a very heavy movement of stock to the California markets. This includes cattle, sheep, and hogs. The movement has grown to a place of importance equal to that of shipments for the East through midwestern stockyards and feeding grounds.

California continues to grow by leaps and bounds, and with its enormous increase in population it is only natural that the consumption of meat and meat products should rise in proportion. All of the railroads serving California have been aware of this situation and the Union Pacific has risen to the situation in a comprehensive and practical manner.

The U.P. began by converting 300 friction-bearing stock cars to Timken roller-bearing equipped cars. This was in March, 1947. The cars also were equipped with Twin-Cushion Draft Gears and painted yellow. In October of that year 500 more stock cars were similarly equipped. These 800 cars were placed in a livestock pool and were assigned to the Los Angeles stock run, just about the hottest thing around.

The livestock shipments mostly originate on the Butte line of the Utah Division, with some moving in from the Idaho Division and some coming through from Wyoming. These cars of stock are consolidated and classified in North Yard at Salt Lake City, where the stock is rested and watered for the last time before starting for Los Angeles.

The run of some 790 miles is made in about 27 hours. Big freight Diesels pull the train—No. 299, the *Stock Special*. The fast-flying stock train leaves North Yard, Salt Lake, at 10:30 A.M. Crews change at Milford, Utah, at 3:50 that afternoon. At 11:15 P.M. both engine and train crews change again at Las Vegas, Nevada. The crew that take over there run through to Yermo, California, arriving at 5:45 A.M.

This red ball schedule is almost always bettered, and it is

#26 new eastbound Twentieth Century Limited hauled by EMC diesel #4029 just after passing through Breakneck Tunnel — Hudson Division. Courtesy N.Y.C. RR.

U.P. #111 streamliner City of Denver — from Chicago to Denver — picking up mail at 80 miles an hour at Fort Morgan, Colorado, on the Colorado Division, Photo by R. H. Kindig.

EMC — 2-unit diesel #1617 solid N.Y.C. meat train west of Rochester on the Syracuse Division being run around by #90, the Chicagoan. Courtesy N.Y.C. RR.

U.P. 3-unit Electro Motive diesel with 110-car westward extra climbing the 0.82% grade west of Green River, Wyoming, on the Utah Division. Photo by R. H. Kindig.

Signal maintainer observes clear motor car indicator as he leaves Clear Lake, Utah, on the U.P.'s California Division Salt Lake City Caliente CTC installation. When the indicator is clear, motor car operator is assured ample time to reach next indicator. A typical device of the railroads of today.

U.P. Extra 1404 west with 4-unit Electro Motive freight diesel hauling roller bearing stock special near Mira Loma, Calif., on the Fourth Subdivision of the California Division. Courtesy Union Pacific RR.

Dispatcher working CTC board at Le Grande, Ore. U.P. has 78 miles of CTC between Le Grande and Rieth, Ore., and 100 miles between Le Grande and Huntington on the Third and Fourth Subdivisions of the Idaho Division.

Extra 1458 east 4-unit EMC diesel takes siding at west end of Gurkee on Third Subdivision of Oregon Division. On this territory heavy grades are frequent, requiring the cutting in and out of helpers at numerous locations. CTC makes it possible to obtain maximum productivity from helpers thereby reducing the numbers needed saving their first cost, maintenance, and operating expense.

C & O #1654 2—6—6—6 type, class H—8 with a westward train of empty coal cars climbing the east slope of the Alleghenies at Moss Run, Virginia, on the Allegheny Subdivision of the Clifton Forge Division unassisted. Courtesy C & O RR.

A real railroad station of today. C & O passenger station at Prince, W. Va., on the New River Subdivision of the Hinton Division. Note the mural. Courtesy C & O RR.

Electro Motive 6000 h.p. F—3 diesel descending grade into Green River, Wyoming, with #28—The Overland—with eighteen cars at 60 miles an hour. Note there is no smoke alongside the train which is being braked with the dynamic brake. Photo by R. H. Kindig.

U.P. Inspection Car B-24 about to leave Ketchum, Idaho, for Pocatello over the Ketchum Branch on the First Subdivision of the Idaho Division with Asst. Supt. Roberts, "B" car's crew, the author and his wife, and the agent at Ketchum also in the picture. Courtesy of Sun Valley Lodge.

rare indeed that the livestock train pulls in late. Credit C.T.C., the Diesel locomotive, and Timken roller bearings, plus a fine roadbed and some real railroaders, from officials down.

The stock train is highly respected the entire length of the U.P.'s California Division, and it gets rights over everything except first-class trains. The *Stock Special* leaves Yermo at 6:15 A.M., climbs Cajon Pass and is through San Bernardino and Riverside by 11:20 A.M. every day, with a 1:30 arrival and delivery that afternoon at the Los Angeles Union Stock Yards.

The livestock train usually consists of 65 to 75 cars and a second section is run almost every day. The average time for the entire run is usually about 30 miles per hour. I have ridden the train several times and we have been on No. 37, the Pony Express's block all the way to Milford and sometimes to Caliente, Nevada.

This solid yellow train, behind a big yellow Diesel, rushing across the mountains and deserts with its valuable cargo, is a beautiful sight—a modern fast freight, the last word in motive power, on today's U.P. trail.

In connection with this livestock move, the Santa Fe also operates a daily stock train, the Hog Special, from Amarillo, Texas, through Belen, New Mexico, to Los Angeles.

There is no question that plenty of fine cattle, sheep, and hogs that formerly made their last trip eastward through the cold country north to the Minneapolis gateway are now having a warmer ride to Southern California. The U.P. has spent over a million dollars in car improvements alone to see that they have it.

Personally, I feel that the Union Pacific's fine board chairman, E. Roland Harriman, is deserving of high commendation for the things he has accomplished. Through his efforts, a great railroad has become even greater, due to the intelligence and foresight of its president and board of directors, in improving, maintaining and constantly strengthening the railroad plant. However, Mr. Harriman would be the last person to take any credit for it.

The Union Pacific Railroad, planned by Lincoln to unify the nation, is today dedicated to the development of the West that it helped to pioneer.

CHAPTER XXV

THE GREAT NORTHERN

Old Bill Rides the Diesels

Probably no railroad emblem in America is better known than "Bill," of the Great Northern. Everyone knows the famous Rocky Mountain goat, the challenging figure, perched atop a mountain peak, surveying the world from more than 30,000 rambling freight cars. The thing about Bill that makes him valuable is the fact that you never forget him, and promptly associate this lordly animal with the Great Northern Railway.

It was the Great Northern that coined the phrase "See America First." The Rocky Mountain goat set the fashion and a lot of Americans took the slogan to heart, to their own advantage as well as that of the Great Northern and a lot more fine American railroads. There was a time when it was fashionable to visit Europe, to see London and Paris, and there was nothing wrong with that. But a lot of Americans got in the habit of groping around in foreign lands for scenery, and turning their backs on just about as fine a selection of out-of-doors, right here in our own back yard, as there is anywhere.

It took a second world war to turn the attention of some of the globe-trotters to such gems as the Colorado Rockies and the Pacific Northwest, as they took a little tip from old Rocky Mountain Bill and headed west, and they are indebted to the old rascal forever more.

The Great Northern has kept pace with the postwar railroad trends to modernization and rehabilitation with a wide program. Much general improvement got under way following the close of the war, including the laying of new steel and other construction—work that a railroad is never through with. A new division office and depot building at Willmar, Minnesota, was a symbol of the program undertaken.

A streamlined version of the famous Empire Builder made its bow, and vast quantities of new equipment, from Diesels to box cars, were appearing on the rails as fast as manufacturers could make deliveries.

As on most of United States railroads, Dieselization has occupied a prominent part in the postwar program on the Great Northern in freight, passenger and switching service. The latter part of 1947 saw most passenger trains handled by Diesels. This included shorter run trains as well as those in transcontinental service. The Empire Builder began operating with Diesel power in February, 1947.

Diesels moved onto the head end of the Red River Limited, the Oriental Limited and Nos. 27 and 28 of the Chicago to Pacific Northwest run of this famous Fast Mail. Diesel power hauls the Oriental Limited and the Fast Mail all the way, except for the electrified portion of the line, extending between Wenatchee and Skykomish, Washington, a distance of 73 miles.

The world's two largest single-cab all-electric locomotives augmented the Great Northern's fleet of electric engines in mid-1947 and began the job of helping move freight and passenger trains over the electrified segment of the road. They were designed and built by the General Electric Company for heavy mountain service. Each locomotive is 101 feet in length. They have a continuous rating of 5,000-horsepower—power enough to pull a 2,000-ton train over the maximum 2.2 per cent grade of the Cascades without helper service.

The new electric locomotives weigh 720,000 pounds each. They are of welded steel construction and streamlined. Two traction motor-generator sets take power from the 11,000-volt overhead electric line, delivering current to the 12 traction motors with which these big, sleek giants are equipped. They can be operated from either end and can be coupled in tandem for multiple operation.

The Great Northern's electrified territory includes the 7.79-

mile-long Cascade Tunnel, the longest in the Western Hemisphere, which pierces the great Cascade Range, thrust up between the Columbia River and Puget Sound on the Pacific.

In the spring of 1948 work was begun on a relocation project in the Cascades, 46 miles west of Wenatchee, Washington. This involved the construction of 4,331 feet of new line, including a 700-foot tunnel and a 650-foot bridge across Nason Creek. Undertaken as part of a postwar improvement program to expedite traffic, the new line will be shorter, with a 2.0 per cent grade compared with an existing 2.2 per cent grade. Scheduled for completion early in 1950, or before, the track will have one curve of four degrees compared with twelve curves having a total of 216 degrees of curvature.

The cost of the project will be in the neighborhood of one million dollars, but these road improvements pay dividends in faster service and better train operation in difficult country. This constant ironing out of the line paves the way for the rush of those bright orange-dark green Diesels that Old Bill rides in the "Evergreen Northwest."

The Great Northern began using E.M.C. Diesels in 1941, increasing the number each year until, by October, 1948, there were 150 on the road. These ranged all the way from the first 360-horsepower switch engine to the last word in 6,000-horsepower freight locomotives. On October 1, 1948, the Great Northern had a total of 33 Diesels on order, with delivery scheduled for late October.

The latter locomotives included one 6,000-horsepower four-unit freight Diesel for use between Havre, Montana, and Appleyard, Washington; one 4,500-horsepower three-unit freight Diesel for use between Laurel, Montana, and Hillyard, Washington; two 3,000-horsepower two-unit freight Diesels for the Butte Division in Montana; two 3,000-horsepower two-unit passenger Diesels for work between St. Paul-Duluth, replacing 2,700-horsepower Diesels on the trains the *Gopher* and the *Badger*; and two 1,500-horsepower one-unit passenger Diesels. The last two being added to the two 2,700-horsepower Diesels running between St. Paul and Duluth, making two three-unit locomotives of 4,200-horsepower each, to handle the Oriental Limited and the Fast Mail between Skykomish, Washington, and Seattle, and to pull trains 459-460 between Seattle and Portland, Oregon.

Delivery of three 6,000-horsepower four-unit freight Diesels were scheduled for delivery some time in the first quarter of 1949, as were ten 1,500-horsepower one-unit road switch engines. Twelve additional switch engines of 1,000-horsepower were set for delivery in 1949—four in July and eight in December.

By late 1947 the bulk of Great Northern passenger trains, both transcontinental and shorter runs, were handled by Diesel power. Diesels were added to the following trains during 1947: Trains Nos. 7 and 8, the Winnipeg Limited; Nos. 235 and 236, operating between Butte and Havre, Montana; Nos. 42-43, running between Billings and Sweet Grass, Montana; Nos. 360-355 and 358-359, Morning and Afternoon Puget Sounder, operating between Seattle, Washington, and Vancouver, B. C.; Nos. 29-30, the Red River Limited; No. 3 and No. 4, the Oriental Limited; and Nos. 27 and 28, Fast Mail, between St. Paul, Minnesota, and Wenatchee, Washington.

The Oriental Limited and the Fast Mail are handled by nine three-unit 4,500-horsepower locomotives. They are maintained in St. Paul and make their runs to Wenatchee and go back to St. Paul. Arriving in St. Paul on No. 28, the locomotive lays over until it goes out on westbound No. 27 the next day. The Diesel coming in on No. 4, of the Oriental Limited, goes out on No. 3 the following morning. This arrangement permits a more than 24-hours layover at St. Paul on every other trip, and a shorter layover on intervening days. At Wenatchee No. 3's locomotive waits several hours and then heads east on No. 28. Westbound No. 27's locomotive returns to St. Paul on No. 4, the eastbound Oriental Limited. (This motive power schedule applied as of October 1, 1948, before Dieselization of these trains had been completed through to Seattle.)

New Equipment

A considerable amount of new equipment, ordered in 1946, had not yet been delivered the latter part of 1948 but was expected to be in service in 1949. This included 15 cars to make up the streamlined Morning Puget Sounder, Afternoon Puget Sounder and the Red River Limited. Each of these trains will operate with a five-car consist and on faster schedules.

The May, 1948, authorization for the purchase of 30 new passenger cars saw delivery set for the fourth quarter of 1949. Cars under construction in company shops in 1948 included one baggage-mail car, one Empire Builder diner and one Empire Builder coffee shop-lounge car, all to be standby equipment. The 30 cars ordered included six 52-seat coaches and twelve 48-seat coaches for the Oriental Limited. One and two of each type were for the six consists. There were also 11 sleepers of 8-bedroom-3-compartment type—two for each of the five Empire Builder trains, plus one extra, and one Empire Builder observation lounge car as standby.

Authorized in September, 1948, were purchases covering 100 covered hopper cars and 500 gondolas. The Great Northern shops at St. Cloud, Minnesota, and Superior, Wisconsin, were ordered to begin construction on 1,000 steel box cars for 1949 delivery. Further construction of 2,000 steel box cars was scheduled for the same company shops during 1949. 500 of these were for the Spokane, Portland & Seattle Railway, a G.N. subsidiary.

The Great Northern shops at Superior, Wisconsin, built the underframes of the 1,000 steel box cars; the balance of the work was done at the company shops in St. Cloud. Production was maintained at 18 complete cars daily for the second lot of 500, finished in early July, 1948. This was the highest production level ever reached at St. Cloud. The previous high was 16 daily when 500 were built in the year's first quarter.

In connection with the box car construction program, it might be pointed out that the Great Northern pioneered the use of "Scotchlite" reflective material on the sides of box cars in 1944. It was applied to the letters making up the words "Great

Northern," to the letters "G. N." and to the monogram on an experimental aluminum car and 24 box cars equipped for passenger train service.

In 1947, Scotchlite was applied to 500 freight box cars of plywood exterior, and in 1948 to 1,000 steel box cars. On these cars Scotchlite was applied to the letters "Great Northern," the letters "G. N.," the monogram of Old Bill, the car numbers and a row of three-inch circular targets across the bottom of car sides. The objective of this Scotchlite application is safety, since this material picks up light rays that shine on it. It also makes the reading of car designations easy. On top of these features, it is the best advertising in the world for this Rocky Mountain goat on a mountain peak out where the Great Northern spins its silver rails across the empire of the Great Northwest.

Facts and Finances

In 1947 the Great Northern's operating revenue was more than $193,750,000, which, except for the three war years of 1943 through 1945, established a record. This was only 7 per cent below the company's all-time peak of approximately $207,-750,000 in 1944. Operating expenses, however, in 1947 were 8 per cent greater than in 1944, a reflection of higher wage and material costs.

The railroad's fixed charges were reduced one million dollars in 1947—to less than $7,750,000, the lowest in 50 years. The 1947 net income of $22,500,000 was nearly one million less than in 1946. President F. J. Gavin reported that in addition to a $13,500,000 dollar increase in taxes, other factors adversely affecting the 1947 net income were wage and fuel increases of $5,750,000 and $3,500,000, respectively.

The "increasing burden" of railway payroll taxes as compared with those paid by other industries was emphasized in the Great Northern Railway's annual report to stockholders. The railway owners were advised by Mr. Gavin that the company's 1947 payroll taxes of nearly $7,500,000 equalled almost fixed charges and that they were greater than interest on funded debt.

"Payroll taxes," stated F. J. Gavin, Great Northern president, "have been an increasing burden on the company's earnings, not only because of the larger payroll base to which the tax is applied, but, more importantly, the huge increase in rates from 1 per cent in 1936 (when this form of taxation was started) to 6½ per cent in 1946 and 8¾ per cent in 1947. The increase in payroll taxes in 1947 over 1946 was more than $2,250,000."

Mr. Gavin further declared: "No other industry carries a Social Security burden as heavy as that imposed on the railways by the Crosser Act, which was enacted in 1946. The tax rate of 8¾ per cent is applied on compensation up to $300 per employee per month as compared with 2.7 per cent on compensation up to $250 per month, generally levied on employers in other industries."

Movement of freight traffic over the Great Northern in 1947 exceeded any previous peacetime year and produced nearly $165 million in revenue, an indication of the growth of the Pacific Northwest country, since approximately 380 new industries that year were located on Great Northern lines.

A total of 202 million bushels of grain were loaded at Great Northern Railway points during 1947, as compared with 206 million bushels in 1946. Lumber, fruit and copper movements were heavier in 1947 than in the preceding year, although less livestock was handled in 1947. An early start of the 1947 ore shipping season gave the Great Northern an increase of nearly 6 million long tons over 1946. More than 23 million long tons of iron were handled at the railway docks in Superior, Wisconsin, during 1947.

The year 1947 saw the inauguration of the new streamlined Empire Builder fleet. The new Empire Builder began operation on a fast daily schedule between Chicago and Seattle-Portland in February, 1947, and it received an enthusiastic endorsement by the traveling public.

Inauguration of this new Empire Builder service resulted in an increase in passenger revenues from civilian business in spite of the almost complete elimination of military travel. The Great Northern's passenger revenues in 1947 declined 18 per cent from the 1946 figures, reflecting a sharp drop in military personnel travel. However, passenger revenues of all other lines in the Western district decreased some 32 per cent.

Annual interest charges, as 1947 ended, were 60 per cent less than in 1935, while the long-term debt was 35 per cent lower.

It was somewhere around 1913, when the Great Northern began to make a speciality of tours to Glacier National Park in Montana, that Old Bill started to appear on just about everything the Great Northern owned. Glacier Park was the natural habitat of the Rocky Mountain goat and it was perfectly fitting that so noble an animal should be chosen as a symbol of the road of Jim Hill, railroad builder and empire builder.

The Pacific Northwest for a long time has been a land of opportunity, and it still is. It is a vacation land beyond compare, a world of breath-taking beauty across which the rails of the Great Northern reach. The continued success of the road and its financial soundness is largely a result of the leadership of its present president, F. J. Gavin, one of the great railroad men of the country plus its able operating vice-president, John Budd.

CHAPTER XXVI

ROCK ISLAND ROCKETS

Coach Yard—Rocket Freight

The first of the Rock Island's fleet of 15 *Rockets* was placed in service between Chicago and Peoria, Illinois, on September 19, 1937—a four-car Diesel-powered train making four trips over the 161 miles each day. The same cars and the same Diesel— No. 601. In the first ten years of operation the *Peoria Rocket* carried an estimated 2,300,000 passengers and piled up an astounding total of 2,500,000 miles.

The *Des Moines Rocket* was also placed in service in the fall of 1937—a Diesel-powered train with full parlor, reclining-seat coach and dining car accommodations. The *Des Moines Rocket* serves such important intermediate cities as Rock Island, Moline, Davenport and Iowa City. It makes one round trip daily.

For ten straight years, this pair of fabulous dayliners made a combined daily average of 1,360 miles at an average of somewhat more than a mile a minute, an astounding performance.

The *Peoria Rocket* was rightly named. The train is as much a part of Peorians' thinking as their hotels or factories. They feel, and logically so, that they have priority rights to its accommodations. It is their "shoppers special," leaving Peoria in the early morning and arriving home in early evening; it also gives the business man a full day in his Chicago office. There is a good deal of sentiment attached to the *Peoria Rocket*. The same nice things can be said about the *Des Moines Rocket*.

In addition to the *Peoria* and *Des Moines Rockets*, the *Rocket* fleet today is comprised in the order in which they were inaugurated: the *Rocky Mountain Rocket* (Chicago-Denver-

Colorado Springs); the *Choctaw Rocket* (Memphis-Amarillo, Texas); the *Zephyr Rocket* (Rock Island operates Minneapolis to Burlington, Iowa—Burlington Railroad operates on to St. Louis); the *Texas Rocket* (Minneapolis to Houston); and the *Corn Belt Rocket*, inaugurated in November, 1947, (Chicago to Omaha).

And what about the *Rocket* earnings?

The *Rockets* brought the Rock Island not only passenger train fame but fortune as well. The first four streamliners paid for themselves in less than two years, and the others have earned proportionally.

In 1947, the *Rocket* fleet amassed a total of 3,680,673 miles and earned a total gross revenue of $10,054,673, with the *Rocky Mountain Rocket*, while competing with faster schedules on other lines, grossed $2,880,628, netting $1,652,873, or a per train-mile revenue of $3.394.

Second in gross revenues in the fleet was the *Twin Star Rocket* (connecting the North Star State of Minnesota with the Lone Star State of Texas) which accumulated $1,678,912 and made a per train-mile revenue of $2.904.

This train was put together of existing *Rocket* equipment during the war to provide the only mid-west North-South rail route west of the Mississippi. It also gave the Rock Island an opportunity to make use of its 1,370-mile mid-continent route and to tie together Minneapolis, St. Paul, Des Moines, Kansas City, Oklahoma City, Dallas, Fort Worth and Houston. The train originally operated sleeping cars only between Minneapolis and Kansas City, but in 1948 postwar equipment deliveries permitted the road to add through all-room sleepers between Minneapolis and Houston.

In outward appearance, the *Rockets*, like the *Hiawathas* and the *Chiefs* and other streamliners of the west, have an individuality that highlights and glamorizes the road that operates them. The sleek-lined red Diesels, and the silver stainless steel of the cars have become a symbol of the Rock Island as they traverse the great Rock Island system. The "Route of the Rockets" has become a reality.

Included in the *Rocket* family also is the *Golden State*, which the Rock Island operates jointly with the Southern Pacific between Chicago and Los Angeles, California. This train, inaugurated in 1902, is an established institution on the Rock Island. It has been completely modernized and placed on a 45-hour extra-fare schedule. New cars added to the consist, including the widely publicized "Fiesta" car, are part of an order for 5½ million dollars worth of new equipment placed with Pullman Standard during the war. The *Golden State* has received a new exterior color design to conform with the road's combination of *Rocket* red and silver.

Returning to earnings of the *Rockets*, the *Corn Belt Rocket* started off with an impressive revenue of $2.75 per train-mile, which was amazing for a new service. The *Corn Belt* provides an over-night run between Chicago and Omaha, and return, leaving Omaha at 11:30 A.M. and arriving at Chicago at 8:30 P.M. All of the new stainless steel equipment in the consist was built by the Pullman Standard Car Manufacturing Company.

In commenting on the performance of the justly famous *Rockets*, John D. Farrington, president of the road, said: "They were a hit from the start. Back in 1937 we knew that to compete with the automobiles and busses we needed lightweight, high-speed equipment, with modern comfortable interiors. Since the first of the *Rockets* were placed in service back in 1937, they have more than met our highest expectations, both in providing high-class service and increased revenues."

New Equipment

Substantial improvements in equipment and service on five of the Rock Island Lines' fleet of Diesel-powered trains were announced in October, 1948.

During this month, new all-room sleeping cars, streamlined, lightweight diners and new observation parlor cars were added to the consist of the *Twin Star Rocket*. Accommodations on the all-private room sleepers include duplex roomettes, roomettes, and double bedrooms. The cars have all of the latest refinements, including individually-controlled lighting, air-conditioning and fluorescent lighting. All have enclosed washroom and toilet facilities.

In addition to the Pullman and dining car accommodations, the *Twin Star* carries 68-seat reclining chair coaches. Like all of the Rock Island *Rockets*, the *Twin Star* operates at no extra fare.

Also in October, 1948, the Rock Island inaugurated all-private-room sleeping car service on the *Corn Belt Rockets*. The new cars leave Chicago at 8:05 P.M. and arrive in Omaha the following morning at 7:25 A.M. The best evening train.

The addition of the new all-room sleeping cars provide both daylight and over-night streamlined passenger train service, including reclining-seat chair cars, parlor-observation cars and dining and club-lounge facilities.

Car Service and Repair

To service and maintain the cars of the Rockets, the Rock Island has completed the construction of a $1,200,000 coach yard and shops in Chicago.

Every day an average of 120 Pullmans and coaches are brought into these yards and cleaned, serviced and turned for the outgoing trip. Often this servicing must be done within a few hours. The *Rocky Mountain Rocket*, for example, arriving in the morning, must be unloaded at the station, backed into the coach yards and undergo a thorough cleaning and scrubbing. The diner must be restocked, the exterior of the train washed, ice and water supplied, equipment thoroughly inspected and repaired if necessary. The cars must be ready for the outgoing trip within a matter of five hours.

Trains arriving are passed through an automatic car washer. The cars then continue through a production-line of rapid service.

The yard layout has thirteen service tracks, which are separated by concrete platforms. There is one track for handling spare wheels. The wheel-drop pit, serving six tracks, is located in the middle of the yard. An enclosure 30 feet by 100 feet provides improved working conditions for doing wheel work and making mechanical repairs.

Yard facilities include a paint shop, oil storage building, machine, cabinet and electric shops; pipe, tin and airbrake shops and office, locker and stock rooms.

The original shops and yards were laid out between 47th and 51st Streets on Wentworth Avenue back in the 1870's, or about the time the rails were pointing West. This area then was a sparsely settled prairie. Here on 47th Street today we find the last word in railroad modernization—the Rock Island Lines testing laboratory.

Rocket Freight

Further Dieselization of the Rock Island Lines' freight service was announced in the last quarter of 1948. At that time five new 3-unit Diesel-electric locomotives were delivered. At that time, three more Diesels were on order. Their delivery gives the Rock Island a total of 34 heavy Diesels for the *Rocket* Freight service on the road's 8,000-mile system. And the Electro-Motive Division of General Motors has more of these locomotives on order at their La Grange, Illinois, plant.

Officials of the Rock Island in October, 1948, announced plans for the immediate use of Diesel power exclusively on the 300-mile Kansas City-St. Louis line and on the Choctaw route, extending from Memphis, Tennessee, to Amarillo, Texas, a distance of 761 miles. These road engines are 4,050-horsepower.

In addition to their fleet of mainline Diesels, the Rock Island has over 100 Diesel switch engines in service. A pioneer in the use of Diesel power, the road now has in operation 185 Diesels with a total of 242,664 horsepower. Diesel horsepower on order at this writing totals 65,500 horsepower.

Rocket freight service was inaugurated on through mainline runs in 1945. This innovation was a result of the successful performance of the Diesel in freight service across the nation. The program was opened with six 5,400-horsepower Diesel locomotives. Later, ten more freight units of 4,050 were added.

Diesel motors are repaired and maintained in a new shop at Silvis, Illinois. In fact, everywhere we look along the lines of the Rock Island we see a continuous modernization program as the road and its pace-setting Rockets move forward with the "Railroads of Today."

CHICAGO, ROCK ISLAND AND PACIFIC RAILROAD COMPANY
PERFORMANCE OF ROCKET TRAINS—YEAR 1947

Operating Between	Chicago & Peoria	Chicago & Des Moines	Minneapolis & Houston	Kansas City & Dallas	Memphis & Amarillo
Train Nos.	501-2-3-4	505-6	507-8	509 to 514	51-52
Train Miles	235,060	261,340	996,682	497,192	554,634
Total Revenues	$746,781	$823,754	$2,804,234	$958,476	$1,010,327
All Direct Expenses	261,013	270,902	1,051,789	521,280	551,178
Interest-Depreciation-Taxes-Insurance	46,871	53,515	163,533	110,395	84,711
NET INCOME 1947	$438,897	$499,337	$1,678,912	$326,801	$374,438
Revenue Per Train Mile	3.177	$ 3.152	$ 2.904	$ 1.928	$ 1.822

Operating Between	Chicago & Denver-Colorado Springs	Burlington & Minneapolis	Omaha to Chicago x	Total all Rocket Trains
Train Nos.	7 and 8	61-62&561-2	10	
Train Miles	848,696	267,623	19,617	3,680,844
Total Revenues	$2,880,628	$686,492	$53,981	$10,054,673
All Direct Expenses	1,079,199	337,973	27,684	4,101,018
Interest-Depreciation-Taxes-Insurance	148,556	55,254	8,643	671,478
NET INCOME 1947	$1,652,873	$293,265	$17,654	$5,282,177
Revenue Per Train Mile	$ 3.394	$ 2.565	$ 2.752	$ 2.732

x Inaugurated November 23, 1947

Office of President
March 10th, 1948

CHAPTER XXVII

BALTIMORE & OHIO

"Sentinel Service" Speeds the Freight Car

In March of 1947, the Baltimore & Ohio Railroad inaugurated one of the most revolutionary methods of handling freight in the history of American railroading. This innovation was called the "Sentinel Service" and it insured the dependable dispatch of fast freight by means of a constantly supervised movement of all trains in transit through a company-owned teletype system, which has under its hand and eye every speeding freight car.

The vast network of "Sentinel Service" reaches out from all of the great industrial centers of the East and the Mid-west, giving the shipper ample notice of the movement and the arrival of his carload shipments, thereby enabling him to arrange in advance for the handling and unloading of the car.

Sentinel Service carload freight moves with the same precision and under the same continuous control as does the passenger traffic. This service is made possible by the adoption of new and modern communications, and by new and more efficient methods of handling freight cars at reclassification and interchange points.

One of the outstanding features of this service is the "Blue Book of Sentinel Service," distributed to freight representatives, shippers, and receivers. Drawn up by B.&O. specialists for the particular industry to which the book has been presented, it presents personalized traffic plans. These individually-tailored plans of traffic show the shipper the day and hour that his carload shipment should be ready on his own siding or team track. There are also plans and descriptive matter regarding public freight facilities, team tracks, and interchange at "Sentinel" cities.

The B.&O. automatic records which record the movement of Sentinel Service inform shippers and receivers immediately of any interruption in established schedules, enabling them to rearrange their plans.

The teletype communications employed in Sentinel Service are time-savers at reclassification points. When a freight train, for example, leaves Chicago for the East the numbers and destinations of its cars are flashed ahead to the next reclassification yard. The yard force, instead of waiting for the train's arrival to determine from the waybills how to make the car distribution, can determine in advance the make-up of the new trains from these teletype reports.

There could be no finer example of the modern railroad trend in the movement of fast freight than this Sentinel Service established by the progressive Baltimore & Ohio. The old days of slipshod railroading are gone, the days of catch-as-catch-can wrestling with freight traffic, of shippers waving their arms helplessly in impotent fury over delays to vital shipments, are lost somewhere in the maze of tracks and terminals.

At this writing more than 30 cities on the B.&O. are linked in a tightly-knit pattern of Sentinel Service, providing more than 400 services for the shipper, who has under his hand the Baltimore & Ohio's traffic plan "Blue Book." More than a year of planning and experimentation went into the development of Sentinel Service, which revolutionized the movement of fast freight.

Planning for the new service was begun immediately following the termination of World War II. It involved thousands of man hours, with freight traffic people consulting continuously with operations and communications personnel. Test movements were made between three seaboard and 17 inland cities. The first movements were gradually expanded and Sentinel Service had its roots down and a healthy growth was begun.

In the beginning there were the usual skeptics and critics, crying that it couldn't be done, that it was money foolishly spent on a crazy venture. The B.&O.'s answer was that money spent in personal service information for carload customers was money well spent. Furthermore, it was not a service that demanded a direct increase in train operating expenses, but was based upon the road's "Quick Dispatch" arranged freight service—the already operating fleet of "Q.D." trains, the famous "90" fast freight movements.

Several years ago a survey by the B.&O.'s traffic department revealed that shippers were more interested in obtaining good performance on existing freight schedules than in a drastic speed-up "on paper." There has been a widespread enthusiasm for Sentinel Service, which by many has been termed "revolutionary," and the Baltimore & Ohio Blue Book today occupies a prominent place on the desk of many shippers.

Many B.&O. freight cars are now a rolling advertisement of Sentinel Service from coast to coast. Painted aluminum, each car carries the "Sentinel Service" emblem in color. This is a bright yellow rectangle bearing the words "B.&O. SENTINEL SERVICE," with a picture of the B.&O. color position light signal set to indicate "All Clear—Proceed."

Traffic "Blue Book"

Probably nothing quite as comprehensive as the Sentinel Service Blue Book has ever come into the hands of the railroad shipper. Bound in loose-leaf form for possible additional or supplementary data it contains indexed information concerning each principal city served by the service. The volume for customers in Chicago presents the pertinent data on B.&O. service to and from Chicago, with all other cities served considered as away-from-home points.

In each edition, the shipper is given a page listing of all B.&O. freight station agents in the city and the local personnel whom he may consult with respect to billing, car inspection, car records, car supply, claims, demurrage, l.c.l. arrivals, packing, rates, reconsignments, schedules, tracing, and weighing.

At the beginning of the page there is a place reserved for the card of the road's traffic representative, giving his name and telephone number. There follow then in alphabetical order loose-leaf data on each city to or from which Sentinel Service is effective. This data comprises, in brief, a full-page facilities map of the city, with separate pages listing terminal facilities, team tracks, specialized facilities (such as automobile unloading, piers, crane-equipped yards) and interchange points, respectively, each of which is "keyed" to the map and for each of which there is given a "latest placement time"—the actual hour and minute —from the east and from the west.

These pages are followed by forms in which the traffic representative inserts actual time of placement or cut-off shipments to or from the destinations listed. Information regarding switch pulls and placements at private sidings can be ascertained by the traffic representative from a special schedule book which has been prepared for each Sentinel city in connection with the new service.

Let us examine this Blue Book set-up a little more closely. We have, let us assume, a manufacturer in Chicago who uses materials which come from Newark, Ohio, a Sentinel city. By reference to the schedule—by days—of the road's arranged or "Quick Dispatch" freight service, he finds that he may expect a two-day service. However, he wishes to know more than this, or the actual time of pickup and placement, so he refers to the "Traffic Manual of Sentinel Service," which is the source of the data on cut-off and latest placement times. This data has been placed in the client's "Blue Book" traffic plan.

Under "Newark" the manufacturer finds the name of the consignor, which has been filled in by the traffic representative, the cut-off time at the local siding in Newark, and the time at which cars made ready at origin at cut-off time will be placed at the manufacturer's own siding in Chicago.

The Chicago manufacturer, of course, ships to a large number of destinations, and all information concerning such shipments will be noted in his Blue Book, ready at his finger-tips for instant reference. For shipments going to a customer at Toledo, Ohio, the traffic representative will write in the cut-off time at the shipper's siding in Chicago and the placement time at the consignee's rack at Toledo.

Now let us assume that there is a firm in Baltimore, Maryland, which is not a regular consignee and does not have a siding. The Chicago manufacturer has only to look at the Baltimore facilities map in his Blue Book to ascertain the location of the proper team track and note down on his traffic plan the latest placement time listed therefor on the printed loose-leaf sheet.

As for a shipment for an off-line point, via Washington, D. C., and a connection at Potomac Yard, Virginia, he has only to glance at the list of latest placement times for individual interchange roads in the Washington sections of his Blue Book to know what he may expect in performance en route from his loading platform to the end of the B.&O. rails.

In each case, the transit time, in days, in relation to Chicago appears prominently on a separate sheet for each point.

Automatic Records

There is a constant automatic check on all movement of Sentinel Service freight movement, with immediate notification of both consignor and consignee if, for any reason, there is a chance that the shipment will not be delivered according to the siding-to-siding schedule set forth in the traffic plan. When neither the shipper nor the consignee receive any news it is good news, and indicates that the placement will be made "on the advertised."

When a road train is made up in an origin yard at a Sentinel point, the waybills are sorted in the yard office and those governing carload shipments eligible for that service are tagged with a prominent Sentinel Service trademark sticker. A teletype of the outgoing train is then put on the printer, each Sentinel car number being suffixed with an "SX," or Sentinel symbol.

The teletype then flashes the record on to Baltimore, the next point at which the train will be yarded, to the traffic department which has jurisdiction over the origin point, and to any interested parties. From then on, until delivered to the consignee or connection, these Sentinel cars are under the constant control of this automatic record system.

Under instructions, formulated jointly by traffic and operations, by trainmasters, by general yardmasters and division superintendents, checks are made to make sure that these "tagged" carload shipments: (1) Are pulled at or before cutoff time; (2) depart in the proper "Quick Dispatch" freight train; (3) remain in the block to reach the destination on schedule; (4) are placed at destination on or before latest placement time.

This check is made by automatic comparison of waybills with teletyped train and transfer consist departure reports. If a "ragged" car is not on Train No. 94, say, out of Willard, Ohio, when it ought to be, the yardmaster must then balance his books by wiring the central Sentinel record office at Baltimore, informing them of the delay, the expected duration, and the cause. Baltimore, in turn, wires the traffic offices serving the consignor and consignee, respectively, and the two parties most interested in the car's movements receive a prompt telephone call or wire, notifying them that their car will probably not reach its destination on schedule.

To provide an even speedier transmission of information to the shipper some Sentinel city traffic offices have made arrangements to receive from classification yards which handle the bulk of their shipments teletyped train consist departure reports. These are often *received* before the train actually leaves the yard. Thus the city traffic office can check against the system passing report, in the case of inbound loads, or against the chief dispatcher's list of cars billed and pulled from origin sidings, in the case of outbound shipments.

Through this arrangement, the Chicago freight traffic staff can tell from teletyped train reports from Willard, Ohio, whether shipments originating in Chicago have departed from Willard on the correct preference freight train, and whether shipments destined to Chicago are likely to arrive on schedule. This special reporting does not supplant the receipt and use of system passing reports from Baltimore, but any action Chicago may take as a result of such information constitutes a double-check on "failure" wires dispatched from the central automatic records' office.

Before Sentinel Service was actually placed in operation by the B.&O., the traffic and operating departments conducted exhaustive tests for a year to make certain that the advertised schedules were sufficiently expansive to cushion the inevitable effects of heavy traffic and equipment shortages. Each schedule and every plan of operation went through a score of initialing, indicating approval by scores of offices, before the present service was finally approved and subsequently announced as ready to take its place as another Baltimore & Ohio "first" and one of the most revolutionary methods of handling freight in the history of American railroads.

Plant Improvement

To make possible a so highly specialized innovation as Sentinel Service required complete modernization of plant and facilities of the B.&O., and the road has employed every resource to maintain its position as one of the really great rail systems of the country.

The postwar improvement and modernization program of the Baltimore & Ohio involved an investment of $116 million. Of this sum more than $26 million was spent for improvements along the road's 6,000 miles of right-of-way. Ninety million dollars went into new rolling stock, including modern locomotives, passenger cars, and thousands of new freight cars.

Additional expenditures totaling more than $250 million for major improvements and new equipment, to meet the growing demand for improved rail transportation, are planned for the next five or ten years, or well on toward 1958, according to president R. B. White, who emphasizes, however, that current net income is too low to provide the funds or to establish the credit necessary for such large expenditures.

A major 1947 improvement was the mighty two million dollar railroad bridge over the Great Kanawha River at Point Pleasant,

West Virginia. This was the largest bridge built by the B.&O. in 25 years and its opening was hailed as an event of great civic and social importance to the entire Middle Ohio Valley region. The bridge is one of 18 along the Ohio River sub-division that has been rebuilt in order to enable the road's short route between the Great Lakes, the Pittsburgh industrial region, and the South to handle the heaviest freight loads through this gateway.

Rich in natural resources, the Ohio Valley is in a position to be known as the "Ruhr Valley" of America, and it was with this in mind, President White stated in his address of dedication, that the Baltimore & Ohio had turned its attention to creating a modern, efficient rail transportation artery capable of serving the industries of the valley as well as the shippers of the great industrial region to the north.

Located about three-quarters of a mile from the point where the Great Kanawha River meets the Ohio, the new bridge, during the first months of its operation, proved its worth to the road. Heavy volumes of traffic, much of which never before routed B.&O., have rolled across it in increasing tonnage.

Completed in December, 1946, the B.&O.'s Cone Yard at East St. Louis has greatly increased the capacity and the facilities of the railroad at this vital gateway. Closer to the Terminal Railroad Association than any other Eastern trunk line yard, the East St. Louis Yard has been for many years the principal terminal facility of the system at this point. The yard's expansion has increased greatly the capacity of the Baltimore & Ohio in this territory, providing expeditious and efficient switching, classification of freight, interchange of cars, and dispatching of trains.

The new track layout for freight trains consists of 24 classification tracks, a new and enlarged car repair yard, and a modern 200-ton track scale. The yard is flood-lighted and its operation is directed through a modern loud-speaking system.

Supporting the yard is a new engine terminal with a ten-stall enginehouse and a 115-foot turntable. There are offices, a machine shop, store, oil houses, water-treating plant, and inspection pits. The engine handling layout includes a completely new and modern coaling station for locomotives, ash conveyors, sand facilities, and locomotive-washing platform.

This improved yard at East St. Louis is a part of the original Ohio and Mississippi Railroad, the oldest railroad connecting St. Louis with the Eastern seaboard. The original line was projected as early as 1832, but it was not until 1848 that it was actually chartered by Indiana, in 1845 by Ohio, and in 1851 by Illinois. On July 11, 1855, it was completed from Vincennes to Illinoistown, now East St. Louis. In two years it reached Cincinnati. Here connection was made with the Marietta and Cincinnati Railroad, which connected at Parkersburg with the B.&O.

The completion of this through route in 1857, called the "Great American Central Route," from St. Louis on the Mississippi to Baltimore on the Atlantic seaboard, was celebrated as a great occasion. For weeks special trains were run over the entire route, and cities and states vied to honor the celebrities who rode the trains as the guests of the railroads. The entire line became the property of the Baltimore & Ohio in 1889. This great main rail artery is still the shortest route from the Mississippi to the Atlantic.

Because of the importance of the new Cone Yard to the B.&O. system in the St. Louis area, President White and the road's board of directors made a special visit to the yard after its completion, inspecting its enormous track layout and operating facilties. The Baltimore & Ohio's huge investment in the new facility is indicative of the company's faith in the continued growth of St. Louis, its environs and the great Southwest territory which stands beyond this gateway.

Since its opening, Cone Yard has demonstrated its ability to expedite freight service in this section, and the B.&O.'s traffic potential in this rich industrial region has risen to new heights.

Communications—Car Retarders

Modern communications are vital to the railroad of today. Sentinel freight service and the speeding passenger train are dependent on quick and sure communication facilities in their conquest of time and distance. And the B.&O.'s communication system is among the most modern in the country.

The road has maintained its position through constant expansion and improvement of its communication facilities, consisting mainly of additions to its long-distance telephone trunk circuits, and the creation of a teletype and train dispatching service. This great communication network links every important terminal, every gateway on the system.

Teletype machines are in operation at every headquarters on every division, with the exception of the Buffalo Division, where plans for teletype installations are under way as this is written.

Radio is taking its place more and more in the Baltimore & Ohio communication world. The classification yard at New Castle was radio-equipped around 1946. The tug fleet at Baltimore is dispatched by radio, as are tugs operated by the B.&O. in New York harbor.

The first commercial radio-telephone call ever made was from the famous "Royal Blue," operating between New York and Washington, on August 15, 1947.

The B.&O.'s Cincinnatian is equipped with both radio reception equipment and a public address system.

It was on the coldest day of the year in the winter of 1947-48 that the new car retarders were placed in operation on the eastbound hump in the yard at Willard, Ohio. Train 394, from Toledo, was put over the hump in freezing temperatures—39 cars, sliding down the hump to the fanned-out classification tracks, at better than one a minute, and this with a crew inexperienced in car-retarder operation.

There are 32 tracks at this location and five retarders, operated from the control tower.

You have to get the "feel" of handling cars through these car retarders, as John Reed, the 40-year veteran at Cumberland Yard, will tell you. John puts it this way: "It takes a couple of weeks to learn just the right amount of pressure, but once you learn it through experience you can apply the retarders without thinking about it. All you do is sort of look at the car to judge its weight and keep in the back of your mind just how far down you want it to stop on the classification track."

Humping cars used to be a rather rugged job in winter, with plenty of frostbites when the thermometer red was hunting the bottom of the glass, but with retarders only one or two hump riders are required for the few cars carrying fragile shipments.

John Reed's equipment, there in the tower, consists of a tele-type machine, over which he receives the lists of the cars to be humped, with their serial numbers, classification symbol, the particular track to which they are to be directed, and special information. Then there are his switch dials, which he sets to route each car or cut, operated by a flick of a finger. Other dials control the "master" retarder, located just below the hump. Below the master retarder, on the diverging lead tracks, there are three other retarders to slow up the cars again if necessary.

Beside the teletype machine and dial panel, there is a microphone connected to a public address system outside of the tower which Reed employs when he has to give verbal orders to the crew of the switch engine. He also controls signals to the extent of being able to stop hump operation when he deems it advisable. There is also a voice box which enables Reed to communicate instantly with the yardmaster's office, and a standard telephone for other contacts.

The eastbound yard at Cumberland is a busy one—one of the busiest on the system—for all the freight from both western main lines funnel into it. About 1,700 cars, or some 20 trains, are humped each 24-hour day.

At Willard, Ohio, the B.&O. rebuilt two large gravity-type classification yards at a cost of around $2,000,000 in order to get trains through the yards quickly and so further facilitate the road's Sentinel Service to shippers. The changes made possible the handling of approximately 2,300 cars daily. The features of the project included a complete modernization of the plant, including the last word in communication. The two eastbound yards were consolidated, which meant making extensive track changes; changes in the westbound yard were limited to the area down the hump and through the switches and retarders. The project also included new office buildings and other improvements.

The improvements at Willard were essential to the kind of service the Baltimore & Ohio planned to give its shippers. Willard is 278 miles east of Chicago on the B.&O.'s main route east through Akron, Ohio, Youngstown and Pittsburgh, Pa., to Washington, D. C., Baltimore, Maryland, Philadelphia and New York.

Willard, Ohio, is the hub of the road's freight operations throughout a large area between Pittsburgh and Chicago, involving five operating divisions. Within the scope of the Willard yard, the B.&O. has three north-and-south lines from ports on Lake Erie to cities and coal fields in southern Ohio, West Virginia and Kentucky.

The year 1948 saw car retarders playing an increasingly important part in speeding freight between shipper and consignee, as more and more gravity-type freight classification yards were equipped with completely modern facilities. The Willard yard is floodlighted with lights mounted on 100-foot-high steel towers; they can be turned on and off by switches in the retarder control towers, or controlled automatically by light-sensitive photoelectric devices on the towers which turn the lights "on" as darkness falls, or "off" as dawn approaches.

The men who operate the modern classification yard are trained railroad specialists and vastly important in the field of mechanical railroading. They are the trained army of the steel rail who make possible the highly developed service rendered by the railroads of today—the kind of service that goes into maintaining the rapid transport of goods necessary to the health and prosperity of America in peacetime and to the defense of America in wartime.

CHAPTER XXVIII

CHESAPEAKE & OHIO

"Show Window" of the C.&O.—Ticket Reservations

White Sulphur Springs and its Greenbrier Hotel have been taken over again by the Chesapeake & Ohio Railroad. Like Sun Valley on the Union Pacific, this is an integral part of the "Railroads of Today" and it is fortunate that one of the nation's great railroad systems, so ably managed, can bring so famous and beautiful a resort within reach of the people.

The White Sulphur Springs property includes three magnificent golf courses, wonderful baths, tennis courts, bridle trails, and all recreational facilities. You can enjoy trout fishing, grouse shooting, horseback riding—almost anything, in fact, that your fancy dictates.

White Sulphur Springs is located on the main line of the C.&O. up the Allegheny grade for the eastbound movement of coal. It is surrounded by mountains—the tumbled ridges that cap some of the richest coal deposits in America.

During the war the government used the great White Sulphur Springs resort as a hospital. Since its return to the Chesapeake & Ohio it has been redecorated as nicely as only a person like Dorothy Draper can do it. Exquisite is the only word for it. Indeed, Miss Draper has shown not only fine taste but also originality. She has done a particularly interesting C.&O. ticket office in the hotel—an illuminated panel of the road's new steam turbine engine, the "500." Commodious facilities are provided for passengers waiting for their tickets.

The Chesapeake & Ohio also designed White Sulphur station, which is one of the finest you will find anywhere. It is built of white-washed brick, with blue and red leather sofas in the waiting room. The ticket office itself bears little resemblance to ticket offices found in the average railroad station.

White Sulphur Springs is also an amazingly fine operational station with a run-around track on the north side of the main line so that when train No. 3, the F. F. V., arrives in the morning it is a simple matter to cut off the sleeper for White Sulphur, allowing later sleep for passengers. The car is picked up later in the morning by train No. 13 and taken to Hinton to be serviced before returning that night on C.&O. No. 6.

White Sulphur station has other admirable operating arrangements, as have so many stations on the lines of the Chesapeake & Ohio. The hotel is ably managed by C. P. Fairless, one of the best hotel men in the country.

The "Pere Marquettes"

The C.&O. has continued to pioneer in improving passenger service—the "show window" of the Chesapeake & Ohio. The growing patronage of the popular streamliners in service on the Pere Marquette District provides tangible evidence that modern equipment and improved service can increase substantially passenger revenues.

The modern quality of the streamlined *Pere Marquettes* extends to every detail of their accommodations. In the dining car, for instance, tables are placed so that the waitress can serve without reaching over seated persons. The no-tipping policy was pioneered on these smartly appointed trains—if you care for it. Some do—others do not.

The *Pere Marquettes* are carrying twice as many passengers between Detroit and Grand Rapids as the conventional-type trains which they replaced in August, 1946.

The reader understands, of course, that the properties of the Pere Marquette Railway Company were merged with those of the Chesapeake & Ohio, and became the Pere Marquette District of the C.&O. on June 6, 1947. The two railroads had been affiliated since 1929. During the intervening years the Pere Marquette materially improved the physical condition of its property, substantially reduced its debt and refunded the balance at a lower interest rate.

The merger added a 1,950-mile system to the 3,106 miles of the C.&O. lines that link the rich coal fields of Virginia, West Virginia, Ohio, and Kentucky with the Atlantic seaboard and the Great Lakes. The added system serves many of Michigan's key production centers and resort areas—Chicago, Milwaukee and two other Lake Michigan ports in Wisconsin, and a prosperous agricultural and industrial territory in the southern part of the Canadian province of Ontario.

Passenger traffic, present and potential, is considerable in the Pere Marquette District; its lines serve populous areas in northern Illinois and Indiana, and extend from southern Michigan to the lakes and woodlands of northern Michigan, drawing vacationists all year long.

Family coaches and their companion units in the new passenger-car fleet were designed by C.&O. engineers and manufactured by the Budd Company. Their distribution over the Chesapeake and Pere Marquette districts has added modern units to the C.&O.'s busiest passenger runs. Twin unit diners, luxury day coaches, and tavern cars have been assigned to both districts. The family and room-dome cars are operating over the Chesapeake District while the observation-dome coaches run exclusively on the Pere Marquette.

Two novel features of the new C.&O. passenger fleet include the Mickey Mouse Theater in the family car and the aquarium filled with tropical fish, together with the unique marine motif, in the tavern lounge. The family car is a welcome haven for the mother with a baby. Here the C.&O. hostess will help out, preparing the bottle in the car's all-stainless steel kitchen, which is equipped with hot plates, a bottle sterilizer, and refrigerator, while mother attends to the baby's needs in a special room where infants can be bathed and the diapers changed and washed.

The rest rooms in all cars invite enthusiasm by the traveler on today's glamour train. They are large and attractively decorated, with fluorescent lights, pedal-operated plumbing and germ-free "Sterilseats," sterilized by ultra-violet rays when not in use. Women passengers enjoy the convenience of lounge chairs, vanity tables and full-length mirrors in the powder rooms.

Electro-pneumatically operated vestibule doors slide open at the slightest touch of a small push-plate. The doors remain open long enough for a passenger to walk through, but should they begin to close before passage has been completed a hidden mechanism automatically re-opens the door at the least contact with a rubber guard.

Temperature controls and filtering systems insure fresh, clean air at all times. The cars themselves offer something new and delightful at every turn. Interior decorations provide lovely color arrangements of dark oak-veneer walls, ivory-cream ceilings, chinese red doors, and upholstery and carpeting in rose.

Anyone who once rode a modern train should want to ride it again.

On board of the Mountaineer in the first chapter you were met by John Jones, the train passenger agent. You were indebted to Mr. Jones for much of the enjoyment and comfort of your trip. From him you learned of the many things that are happening on the "Railroads of Today." On the C.&O. Pere Marquettes you meet his counterpart in the passenger representative, except that on the Chesapeake & Ohio his duties concern passengers who hold "pay-on-train" tickets.

When the C.&O.'s travel on credit and train reservations-by-telephone plans were introduced to American railroading, 12 young men in the new position of passenger representatives were introduced to the Chesapeake & Ohio's Pere Marquettes and passengers. The success or failure of the revolutionary charge account for rail service and no-waiting-in-ticket-lines systems depended largely on the men who would be the go-betweens on the trains between the public and the company. It is an established fact that the systems are successful and have the unqualified support of the traveling public.

The C.&O. passenger representatives are among the most smartly uniformed railroad personnel in the country. Their job is

C & O #90 the Expediter, crack Manifest freight train, heading east out of Stevens Yard, Kentucky, on the Cincinnati Division. Courtesy C & O RR.

EMC diesel #18 6000 h.p. F–3 on #18, the Super Chief, climbing the 3% grade through Apache Canyon up Glorietta Pass, 20 miles an hour with twelve cars and no helper. Photo by Preston George.

Sentinel freight really crosses the Alleghenies B & O Manifest CSD–95 leaving Altamount behind one of the great EM–1 engines on Cumberland Division. Photo by H. W. Pontin, Rail Photo Service.

Elevated platforms provide working areas at the same level in the Great Northern diesel shops at Havre, Montana. Courtesy G. N. RR.

Great Northern diesel shop at Havre, Montana, went into operation in November, 1945. This was the railroad's first shop built exclusively for diesel motor power. Courtesy G. N. RR.

The new C & O Central reservation ticket drums at Huntington, W. Va. It is possible for passengers to phone from many outlying points to this bureau to reserve accommodations. Courtesy C & O RR.

C & O #1601, class H—8, with an eastbound manifest train running around another engine of the same class which has stopped at Allegheny Tower to cut off its pusher. Clifton Forge Division. Courtesy C & O RR.

New diner lounge cars now in service on the Rock Island Rocky Mt. Rocket between Chicago and Colorado Springs. Note the diagonal seating. Courtesy Rock Island Lines.

C & O #3007, the great 2–10–4 type, class T-1, west of Greenup, Kentucky, on the Cincinnati Division enroute to Parsons Yard, Columbus, Toledo, and the Lakes with 160 loads totaling 13,500 tons. Courtesy C & O RR.

Electro Motive 4-unit 6000 h.p. freight diesel climbing Sherman Hill unassisted with a fifty-one-car stock train at 30 miles an hour. Wyoming Division. Photo by R. H. Kindig.

New type of dining-car seating with conventional tables on the new streamlined Pere Marquette. Courtesy C & O RR.

EMC 4000 h.p. passenger diesel #4009 eastbound with train #48 the new Detroiter running over the Hudson Division above Peekskill, New York. Courtesy N.Y.C. RR.

M P Fairbanks Morse diesel #306 with solid train of green fruit from the lower Rio Grande Valley just north of Harlingen, Texas. Courtesy Missouri Pacific RR.

one of liaison between the ticket office employees who make reservations over the telephone for prospective travelers and the person boarding the train after having made such a reservation. The passenger representative secures the tickets from the office and delivers them to the travelers aboard the train. There he either collects a cash payment for the amount of the fare or he makes out the necessary bill if the recipient is a credit card holder.

The passenger representative is also charged with assigning passengers to their designated seats, making sure they have the proper tickets and ironing out any misunderstanding among passengers over space assignments. He has a chart of reserved-seat coaches similar to those used in Pullman cars.

As travelers board the train the passenger representative locates those for whom he holds pay-on-train tickets, assigns them their space, and delivers their tickets to them. When the conductor comes through collecting tickets he does not know whether the tickets were purchased at a ticket office, or reserved by telephone and paid for or charged on the train.

Passenger representatives on the C.&O. are constantly on the alert to perform any of the many little duties that improve the service rendered by the road. At principal operating points, representatives check at ticket offices for further reservations and wire ahead to determine whether any space has been released. In this way they know at all times which space has been reserved and which space is available as the run progresses.

We will turn now to the C.&O. Central Reservation Bureau.

Central Ticket Reservation Bureau

In January of 1948, the Chesapeake & Ohio announced the inauguration of a Central Reservation Bureau at Huntington, West Virginia. This completed plans made in the preceding months for the establishment of a system whereby the prospective passenger could arrange in advance for reservations by simply picking up the nearest telephone and making a five-cent call from New York, Cleveland, or any of the principal cities on the lines of the C.&O.

The prospective passenger informs the central reservationist of the date of departure from a certain point and is immediately assigned available accommodations. If the traveler is a holder of a Chesapeake & Ohio credit card the ticket reservations are either charged to his account, or he can pay for them when he boards the train.

Let us assume the prospective passenger intends to make a trip from Washington, D. C., to Huntington, West Virginia. He simply looks up the telephone number listed under "C. & O. Reservations," dials, and is connected with the C.&O. central bureau switchboard operator in Huntington. After being informed of the passenger's requirements, the call is dispatched to the operator handling westbound sleeper reservations.

The second operator requests complete details from the prospective passenger, then looks at a reservation table to determine whether the desired space is available. On the table before the operator is a panel resembling a cribbage board, in which are stuck various colored pegs representing the different types of accommodations. A peg in a spot for the particular date and space the traveler desires would indicate that the space is open. If the peg is not there it indicates that the space has been sold. The peg is removed after the accommodation has been assigned, and the reservation is recorded in the indexed diagram cards. Another feature of the central control bureau is an arrangement whereby the reservationist is in a position to give comprehensive reports of possible accommodations on any train 56 days in advance.

The Chesapeake & Ohio reports that the central reservation bureau was devised by the road's own engineers in co-operation with the Wassell Organization. It necessitates a widespread network of direct telephone lines between major on-line cities and the bureau, as well as the use of four visual reservation units.

These reservation units or tables, one each for eastbound and westbound sleeping car and coach reservations, are mounted on three free-swinging rotating drums around which the operators are seated. The drum, with its ball-bearing mounting, may be swung around to give the several operators a chance to work on the table at once. Reservationists wear the new-type headphones and are seated so that all three drums of the reservation table are within easy reach.

A staff of trained reservationists operates the bureau. The girls are given intensive preliminary training in telephone etiquette, the operation of reservation boards, and all other phases of the system. Operators work in a glass-enclosed, soundproof room. The bureau is located in the C.&O. building in Huntington and is under the supervision of Arthur S. Gent, vice-president of traffic. David F. O'Connel, formerly assistant manager of the reservation bureau at Grand Central Terminal, New York City, is manager of the bureau.

Reservations for the following trains are handled by the bureau: The "George Washington," operating between Cincinnati and Washington and Phoebus, Virginia, and between Ashland, Kentucky, and Louisville; the "Sportsman," between Cincinnati and Washington and between Phoebus and Detroit, Michigan; and the "Fast Flying Virginian," between Cincinnati and Washington and between Phoebus and Cincinnati.

The reservation bureau does away with a lot of effort and waste motion. You merely pick up your telephone, or step into a convenient booth, call C.&O. Reservations and tell the pleasant-voiced young lady your transportation problem. That is all there is to it. This is simply another of the parade of innovations that await your pleasure on the "Railroads of Today."

The C.&O.'s new president Walter J. Tuohy is one of this country's leading coal experts which should help the C.&O. and her many friends in the business. He is also a real railroader with plenty of modern ideas.

CHAPTER XXIX

THE MISSOURI PACIFIC

Green Fruit Movement—Instruction Car

The number of trains for perishables has grown from a thin trickle 60 years ago to a great flood of rolling cars. The health of America rides the fruit trains, traveling swiftly from the rich valleys of California, Arizona, Texas; from fertile flat lands of Florida to the industrial and metropolitan centers of the country.

During the 1947-48 season, 41,768 cars of fresh fruits and vegetables were shipped over the Missouri Pacific Lines from the great Rio Grande Valley of Texas. These included 34 varieties of fruits and vegetables, which were shipped from 41 separate loading stations. This green fruit, originating on the Missouri Pacific, went to every state in the Union, to Canada, and several European countries.

Down in the Rio Grande Valley the harvest season begins each year in October and continues through July of the following year. The movement of perishables starts slowly; then increases rapidly to the peak months of January, February, and March; loadings then taper off to the end of the season.

An indication of the manner in which car loadings progress from month to month is shown on the following table:

October	555 cars		March	6,247 "
November	2,767 "		April	5,774 "
December	4,600 "		May	4,291 "
January	7,683 "		June	2,298 "
February	7,353 "		July	199 "

Of the total car movement during the 1947-48 season over the Missouri Pacific Lines, 17,100 cars were citrus fruits and 24,668 cars were fresh vegetables.

The Rio Grande Valley produces a wide variety of green fruit. In addition to oranges and grapefruit, we find tomatoes, carrots, potatoes, onions, spinach, cabbage, squash, green corn, beets, and parsley. Lesser quantities of anise, broccoli, cauliflower, green beans, cucumbers, eggplant, endive, lettuce, turnips, radishes, peas, peppers, and watermelons are loaded aboard the refrigerator cars that will speed the crops to the far-flung markets of the country.

Of the 41 loading stations along the Missouri Pacific, Weslaco, Pharr, San Benito, Raymondville, Mercedes, Mission, Alamo, McAllen, Edinburg, Edcouch, Harlingen, Donna, and La Feria, all load in excess of 1,200 cars of fruits and vegetables annually. Ten of the remaining stations load in excess of 500 cars annually.

Some miles north of this Rio Grande Valley country in what is known as the "Coastal Bend," which comprises the Corpus Christi-Robstown district, 1,146 cars of vegetables were loaded during the 1947-48 season.

There are two routes by which these perishables of the Rio Grande Valley move to the principal markets of the country. Sixty per cent travel the coastal route through Kinder to Northern and Eastern market destinations. Twenty-nine per cent move to the midwest and western markets through the Texarkana gateway. Eleven per cent are distributed to what is generally known as local markets. Aside from the freight loadings of this produce, something like 300 cars are moved by express.

None of the figures we have indicated includes fruits and vegetables that go into cans. Approximately 33 per cent of the Rio Grande Valley production is taken by the canners.

"King Cotton" is still a major source of income in this great garden valley of the Rio Grande. In 1948 more than 300,000 bales were produced.

Adjacent to and just north of the Lower Rio Grande Valley is a vast cattle empire. From this district thousands of head of beef cattle move to market each year. Located in this region is the most famous cattle ranch in the world—the fabulous and historic King Ranch, the largest not only in the United States but in the whole world. The King Ranch breeds its own strain of beef cattle and also breeds fine race horses. An adjacent ranch for many years has been in the business of breeding polo ponies.

Some of the country's best duck shooting can be enjoyed in this great valley; quail and doves are also plentiful. In fact, this country reached by the Missouri Pacific is a sportsman's paradise, offering even great tarpon fishing in the waters of the adjacent gulf.

Again, getting better acquainted with America's railroads means getting better acquainted with America.

In another chapter we have reviewed the beautiful new Eagles of the Missouri Pacific and Texas Pacific, a pleasant adventure in themselves, as they provide a comfortable, luxurious way of visiting the fascinating Rio Grande Valley and the romantic and glamorous Gulf Coast country of Texas. Just as Presidents Neff and Volmer of these two roads would want it to be. They both know their properties and the country they operate in.

This is history, this Texas, rich in color and legend, from the days of Cabeza De Vaca in 1528, who passed this way with his slogging caravans, to the days of the modern Eagle trains, shining in the Texas sun.

"Classroom on Wheels"

The use of an air-brake instruction car is not new to Missouri Pacific crew and repair men for such a car has been employed since 1926. However, in 1948 a new car of this type was equipped and placed in service. It was designed for the practical demonstration of air-brake operation and arranged to provide an opportunity for all motive power employees and shop and maintenance men to learn more about air-brake details.

The car will be an aid to newer railroaders and will serve as a means of refreshing the minds of the older men and helping to clarify their extensive experience with air-brake operation or repairing, and at the same time provide them with an opportunity to learn about the newest and latest equipment.

This air-brake class room car was originally an all-steel Pullman. It was completely rebuilt and outfitted at the Sedalia, Missouri, shops of the Missouri Pacific. It is equipped with working, full-size brake equipment such as is used on locomotives and cars in passenger and freight service, and includes electro-pneumatic brakes installed on modern streamlined passenger trains.

The car has comfortable seats for 48 persons, but up to 60 can be accommodated. It serves the major purpose of making possible study of air-brake equipment by groups assembled at designated points along the lines of the system. It also affords means whereby running tests can be made while the car is en route from place to place. The interior arrangement of the car includes an instrument room, a large instruction room, and two staterooms for the traveling instructors, or inspectors, when the car is being used to make running tests. Each stateroom has one permanent bed and a shower bath.

An operative set of D-24-RL brake equipment with electro-pneumatic devices is mounted on a vertical steel panel at one end of the instruction room. This equipment is the same used on the new Diesel passenger locomotives. A speed-governor generator and a Reeves variable-speed drive unit are mounted as an auxiliary assembly, thus making it possible to simulate actual road operating conditions at speeds from 10 to more than a 100 miles an hour. These various speeds are shown on the General Electric speed indicator.

On the side wall of the car are located sets of No. 8 empty-and-loaded freight-car equipment, No. 6-ET locomotive brake equipment, AB-1B high-speed freight-car brake equipment which can also be used to demonstrate operation of standard AB freight-car brake equipment, and UC passenger-car brakes and the K-2 type for freight cars.

Demonstrator equipment has been so installed that all of it is along the side walls of the car, but the tell-tale gauges that register operation of the mechanism have been arranged on brackets which can be swung out across the center aisle of the car so that they are visible to everyone in the room. The No. 6-ET, the AB, UC, and K-type equipments are applied, in the same way, with sections of rubber hose substituting for the rigid piping used on locomotives.

At other locations on the side walls are various locomotive devices cut away to show the interior construction and the operation. These units include a No. 4 vent valve, ADA super-governor, SD-6 compressor governor, Edna Type-A mechanical lubricator, firedoor cylinder, and other small devices. This miscellaneous equipment is valuable for classes of locomotive enginemen and firemen.

Class sessions usually last about one and a half hours. The car may remain at one location anywhere from a few days to two weeks. No predetermined course of study is followed. One day there may be repair and maintenance men present, while the next day the class may be made up of apprentices, or, perhaps, electricians interested mainly in the electric brake service.

The lecturer or instructor is aided by the car's public-address system, and he wears a microphone which permits freedom of movement around the equipment. Visual aids include projection equipment, manufacturers charts and graphs, and other explanatory literature.

The instrument room in the car is equipped with various devices for the accurate recording of data incident to actual train operation as the car is moving from place to place. A steel pedestal supports a heavy table on which are mounted three Essterline Angus recording instruments. One pen records the speed of the moving car; the second records the pressure in the brake pipe under the car; the third records brake-cylinder pressure on the locomotive when the car is placed next to the locomotive in a train.

On the left margin of each recording tape a timing pen marks in seconds the elapsed time. On the right margin of the tapes a pen records each ten revolutions of the car wheels under the car. These instruments are used to record accurately the speed of the train in which the car may be running, the distance required to stop the train after application of the brakes, and the time consumed in making the stop.

Other important data may be obtained through the use of these instruments. The proper spacing of block signals can be checked against the time required for trains to make stops in response to signal indication. The exact air pressures indicating brake applications can be watched, and other details of train handling observed and recorded.

Impact Recorders

Two impact recorders are included in the instrument sets, one for use on passenger trains, the other for use on freights. These units record automatically the shocks of train handling. Jolts and jars are recorded on a time-calibrated tape.

When checking on freight trains one recording instrument remains in the car and is usually placed behind the locomotive where the impacts are the lightest; the other is placed in the caboose. These recorders will show up the shocks of starting, or the amount of impact due to slack action between the cars when a brake application is made and subsequently released.

A study of the recording instrument tapes will reveal at what time the impacts occurred and the extent of possible effects on merchandise in the cars of the train. This provides an accurate story of what actually happened, and it paves the way for an intelligent discussion of means and methods of avoiding rough handling in the future.

Particularly this phase of the Missouri Pacific's new car has proved increasingly beneficial, and there is no doubt that these impact recorders have been instrumental in reducing loss and damage claims to some extent.

CHAPTER XXX

THE SANTA FE TODAY

Canyon Diablo Bridge—Argentine Yard

The dream of Cyrus K. Holliday for a railroad that would join Kansas and the ports of the Pacific Coast materialized into a great rail system which has a grand total of 21,176 miles of track. Thirteen thousand eighty-four of these miles are operated track which speed the roaring trains of the Atchison, Topeka and Santa Fe from a few feet above sea level to the summit of Raton Pass, more than 7,000 feet high.

It is difficult to visualize the size of this railroad plant unless it is broken down into quantities and elements that can be grasped by the mind. Even then one is a little bewildered by the figures presented. Let us take Santa Fe bridges, for example. A train making a tour of the system would travel 218 miles on bridges, trestles, and viaducts alone. The Illinois River bridge, which is double track, is 1,695 feet long. The Mississippi River Bridge at Fort Madison reaches a length of 3,347 feet. This is also double-track. The Missouri River bridge at Sibley, Missouri—considered one of the most picturesque of all Santa Fe bridges—is 4,057 feet long. All three original bridge structures were built in 1887.

Then there is Canyon Diablo bridge, the highest bridge on the system, which will be described in detail in these pages.

Any railroad's physical plant begins with the right-of-way, and it includes ballast, ties, rails, signals, towers, switches, sidings, bridges, telephone and telegraph lines, depots, freight houses, signposts, mail cranes, pipe lines, stock chutes, snow fences, and telegraph offices. The maintenance of these facilities is a mighty

276

operation in itself, demanding a well-staffed engineering department and the latest and best materials and machines available.

At the end of 1946 the crossties supporting Santa Fe tracks totaled more than 58 millions. The Santa Fe system uses two and a quarter million cross, switch, and bridge ties annually. A railroad tie in itself is just a sizable chunk of timber eight feet long, seven inches thick and about ten inches across the face, but after it has been treated chemically and planted firmly beneath a pair of rails it becomes the cornerstone of railroad transportation. For all of the inventive genius of mankind, no suitable substitute for a plain old wood tie has been discovered.

The standard tie for Santa Fe high-speed main track is nine feet in length—which is one foot longer than the regulation standard. All Santa Fe high-speed transcontinental lines have been designated as 131-132-pound rail territory. This means that much of the mileage and all new rail laid in that territory is 131-132-pound rail except in yards and other localities where lighter rail is preferable.

Thousands of trains, containing millions of passengers and tens of millions of tons of freight, annually move over Santa Fe rails. Santa Fe people feel that there is no smoother, finer, safer track or roadbed in the country.

In these later years, heavier rail, longer ties, sturdier and heavier joints, the use of heat-treated bolts, heat treating and surface grinding of new rail ends, use of larger and heavier tie plates and anchor spikes, hydraulic pressure grouting, and other efforts directed toward increased roadbed stabilization, have resulted in trackage facilities which permit the movement of volume traffic at high speeds.

On a railway of the length of the Santa Fe there are unending maintenance problems. Most present-day Santa Fe construction consists of track extensions (additional second and third main line track), the elimination or separation of highway grade crossings by the construction of underpasses or overhead bridges, drainage work, curve reduction and other alignment changes, relaying rail, and the replacing and strengthening of bridges.

The Santa Fe's original transcontinental route, Chicago to the

Pacific, which is today's northern route, experiences a continuous rise west of Newton, Kansas. Beyond Trinidad, Colorado, the grade ascends Raton Mountain, a lateral spur of the Rockies, a rise of 1,632 feet in 15 miles at a ruling grade of 3½ per cent. The highest point on the Santa Fe system lines, the 7,622-foot Raton Summit, is the crest of this grade. Located at this point we find separate east and westbound tunnels, the first 2,040 feet long and the second 2,789 feet.

The grade breaks at the west end of these tunnels at approximately 7,587 feet, falling away to 5,832 feet at Springer, New Mexico. This is a ruling 3.3 per cent grade. From Springer the line rises to 6,041 feet at Las Vegas, New Mexico, and moves on across the main chain of the Rocky Mountains to Glorieta, New Mexico, 7,437 feet.

Originally the Santa Fe's pioneer builders planned to follow the 37th parallel, but beyond Las Vegas it was necessary to turn the line southward in search of more suitable grades, for the lowest pass west and northwest of Las Vegas exceeded 10,000 feet.

A long, steep climb was located west of Glorieta to Glorieta Pass. The approach from the east, however, is much less pronounced than the ruling 3 per cent grade of the western slope. The line drops to Albuquerque, at 4,953 feet; then begins the long, steady climb to the Continental Divide, lifting about 32 feet per mile. The Divide lies in a broad east-west depression known as Campbell's Pass. The summit is reached just west of Gonzales station at 7,248 feet, 374 feet lower than Raton Pass.

The Santa Fe rails then follow across Arizona's northern plateau country, crossing the Arizona Divide at 7,311 feet at Riordan, west of Flagstaff. The grades are moderate, dropping to 483 feet at the Colorado River bottoms near Needles, California. Crossing the great Mojave Desert, the line enters Southern California through a gap between the San Bernardino and the San Gabriel mountain ranges. This is the famous Cajon (pronounced Kah-hoon) Pass, with a 2.2 per cent grade on its western slope and a ruling 1.6 per cent grade on the eastern slope. Trains branching off at Barstow, the San Joaquin Valley and San Francisco junction point, cross the Tehachapi mountain barrier on a ruling 2.2 per cent grade.

The southern route of the Santa Fe, via Amarillo, Texas, and Clovis, New Mexico, reaches its highest point at Mountainair, New Mexico, at 6,492 feet. The greater proportion of transcontinental freight tonnage uses this route between Newton, Kansas, and Belen, New Mexico. Westward tonnage from points east joins the tonnage from the Gulf lines at Texico, New Mexico, near Clovis, and moves across the Pecos Division to the entrance of the coast lines doubletrack at Belen.

This southern route differs from the northern route in that its rise westward from Newton is moderate to Fort Sumner, New Mexico. From this point to Mountainair, 139 miles, it lifts 2,428 feet over a ruling grade of 0.6 per cent; then drops 1,686 feet in the 41 miles to Belen at a ruling 1.25 per cent grade.

When the Santa Fe began construction at Topeka, Kansas, in 1868, its goal was Santa Fe, New Mexico. Reaching Santa Fe, the line was extended across New Mexico, Arizona, and California to the Pacific Coast. It also reached northward to Denver, Colorado, southward to Galveston and El Paso, Texas, and eastward to Chicago. The line then penetrated California's great Central Valley to San Francisco. From Mojave to Bakersfield, California, across the rugged Tehachapi Mountains, the track is used jointly with the Southern Pacific.

The Santa Fe has 220 interlocking plants located at terminals and important operating points, and 36 automatic interlocking plants at railway crossings whereby trains approaching the crossing on two or more intersecting lines are automatically protected against each other.

In December, 1948, the Santa Fe had some 800 miles of centralized traffic control intallations in operation. These are being broadened continually.

Safety is the basic ingredient in all signal installations, operations, and practices. With safety established, attention is directed toward higher speeds which will permit expeditious movement of passenger and freight trains. To accomplish this, the signal department's system-wide organization constantly applies its skill and resources.

To return for a moment to the humble and lowly railroad tie, we find that the first Santa Fe timber treating plant was erected at Las Vegas, New Mexico, in 1885. During that year over 111,000 ties were treated. Today the Santa Fe has under observation 57 test installations of crossties in 424 miles of track. These tests began in 1902 with the establishment of a "test section" at Cleveland, Texas, to demonstrate the value of various kinds of preservative tie treatment.

For more than four decades, the Santa Fe has carried out one of the most outstanding examples of scientific research ever undertaken by an individual railroad. Crosstie investigation has involved the study and observation of well over two million individual crossties treated with 41 different timber preservatives or combinations of preservatives, and involving 31 different species of domestic and five varieties of foreign woods. Of these ties, nearly a million are still in Santa Fe service and under observation, the remainder having been removed because of decay or other types of failure.

The Santa Fe's experience with treated timber dates back to 1875, when piling for the construction of a Santa Fe trestle across Galveston Bay was creosoted. A few hundred ties, purchased from a wood preserving works in St. Louis, were placed in Santa Fe tracks near Topeka, Kansas, and La Junta, Colorado, in 1881 and 1882.

In the latter part of the last century the pressure treatment of wood with creosote began to assume a position of major importance. Such treatments were generally successful but required a considerable amount of creosote which was high in price. That brought into being the first of the "empty-cell" processes known as the Rueping process, named after Max Rueping, a German, in 1902. A second empty-cell process was patented by C. B. Lowry in 1906.

In the Rueping process, air is forced into the wood under pressure, driving the preservative into the timber. The Santa Fe was the first, not only in this country but in the world, to adopt the Rueping process. This was at the Santa Fe's Somerville, Texas, treating plant on February 22, 1906. It was not until four years later that Germany, where Rueping developed the process, began to use it commercially.

The Santa Fe has continued to use the Rueping process for the treatment of ties, switch ties, signal poles, crossing planks and various other forms of wood from 1906 to the present time.

For the past 20 years, practically all Santa Fe crossties have been prebored and pre-adzed, trimmed and branded prior to treatment. All treating plants are equipped with special machinery for that purpose. The Santa Fe was among the first railroads to adopt the preframing of all timbers and wooden parts used in the erection of bridges or other structures. This allowed the assembly of the finished structure without danger of exposed untreated wood areas which would decay and shorten the life of the structure.

All this comes under the engineering department and the road's chief engineer E. H. Blair is one of the best in the game today.

New Argentine Hump Yard

1948 was a "Car Retarder Year." We notice that the designation, "hump yard," is gradually becoming obsolete, as more and more of the important yards of the country are equipped with car retarder facilities.

Argentine Yard, in Greater Kansas City, is the largest terminal on the Santa Fe. Argentine, Wyandotte County, Kansas—these yards are approximately ten miles long. There are 56 tracks in the classification yard, which indicates something of the size and importance of Argentine.

The Union Switch and Signal Company installed the new retarder facilities. There are two tracks over the hump and nine retarders. The yard has all of the modern car inspection facilities.

The Santa Fe, as this is written, is also building a new hump and retarder yard at Pueblo, Colorado.

Canyon Diablo Bridge

Long, long ago Spanish explorers came to a great gash in the northern Arizona tableland, and they called it Canyon Diablo—Devil Canyon. This was more than 300 years before Santa Fe steel came creeping west from old Fort Wingate in the year 1881 to make a railhead at the brink of the Devil's Canyon chasm. Work on the bridge had already been started, with structural segments being freighted long miles across the high deserts.

Track construction was stopped for six months, awaiting the completion of the great span, which was 15 months in building. Two hundred and twenty-five feet above the canyon bottom, the bridge length was 560 feet and the cost was $250,000—a fabulous sum in those days.

This first Canyon Diablo bridge was of the viaduct type with deck trusses or girders reaching between high steel towers. In 1900 a second bridge was built. Both of these bridges were constructed to carry only one track. In 1913, the second structure was provided with a gauntlet track arrangement.

Engineers in those days did not dream of the size and weight of the engines and trains that would boom across Arizona in years to come. But the day came when the weight of some of the heavier steam locomotives made necessary "slow orders" of ten miles per hour over the Devil Canyon structure. This created a bottleneck for the roaring traffic carried by the Santa Fe main line and plans were made to eliminate the gauntlet track arrangement and to free the flow of trains.

Planning and construction of the proposed new bridge was carried out under the general direction of G. W. Harris, then chief engineer of the Santa Fe System, M. C. Blanchard, chief engineer of the company's Coast Lines, and R. A. Van Ness, bridge engineer of the system. C. H. Sandberg, assistant bridge engineer of the Santa Fe, served as resident engineer. We are indebted to Mr. Sandberg for the major portion of the description of technical details concerning the construction of the new doubletrack bridge across the Canyon Diablo in this chapter.

In order to maintain the traffic flow during its construction,

The latest of the great Chiefs—Santa Fe #16, the new Texas Chief—just north of Oklahoma City on the First District of the Oklahoma Division hauled by an Alco diesel. Photo by Preston George.

First #23, crack streamliner "Grand Canyon," near Taiban, N.M., on the First District of the Pecos Division with diesel #165, one of the 5400 h.p. freight diesels that were converted to passenger service and which perform so excellently. Photo by Preston George.

Santa Fe diesel #167 with green signals first #8 Fast Mail crossing new Canyon Diablo Bridge over Third District of the Albuquerque Division. Courtesy Santa Fe RR.

N&W New Pier N left at Lambert Point, Va., serves Norfolk and the railroad. Built at a cost of $6,000,000 this new ocean terminal facility is one of the most modern piers in the nation and is the largest single deck pier on the Atlantic coast. Courtesy N&W RR.

Interior of new C & O lightweight coaches which are rapidly going into service all over the system. Note the clock on the left, the smoking compartment in foreground. Courtesy C & O RR.

A freight pulls into Goshen, Va., Mountain Subdivision of the Clifton Forge Division passing siding on signal indication. With switch power operation, engineer needn't stop or drift along slowly while brakeman closes switch. Valuable minutes are saved.

Fine new N. Y. Central parlor observation car used on the Sycamore, Twilight, Knickerbocker, and other crack trains of the great N.Y.C. passenger fleet. Courtesy N.Y.C. RR.

Rear end of N. Y. Central #1, the new Pacemaker, at Garrison, N.Y., on the Hudson Division as it starts its overnight trip to Chicago. Courtesy N.Y.C. RR.

the new structure was located about 60 feet north of the old bridge. This necessitated a short line change to allow for connections with the existing alignment.

The new bridge was completed and opened to traffic in September, 1947, and trains began speeding over it without pause or slow-down, marking another forward step in fast rail transport over the lines of the Sante Fe. Thus, three time since 1881 the great Atchison, Topeka and Santa Fe has conquered Arizona's great Devil Canyon with men of brawn and rails of steel, reaching almost 600 feet, from rim to rim, across this 222-foot rock gorge.

When you are riding west on the Santa Fe you will find this famous Canyon Diablo 26 miles west of the bustling railroad town of Winslow, and you will hear the wheels singing their song of triumph high above the canyon bottom.

This new bridge is a thing of strength and beauty in a land little changed in the ages. The span is a graceful structure incorporating a 300-foot two-hinged arch, flanked by a 120-foot simple deck-truss span at each end. Particular interest is attached to the structure because of a number of special details in design, including the provision of an extensive system of walkways, reaching to all important points of the bridge. These permit careful inspection, which can be made in complete safety. Another aspect of interest is the extensive intrusion of grout into the sidewalls of the canyon in the vicinity of the arch footings to insure that adequate support for the structure be provided.

During its construction every safety measure was employed to insure the safety of workmen. Nets were used during the erection of the steel arch; delivery of rivets was through pneumatic tubes —an important safety feature. Due to these and other measures, together with the vigilance of the contractors, the work was completed without serious accident. This included the dismantling of the old structure which followed the completion of the new bridge.

The steel superstructure of the new bridge was designed for double-track, E72 loading. The arch span is 25 feet deep at the center and 80 feet two inches deep at the haunches. Panel lengths are 30 feet. The truss system is of the Pratt type.

The bridge foundations consist of concrete abutments at each end of the arch haunches. Each of these piers has a horizontal surface and a sloping surface to conform to the shape of the arch shoes, which are designed to transmit vertical loads as well as the diagonal thrust of the main arch. The arch shoes are six feet wide and seven feet six inches long at the bottom. At each haunch the load is transmitted to the arch shoe through a pin 16 inches in diameter. At the abutment ends of the 120-foot spans rocker shoes are provided to permit expansion.

At the arch end of each 120-foot span the top chords are connected to the upper ends of the vertical posts of the arch by ten-inch pins. For the sake of appearance, erection procedure, and also to add to their lateral stability, the lower chords of the 120-foot spans are extended downward in a half-arch shape to connect with the arch shoes. However, to permit freedom of movement of these lower chords a slip joint is provided at the first panel point from each arch shoe.

One of the features of the new Canyon Diablo bridge is the box sections for the main truss members. The four angles incorporated in each of these sections are turned inward so that the members are given a streamlined appearance. In addition, "perforated" plates are used on the bottoms of the chords and the sides of the diagonals in place of the customary lacing bars.

The inspection walkways, which we have mentioned, are guarded with handrails. One extends the full length of the bridge on the centerline at the bottom-chord level as well as directly under the deck. Also, crosswalks at each panel point extend to both top and bottom chords. Handrails are provided along both sides of all bottom chord members. These were connected before erection and served as additional safety measures.

Each track on the bridge is carried on four longitudinal wide-flange beams, 36 inches deep, supported on rib bearings at each transverse floorbeam. At every fourth floorbeam a traction truss transmits the braking and traction forces into the top lateral system. These trusses consist of rolled 14-inch-wide flange beam sections and are placed directly under the floor stringers.

The deck is of the solid-floor ballasted type that is standard for bridges on the main line of the Santa Fe. The floor of the deck for each track consists of six-inch treated timbers, 16 feet long, with eight inches of crushed rock ballast under the ties. The deck timbers are made 16 feet long so that they extend over the top chords, thereby providing protection against damage to the steel in case of a derailment. A walkway two feet wide, with a steel handrail, is provided on each side of the deck. Wearing surfaces of walkways are of asphalt plank with a mopped-on coating of hot asphalt and sand.

The curbs and all exposed timber surfaces on the deck are sheathed with galvanized metal to protect them from fire. Before the deck timbers were set in position the top flanges were covered with a heavy protective coating of rust inhibitive petrolatum.

The sloping walls of Canyon Diablo are of solid limestone, furnishing an ideal foundation for arch construction. However, a preliminary examination disclosed a number of vertical and horizontal cracks in the rock, some relatively large in size, which indicated the need for special measures to assure that a proper bearing for the footings would be provided. These measures included thorough cleaning of the cracks by water and air, after which they were closed at the surface with Prepakt concrete. Numerous two-inch holes were then drilled in the vicinity of the pier areas to intersect any possible cracks beneath the surface. The maximum depth of these holes was 40 feet. Sand-cement grout was then pumped into the cracks that had been closed with Prepakt concrete and was pumped also into the drilled holes. An indication of the extensive nature of this work is revealed by the fact that five carloads of sand, 2,900 sacks of cement, 1,400 sacks of filler and 4,500 pounds of intrusion agent were consumed in the grouting of these footing areas.

The forms for the concrete piers were anchored to the rock walls of the excavation by Cinch anchors. Reinforcing rods were placed on two-foot centers in both directions. All concrete was designed for a compressive strength of 3,000 pounds per square foot at 28 days, using an admixture of Pozzolith.

To facilitate the work of setting and adjusting the arch shoes to the correct position and elevation, a recess 12 inches deep and somewhat larger than the arch shoe was provided in the horizontal and sloping surfaces of each arch pier. After each arch shoe had been set in exact position with transit and level, the recess was filled with concrete up to the underside of the shoe. Because of the height of the arch piers and the steep slopes on which they were located a steel handrail was placed around the top of each pier as a safety measure.

The erection of the bridge was carried out by working from both ends. First came the 120-foot simple spans. These were erected on falsework bents placed at the panel points. Each half of the arch was then erected by cantilevering it out from the arch piers. During the erection the arch sections were connected to the simple spans, and to prevent uplift of these spans they were anchored to the concrete of the abutments.

This anchorage was accomplished at each abutment by placing two 40-feet-long channels transverse to the center line of the bridge and at a depth of five feet below the bridge seat, where they were encased in the concrete of the abutment. To these channels were connected four vertical anchor rods at each bearing. The upper ends of these anchor rods were fastened to heavy steel slabs placed over the tops of the top chords.

During the erection of the arch, and until it was closed at the center, the end floorbeam at the abutment of each 120-foot span was supported on two hydraulic jacks so that, during the closure of the arch at the center, these jacks could be used to tip the outer ends of the arch sections downward as necessary to effect the change.

While, as stated, the arch is of the two-hinged type under live loads, it was designed and erected on the basis of a three-hinged arch under dead load. Therefore, during the erection after the dead load, including the deck, the ballast, and the track, were in place on each half to within 30 feet of the center, the arch was closed in the center members by riveting.

The handling of "hot" rivets through pneumatic tubes, from heater to riveting crews, did much to expedite all of the riveting work, especially at the top and bottom chords where it was possible to deliver the rivets directly to men working inside the members.

Today the great Devil Canyon, first conquered in 1881, carries the surging traffic of the Santa Fe main line speedily and safely on the steel sinews of the bridge across the deep gorge called Canyon Diablo on the road of the Holy Cross.

The train traveler is more or less prone to think of rail transportation in terms of colorful, streamlined trains, setting new speed records, forgetting that first there must be the roadbed and the steel to sustain these fast trains. Track engineering is, first and foremost, the foundation upon which the speed and safety of trains of today are built.

Concrete poured into the rocks 225 feet below the rail in the Canyon Diablo, rosy-red rivets darting through pneumatic tubes to the end of the last steel beam, riveting hammers singing in the canyon depths, brawny iron workers on the catwalks behind the scenes—these are the invisible and often forgotten links that forge the chain of modern rail transportation.

This bridge is typical of the Santa Fe and her family. She always was and always will be a Railroad of Today, and with President Fred Gurley and Operating Vice President George Minchin running it, there won't be any slow orders.

CHAPTER XXXI

LOOKING AT TOMORROW

Improvements on Norfolk and Western

Better railroading and better railroad service is a job which is never finished. It is a job that calls for unceasing planning, preparation, and improvements. At the beginning of 1949, the Norfolk and Western had completed, had under way, or had the blueprints for major improvements which, when completed, will total $43 million.

An example of the kind of jobs the Norfolk and Western tackled in its postwar program is the $12,000,000 Elkhorn tunnel and track relocation project on the main line near Maybeury, West Virginia. This, when finished, will include the relocation of 5.27 miles of doubletrack and the boring of a 7,052-foot doubletrack tunnel. January 1, 1949, found the Elkhorn Tunnel job slightly over 52 per cent completed.

This relocation was done to reduce heavy grades and sharp curves. It is claimed the improvements will increase operating efficiency, make for greater safety and enable the road to handle much more traffic. The line will employ centralized traffic control, making possible train operation in both directions on both tracks.

Diverging from the present line at Lick Branch and Cooper, the level of the new tunnel will be some 100 feet below the old tunnel. Eastbound, the new line will have a maximum 1.4 per cent grade compared with the 2 per cent grade on the old line. The westbound 1.2 per cent grade will be practically eliminated. Maximum 12 degree curvatures will not exceed six degrees. The

288

grade of the new tunnel will be one per cent against eastbound traffic as compared with 1.4 per cent grade in the old tunnel.

Elimination of Elkhorn tunnel will mark the passing of a historical milestone in the development of the Norfolk and Western Railway. Work on the old tunnel, which followed a seam of Pocahontas coal, was begun in 1887 and completed in 1888.

The close of 1948 saw the Norfolk and Western laying out the plans for the following improvements:

1. Replacement of semaphore signals with position lights on the main line, Iaeger to Williamson, West Virginia. $541,000.
2. Completely new engine facilities and power plant at Portsmouth, Ohio, including construction of several buildings and relocation of tracks. $1,514,000.
3. Removal of engine terminal near Petersburg, Virginia, passenger station to Broadway Yard on the edge of town, and other improvements. $475,000.
4. Installation of centralized traffic control from Auville, to Susanna, West Virginia, on Dry Fork Branch. $308,000.
5. Water supply improvements, including a new water softener at Bluefield, West Virginia. $160,000.
6. New fireproof wash and locker building at Bristol, Virginia. $10,600.

The installation of position lights recorded in the foregoing improvement schedule between Iaeger and Williamson is in line with the Norfolk and Western's policy of establishing a uniform and up-to-date signal and communication system along its major routes.

The full list of improvements is far too long to be included here, because it would fill many chapters. These betterments extend all along the line from Norfolk to Cincinnati and reach out to the road's important feeder lines which are really most important main lines in themselves. There is, for instance, that new engine terminal at Winston-Salem, North Carolina, costing $367,000.

We find such new ocean terminal facilities at the great new merchandise freight pier at the port of Norfolk. More about this later. . . . We move on down the list—new engine terminals, new heavy-duty freight engines, two experimental switch engines, fleets of new coal cars, new passenger station, modernized passenger stations, new offices, modernized offices, modernized signals, tracks, bridges, and we are just skimming the surfaces.

Each postwar year on the Norfolk and Western has seen millions of dollars poured into the job of improving and expanding the facilities of another "Railroad of Today."

In the chapter on the new Powhatan Arrow, we mentioned the beautifully rebuilt station at Roanoke and the modernization of the Lynchburg station. Let us take time out for a moment to see what happens to the typical old railroad depot that so many of us are familiar with. For one thing, it was apt to be an eyesore; it was cold and barny and smelly and inconvenient. In taking a trip it was nothing but a necessary evil. It was not a building that you could point out with pride to visiting lodge members. It was something associated with the Gay Nineties—that dear old railroad "dep-po."

Now let us look at the modernized version here at Lynchburg, Virginia. It is a two-story structure. Both floors are included in the rearrangements. There is new plumbing, fluorescent lighting, radiant heat and forced draft ventilation.

The first or track-level floor houses waiting and rest rooms, an open-counter ticket office, restaurant, kitchen, and check rooms. Terazzo flooring is installed. There is a seven-foot marble or tile wainscot, and an acoustical ceiling. The ticket office has Formica counters. Restaurant fixtures are all new.

Railroad offices are on the second floor. All sheds have been replaced by the butterfly type. The main shed extends to provide protection to patrons entering or leaving the station by automobile. This is an age when the comfort of the traveler comes first.

Pipes for the first floor radiant heating are set in the concrete flooring. Interior and exterior colors are modern and pleasing—even attractive. Approaching today's rebuilt or new station, the traveler is pleased at the changes since he or she last took a train.

This is the beginning of an adventure—a pleasant adventure that continues after the train is boarded—this new train of comfort, convenience, and luxury.

In the last two weeks of 1948, the Norfolk and Western announced improvements amounting to almost $7 million. This sum included a general storehouse in the Roanoke shops. It is interesting to note that since 1926 all new engines acquired by the N&W—127 at this writing—have been designed and built in the road's Roanoke shops.

New engines built by the Norfolk and Western in 1948-49 included 12 powerful brutes which cost three million dollars. These were followed by 10 more. Seven of the former group were Class Y6b's, compound Mallets of 2-8-8-2 wheel arrangement, numbered in the 2,100's. These are similar to the ten-group and to the earlier 70 Class Y5's and Y6's. Five of the 12-group are Class A, numbered in the 1,200's and with 2-6-6-4 wheel arrangement. Thirty-five Class A's now haul both freight and heavy passenger trains over the lines of the N&W.

Heaviest and most powerful of N&W locomotives, the Y6 has a simple tractive effort of 152,206 pounds, a compound tractive effort of 126,838 pounds. These engines have proven highly successful in the movement of heavy coal and merchandise trains in mountainous territory. They can attain a speed of 50 miles an hour with tonnage. The versatile Class A, a single expansion locomotive with a tractive effort of 114,000 pounds, is to be used in both heavy coal and fast through freight service, and, occasionally, for heavy passenger trains. It can sustain a speed of over 70 miles an hour in heavy passenger service where operating conditions permit.

In April, 1948, the Norfolk and Western ordered one hundred 70-ton covered steel hopper cars, costing approximately three quarters of a million dollars. The road owns at this writing 335 special service cars of this covered hopper type. These cars are used for the transportation of bulk commodities which have to be protected from the weather, such as ground limestone, bulk cement, feldspar and soda ash. The lading can be unloaded easily at its destination through the hopper bottoms.

On December 31, 1947, the N&W owned 59,657 freight cars of various classifications. At the time the road ordered the 100 covered hopper cars we have just mentioned, work was progressing in the great Roanoke shops on an order of 3,000 all-steel 70-ton hopper cars.

In connection with the Roanoke shops and the new boilers installed there, an "electric eye" smoke detector was included in the stack arrangements. This device automatically turns on a red light and rings a gong when heavy smoke goes up the stack. Engineers claim they can control the smoke in 30 seconds, once they know about it.

Shop improvements scheduled replacement of seven boilers, which were among the first in the country to burn pulverized coal, by three bent-tube, spreader stoker-fired, continuous ash discharge boilers, each with a capacity of 60,000 pounds of steam per hour.

Planned in November, 1948, was the construction of an extension to the Norfolk and Western's Motive Power Building, costing $275,000. A beautiful new N&W office building went up in Bluefield, West Virginia, at a cost of $790,000. Every dollar spent was a dollar toward better railroad service.

A Great New Pier—Pier "N"

Early in 1948, a "modern pier for a modern port" was opened at the Port of Norfolk, Virginia, by the Norfolk and Western Railway. Pier "N," as it is designated, is 390 feet wide and 1,100 feet long. It covers an over-water area of about ten acres.

Four of the largest ocean-going freighters can be accommodated simultaneously at Pier "N." The pier shed is 320 feet wide and 1,050 feet long and has sufficient floor space to lay out the entire cargoes of the four ships.

Pier "N" is served by six tracks, two within the shed and two on each of the 35-foot aprons on either side of the pier shed. Cars on these tracks can be loaded or unloaded directly from or into the ships. Two large warehouses, each 108 feet wide and 1,000 feet long have a combined storage space of an additional 216,000 square feet. They are connected to the piers by covered runways. A 535-car supporting yard adjacent to the pier serves both warehouses and the pier.

Facilities for fast handling of freight include five-ton cargo masts on each side which extend over the length of the pier above the shed; two 15-ton gantry revolving cranes; four motorized winches on each side for spotting freight cars; and 51 large electrically-operated overhead steel doors, 14 by 15 feet, spaced approximately 50 feet apart.

The piers have a depth of 35 feet below mean low water level. Pier "N" rests on 5,406 concrete piles. 1,470 treated wood piles were used in the construction of the land bulkheads. The pier floor can sustain a load of 1,000 pounds per square foot.

Facilities include a modern plant for the fumigation of cotton, tobacco and other commodities which require fumigation at the port of importation. There are fresh water lines extending down the pier for serving ships at berth. Motorized vertical lift bridges, providing passage over the depressed pier tracks and concrete driveways on the land end, serve the warehouse and pier.

Other N&W merchandise freight pier facilities at Norfolk include Pier "L" and Pier "S" and adjacent warehouses. Piers "A" and "B" and their warehouses also go to make up this great terminal, which includes a modern 750,000-bushel grain elevator close by. The total pier and warehouse floor space is nearly two million square feet.

Pier "N" is the largest single-deck merchandise freight pier on the Atlantic seaboard. It is an important addition to the facilities of the Norfolk and Western's ocean terminal, and it enhances the unique natural advantages of the spacious, year-round, ice-free port of Norfolk.

"Land of Plenty"—Industrial Development

The Norfolk and Western is doing a splendid public relations job in emphasizing the industrial development of the territory it serves, and in revealing the opportunities and industrial advantages offered. The N&W has served this area for more than a century and is in a position to know fully its possibilities for further growth.

The rich six-state area along the lines of the Norfolk and Western occupies a strategic location by operating North, South, East, and West, with direct connections to major trunk lines reaching out to every principal consuming market in every section of the nation. One great advantage is the road's main line direct to shipside at Norfolk, a gateway to world commerce.

This section of the country is a veritable mineral storehouse. The finest, all-purpose coal in the world is located in this area in vast quantities. Coal is the most important economic mineral known to man. Coal is the greatest natural resource in this "Land of Plenty." It is employed in the manufacture of countless articles, including dyes, adhesives, pharmaceuticals, explosives, germicides, perfumes, plastics, soaps, paints, ink, preservatives, fertilizers, cosmetics, and others.

Most important to any area of natural resources is dependable transportation. The Norfolk and Western in its one hundred years of operation has always closely co-operated with shippers. The road maintains a staff of traffic experts and of foreign freight experts.

Let us take a brief look at the things produced in the Piedmont and Midland area. They include tobacco, lumber, pulpwood, furniture, veneers, shoes, textiles, machinery, fruit, vegetables, milk, fertilizer, feed. The region is heavily forested, and there is Virginia pine and upland hardwoods. There are minerals —shale, clays, feldspar, granite, greenstone, kyanite, mica, soapstone, ocher, talc, and quartzite.

The territory here includes parts of the Appalachian area, the valleys of the Potomac, Shenandoah, James, Roanoke, New, Holston and Clinch Rivers. Here are famous bluegrass and large livestock operations, and apples, peaches and general farming are major sources of agricultural income.

There are the great coal fields, and, beyond, the Ohio River Valley, teeming with industry, rich in raw materials, rich in opportunity. Here the Norfolk and Western serves—an old railroad, a modern railroad, a friendly railroad. We see, north from Portsmouth, Ohio, the fields and factories of the Scioto River Valley. Again it is a land of fabulous agricultural areas, a source of untold raw materials.

Few areas anywhere are possessed of such concentrated wealth, and for that reason the Norfolk and Western Railway for almost half a century has maintained an Industrial and Agricultural Department, staffed by experienced men who know the resources of the territory served.

Begun in 1948 and continued in 1949, the N&W's vigorous advertising campaign, as it has concerned this "Land of Plenty," has attracted considerable attention. It shows what a modern railroad can do to bring attention to the area it serves. Not only does it arouse interest and create inquiries, but it also brings business—business that keeps the wheels rolling down the steel rails.

It is estimated that in 1948, 56,500,000 revenue tons of coal passed over the lines of the Norfolk and Western, compared with the 1947 record total of 54,809,000 tons, which, surprisingly, exceeded even the peak war year of 1943. About 68 per cent of this tonnage rolled westward to the Lakes, to Chicago and other great industrial centers—and all of that 68 per cent moved through Portsmouth's vast yard.

The largest single Norfolk and Western improvement, which was scheduled to start in the spring of 1949, was the Portsmouth, Ohio, yard project, costing around $1,514,000. This embraced an all-inclusive engine service building, the construction of many other modern facilities, and the relocation of tracks.

1948 saw the final touches put on the $3,678,000 Cincinnati District track relocation and centralized traffic control project. This C.T.C. project is covered in the chapter reporting train movements by means of this modern miracle dispatcher, Portsmouth to Cincinnati.

The work goes on. The Norfolk and Western's President Smith and his employees continue their efforts to provide better service in the interests of better railroading. This fine road has faith in the nation and its economic system—and the dollars to back it up.

INDEX

A

AB brake equipment, 41-42, 273, 274
AB-1B brake equipment, 273
ADA super-governor, 274
Adhesion, rail, 40
Air-brake instruction car, 272-275
Air brakes, 36, 272-275 (see also "HSC" Electro-Pneumatic brake)
Akron, Canton and Youngstown Railroad, 216
Albuquerque, New Mexico, 47, 54
All-room sleeping cars:
  on Rock Island, 247
  on Twentieth Century Limited, 24
  on Union Pacific, 64
Alternating-current track circuits, 107, 112
Alumnalum, 145
Amarillo, Texas, 114, 115, 116-117, 120, 121, 235, 248, 279
American Association of Railroads, 213, 217
American Car and Foundry Company, 51
American Locomotive Company, 17, 168-169
A.P.B. signaling, 112
"AP" Decelostat equipment, 40-41
Arcadia, Ohio, 153, 154
Argentine Yard (Santa Fe), 281
Armourdale Yard (Rock Island), 102
Armstrong, George R., 50
Ash Fork, Arizona, 53, 54
Aspen Tunnel, 63, 64, 76-77
Association of American Railroads, 41, 141, 146
Atchison, Topeka and Santa Fe Railway System (see Santa Fe Railroad)
Atlanta, Georgia, 157, 158, 159, 160, 163
Atlantic Coast Line, development of Diesel operation recorder on, 183-189
Atlantic Shore, the (Twentieth Century Limited), 29, 32
Automatic control, 25, 148

B

"B" cars, 229-230
Badger, the (Great Northern), 238
Bakersfield, California, 191, 279
Baldwin Diesels, 17, 170
Ballast-tamping hammers, 202
Baltimore & Ohio, the:
  and the New York Central, 201
  and the Nickel Plate, 153
  and the Western Maryland, 80
  car retarders of, 260-262
  Cincinnatian, the, 123-129 (see also Cincinnatian, the)

communication system of, 259-260
Cone Yard of, 158-159
Cumberland Yard of, 261
East St. Louis Yard of, 258-259
Great Kanawha River bridge on, 257-258
plant improvement by, 257-259
"Quick Dispatch" freight service of, 253
"Sentinel Service" of, 251-257
Willard Yard of, 260, 261-262
Baltimore, Maryland, 79, 80, 83, 84, 123
Barstow, California, 15, 191
Bearing temperature, control of, 43-45
Bearings:
  friction, 210, 218, 221, 223
  roller (see Roller bearings)
Beaver Pond line (Norfolk and Western), 176
Beebe, Lucius, 32
Belen, New Mexico, 114, 191, 235, 279
Bellevue, Ohio, 147, 153
Bellevue yard (Nickel Plate), 150
Berkshire type steam locomotives, 151
Bernet, John J., 148-149
"Big Boys," 4-8-8-4 steam locomotives, 65
Big Four, the, 199
"Bill" of the Great Northern, 236, 241, 243
Blair, E. H., 281
Blanchard, M. C., 282
Block signal, automatic, 103, 105, 106, 107, 174
"Blue Book of Sentinel Service," the, 251, 253-255
Bluefield, West Virginia, 289, 292
Blue Mountains, 228
"Bob Elson on the Century," 32
Boise City Branch (Santa Fe), 118
Boise, Idaho, 66, 232
Boston & Albany, the, 199, 200
Brake valves:
  independent, 39
  "self-lapping," 39, 40
Brakes:
  "AB" freight, 41-42
  air, 36, 192, 272-275
  dynamic, 192-193
  electro-pneumatic, 25, 42, 134, 273 (see also "HSC" Electro-Pneumatic brake)
  instruction on, 272-275
  on Empire Builder, 89
  pneumatic, 37-38, 39, 40
Braking:
  by "AB" freight brake, 41-42
  by Diesel, 10-11, 192, 193
  by "HSC" Electro-Pneumatic brake, 36-40, 42
  by 24-RL equipment, 42, 134
Break-in-two's, 121-122

297

Bridge, John, 64-65
Bright Angel Lodge, 47
Broadway Limited, the (Pennsylvania), 48
Bruceton, Tennessee, 158, 160, 163
Bryce Canyon, 226
Buda motors, 229-230
Budd Company, 265
Budd, John, 243
Buffalo, New York, 147, 150, 200, 201
Buffalo Division, the (Nickel Plate), 148
Bunjer, J. A., 73
Burlington Railroad, 17, 101, 245
Butte, Montana, 66, 232, 239

C

Cajon Pass, 278
Caliente, Nevada, 224, 225
California Limited, the (Santa Fe), 190
Calumet yard (Nickel Plate), 150
Campbell's Pass, 278
Canadian River, 97
Canadian, Texas, 114, 117, 120
Canadian-Waynoka District (Santa Fe), 115
Canyon Diablo bridge:
   construction of present, 282-287
   early, 282
Canyon, Texas, 114, 121
Capitol Limited, the (Baltimore & Ohio), 48
Car retarders, 260-262
Carrier control, coded (*see* Coded carrier control)
Carrier frequencies, coded carrier control, 109, 110, 111
Cascade, the (Southern Pacific), 169, 170
Cascade Tunnel, 238
Cavalier, the (Norfolk and Western), 175
Cedar City Branch (Union Pacific), 225-226
Centerville-Paris project (Rock Island), 96
Central States Dispatch, 80
Central Ticket Reservation Bureau (Chesapeake & Ohio), 267-269
Centralized traffic control (*see* C.T.C.)
Century, the (*see* Twentieth Century Limited, the)
CFM blowers, 133-134
Challenger Inn, Sun Valley, 231
Chariton River, 96
Chats, used as ballast, 97
Chattahoochee River Bridge, 159
Chattanooga, Tennessee, 158, 160, 163, 165
Chesapeake & Ohio Railroad:
   accommodations on, 265-266
   and the Nickel Plate, 153
   Central Reservation Bureau of, 167-169
   "500" of, 130-135
   Greenbrier Hotel, operation of, 263
   hopper cars of, 213
   merger of, with Pere Marquette Railway Company, 264-265
   new equipment on, 265-266
   passenger services of, 266-269
   Pere Marquettes, the, 264-266
   steam turbine-electric locomotive of, 130-135
   vista dome cars of, 17
Chesapeake District (Chesapeake & Ohio), 265
Chicago, Illinois, 94, 96, 100, 147, 153, 191, 247
Chicago, Milwaukee, St. Paul & Pacific Railroad, 222

Chicago, Rock Island & Pacific Railroad Company (*see also* Rock Island lines, the), 93
   tables, 99, 250
Chicago and Northwestern Railroad, 50, 168
Chief, the (Santa Fe), 16, 47-48, 49, 54, 192, 222
Children, accommodations for, 3, 9-10 265
Choctaw Rocket, the (Rock Island), 245
Cimarron Bridge, 95
Cincinnati, Ohio, 123, 135, 269
Cincinnatian, the (Baltimore & Ohio):
   air-conditioning on, 129
   appointments of, 125-127
   features of, 124-125
   interior decoration of, 126-127
   lighting on, 128
   make-up of, 125
   public address system on, 127-128
   radio reception on, 127-128
   stewardess' quarters on, 128-129
   telephone system on, 128
City of Memphis, the (Nashville, Chattanooga & St. Louis), 162
City of New Orleans, the (Illinois Central), 20
City of San Francisco, the (Southern Pacific), 168, 169, 170
Civil Service Commission, 52-53
Clare Yard, Cincinnati, 175
Cleveland, Ohio, 147
Clovis, New Mexico, 114, 279
Coal-burning steam-turbine locomotives, 130-135
Coal movement, on Western Maryland, 81-83
Coal roads:
   Norfolk and Western, 59
   Western Maryland, 80
"Coastal Bend," the, 271
Code-following track relay, 104, 107
Code transmitter, 104
Coded carrier control:
   advantages of, 109-110
   and line wires, 108-113
   change-over equipment in, 111
   coded carrier repeater in, 111
   control point for, location of, 109-110
   emergency conditions in, 111-112
   operation of, 109-113
   stand-by equipment for, 110-111
Coded carrier repeater, 111
"Coded track circuit control," 106
Coded track circuits:
   advantages of, 104-105
   code systems used in, 106-107
   compared with steady-energy circuits, 104-105, 106, 107-108
   development of, 103
   functions of, 104-108
   maximum operable length of, 108
   Norfolk & Western, 112-113, 174
   operation of, 104-108
   shunting sensitivity of, 107
   two-code, 105
   types of code in, 106-107
Codes:
   control, 109
   indication, 109, 111-112
   signal (*see* Coded track circuits)
Colfax, Kansas, 97
Collinwood, Ohio, 200
"Colorado Eagle," the (Missouri Pacific-Texas & Pacific), 137, 138
Colorado Southern, the, 118
Combustion Engineering Company, 165
Commodore Vanderbilt, the (New York Central), 197

298

"Company Manners," a booklet, 208
Cone Yard (Baltimore & Ohio), 258-259
Consolidation 2-8-0, Class H-9 locomotives, 80
Control codes, 109
Corn Belt Rocket, the (Rock Island), 245, 246, 247
Coronet magazine, 32
Cor-Ten steel, 58
Count code, 106-107
"Course in Public Relations, A," a booklet, 206-207
Craters of the Moon National Monument, 226
Creosote, treatment of ties with, 280
Crew's quarters, 5, 142
Crosser Act, 242
Cross-over:
  center, 116
  double, 115-116
  intermediate, 115
CSD, 80
C.T.C. (centralized traffic control):
  and coded carrier control, 106, 107, 108-113
  approach-medium aspect of, 180-181
  at water stops, 179-180
  change-over circuits in, 111
  control point for, location of, 110
  "doubling the hill" by, 177-179
  emergency uses of, 118-119
  grade signal aspect of, 181
  machines for, 120, 224-225, 226
  motor car indicators in, 119-120, 228-229
  on Nashville, Chattanooga & St. Louis, 158
  on Nickel Plate, 148, 153
  on Norfolk and Western, 174-182
  on Rock Island, 98
  on Santa Fe, 114-122, 279
  on Union Pacific, 63, 64, 224-229 235
Cumberland Mountain tunnel, 166
Cumberland yard (Baltimore & Ohio), 261
"Current and Electromotive Force," a film, 194
Cushioned draft gears, 25

D

D-24-RL brake equipment, 273
"Da-lite" blinds, 126
Daniels, George Henry, 21, 32
Davin, J. W., 152
Davis, William A., 49, 50
"Daylight" type steam locomotives, 169
Decapod type locomotives, 80
"Delta Eagle," the (Missouri Pacific-Texas & Pacific), 137
Denver and Rio Grande, the, 17
Des Moines Rocket, the (Rock Island), 244
Detecting systems, 104-105, 112
Detroit, Michigan, 269
Detroiter, the (New York Central), 197
De Vaca, Cabeza, 272
Devil Canyon bridge, 282-287
De Witt Yard (New York Central), 201
Dickinson, L. D., 73
Dictaphone service, Twentieth Century Limited, 34-35
Diesel, braking by, 10-11
Diesel instruction cars, 193-195, 200-201
Diesel operation recorder, development of, 183-189
Diesels (*see also* Diesels, Electro-Motive):
  on Atlantic Coast Line, 183-189

on Empire Builder, 89
on Great Northern, 237, 238-239
on Nashville, Chattanooga & St. Louis, 167
on New York Central, 197, 198, 200-201
on Nickel Plate, 151
on Rock Island, 93-94, 245, 246, 248-249
on Southern Pacific, 168-169, 170
on Twentieth Century Limited, 28-29
on Union Pacific, 62, 225
Diesels, Electro-Motive (*see also* Diesels):
  advantages of, 14
  cold-weather performance of, 14
  converted freight, 16
  development of, 13
  driving mechanism of, 28-29
  5,400 horsepower, 15, 16
  instruction on, 193-195, 200-201
  maintenance of, 14
  operation of, 183
  operation recorders on, 183-189
  6,000 horsepower F-3, 15, 16, 19-20
  switch engines, 16
  traction motors on, 14
  transcontinental service by, 190-192
  two-cycle, 19, 194
Diesels, General Motors (*see* Diesels, Electro-Motive)
Dining cars:
  on Empire Builder, 88
  on *Powhatan Arrow*, 57
  on *Super Chief*, 46, 47
  on Twentieth Century Limited, 25
Direct-current track circuits, 106, 107, 108
Dispatching by C.T.C., 108-109, 176, 227
"Dixie Line, the" (*see* Nashville, Chattanooga & St. Louis, the)
Doors, pneumatically-operated, 24, 59, 266
Dormitory coaches, 5, 24, 139, 142
Double cross-over, 115-116
"Doubling the hill," 177-179
Draper, Dorothy, 263
Dreyfuss, Henry, 27
Drive, Diesel, 28-29
Driving axles, Diesel, 29
DRK steam generator, 193
Dry Fork Branch (Norfolk & Western), 289
Duplex-roomette sleeping cars, 87
Dynamic brake, 10-11, 14, 134, 192-193

E

"Eagles," the (Missouri Pacific-Texas & Pacific) (*see also* listings of individual trains):
  accommodations on, 141-144
  brake equipment on, 145
  design of, 141, 222
  interior decoration of, 141-142, 143-144
  lighting on, 144-145
  sleeping cars on, 143-144
East St. Louis, Missouri, 258-259
East St. Louis Yard (Baltimore & Ohio), 258-259
Edna Type-A mechanical lubricator, 274
El Capitan, the (Santa Fe), 16, 48, 49, 222
Electric-pneumatic brakes, 25 (*see also* "HSC" Electro-Pneumatic brake)
Electro-mechanical refrigeration, 57
Electro-Motive Corporation, 13, 18, 190
Electro-Motive Diesels (*see* Diesels, Electro-Motive)
Electro-Motive Division, General Motors Corporation, 13-20, 29, 94, 168, 248

Electro-Motive Engineering Corporation, 13
Electro-Pneumatic Master Controller, 39, 40
Elgin, Joliet & Eastern, the, 150
El Paso, Texas, 139, 279
Elson, Bob, 32
El Tovar, the, 47
EMD-567 type engine, 193
Empire Builder, the (Great Northern):
  accommodations on, 87-89
  brakes on, 89
  consist of trains on, 87
  Diesel power on, 237
  dining cars on, 87
  inauguration of, 242
  motive power of, 89-90
  new equipment on, 240
  roller bearings on, 222
  safety features of, 89
  sleeping cars on, 87
Empire State Express, the (New York Central), 31, 198
"Employes Educational Service" (Nashville, Chattanooga & St. Louis), 166
England, handling of mail in, 50
Esterline Angus recording instruments, 274
Etowah River Bridge, 159
Evans, Michael, 32
Exposition Flyer, the, 22
Express and mail traffic department (Santa Fe), 54

F

F-3 Diesel, 15, 16, 19-20
Fairbanks-Morse Diesel, 17
Fairbanks-Morse switching locomotive, 17
Fairless, C. P., 264
Farrington, John D., 101-102, 246
"Fast Flying Virginian," the (Chesapeake & Ohio), 269
Fast Mail, the (Great Northern), 237, 239
Fast Mail, the (Santa Fe), 16, 191, 192
Fast Mail and Express, the (Santa Fe), 48-49, 52, 53, 54
F.F.V., the (Chesapeake & Ohio), 264
Fiberglas, 145
"Fiesta" car (Golden State), 246
"500," Chesapeake & Ohio's:
  advantages of, 133
  brake equipment on, 134, 135
  design of, 131-133
  introduction of, 130-131
  operation of, 132-135
  performance of, 135
5,000 Type 4-8-4 locomotives, 100, 117
Flat spots, prevention of, 10, 40-41
FM radio communication, 201
Foreign currents, in track circuit, 107-108
Formica table tops, 9, 26, 27, 290
Fort Hall, Idaho, 64
Fort Sumner, New Mexico, 279
Fort Wayne, Indiana, 148
Fort Worth, Texas, 139
Fostoria, Ohio, 153
4-8-8-4 type locomotives, 65
4-8-4 type engines:
  on Norfolk and Western, 59
  on Western Maryland, 80
4-6-6-4 type locomotives, 80
4,000 Class locomotives, 100
Four-wheel trucks, Diesel, 14
Frankfort, Indiana, 150, 153, 154
Frankfort shops (Nickel Plate), 152
Franklin Institute, 41-42
Freight brake equipment, 24-RL, 42-43

Freight Train Timetable, 199
Frequency code system, 106-107, 109
Friction bearings, 210, 218, 221, 223
Frigidaire air-conditioning, 145
Frontier Index, a newspaper, 76
FT type electrical equipment, 193
Fuel efficiency, on Nickel Plate, 148-149

G

Gardenville Yard (New York Central), 201
Garis, Professor Roy L., 166
Gates, John W. "Bet-a-Million," 22
Gavin, F. J., 91, 241-242, 243
General Electric Company, 237
General Electric speed indicator, 273
General Electric water coolers, 145
General Motors Acceptance Corporation, 94
General Motors Company:
  Diesel school of, 20
  Electro-Motive Division of, 13-20, 94
  instruction system of, 16
  public relations system of, 16
Gent, Arthur S., 269
"George Washington," the (Chesapeake & Ohio), 269
Georgia Railroad, 156
Gilbertsville Dam, 159
Glacier National Park, 88, 90
Glorieta, New Mexico, 278
Golden State, the (Rock Island-Southern Pacific), 169, 170, 246
"Good Will Department," Twentieth Century Limited, 31, 206
Gopher, the (Great Northern), 238
Grand Canyon, the (Santa Fe), 114, 116, 192
Grand Central Galleries, 21, 27
"Great American Central Route," the, 259
Great Northern Railway:
  Badger, the, 238
  Butte Division of, 238
  Diesels on, 237, 238-239
  electric engines on, 237
  electrified territory of, 237-238
  Empire Builder, the, 86-90, 91, 92, 237
  Empire Builder fleet, 90, 92
  Fast Mail, the, 237, 239
  financial statistics on, 241-243
  freight activities of, 242
  Gopher, the, 238
  new equipment on, 240-241
  Oriental Limited, the, 90-92, 237, 239, 240
  postwar improvement program of, 238
  Puget Sounders, the, 239, 240
  Red River Limited, the, 237, 239, 240
  Wenatchee relocation project of, 238
  Winnipeg Limited, the, 239
Greenbrier Hotel, White Sulphur Springs, 263
Gulf Curve, elimination of, 203-204
Gulf, Mobile and Ohio, the, 222
Gurley, Fred, 287

H

H-8 Class locomotives, 80, 81
H-9 Class locomotives, 80, 81
Hackworth, W. S., 167
Hagerstown, Maryland, 80, 83
Hamilton, H. L., 13, 18, 19
Hamilton Works, 151
Hannibal & St. Joseph Railroad, 49-50
Harmon, New York, 28, 200

Harriman, E. H., 61
Harriman, E. Roland, 61, 235
Harriman Memorial Gold Medal, 60
Harriman, W. A., 231
Harris, G. W., 282
Harvey, Fred, 46-47, 49
Harvey girl, the, 46
Harvey houses, 47, 49, 54
Harworth, G. R., 85
Hastings, Nebraska, 74
Havre, Montana, 90, 238, 239
Heywood-Wakefield, 126
Hiawathas, the (Milwaukee), 222
Hill, James J., 90, 243
Hillis, W. H., 102
Hillyard, Washington, 238
Hobbie, Selah R., 50
Hobbs Island, 162
Hog Special, the (Union Pacific), 235
Holiday magazine, 32
Holliday, Cyrus K., 276
Hope, Arkansas, 139
Hot bearing detectors, 10, 43-45
Hot Springs, Arkansas, 139
Houdaille vertical shock absorbers, 144
Houston, Texas, 137, 138
"HSC" Electro-Pneumatic brake:
    "circuit checking equipment" of, 37
    development of, 36, 37
    Electro-Pneumatic Master Controller, 39, 40
    emergency application of, 38-39
    equipment for, 42
    features of, 38-39
    on the Eagles, 145
    operation of, 38
    "self-lapping" brake valve on, 39
Hudson 4-6-4 type engine, 23
Huntington, West Virginia, 267, 268, 269
Hyatt roller bearings, 146

I

Idler wheel, absence of, in G-M Diesel, 14
Illinois Central, the, 166, 222
Illinois River Bridge, 276
Impact recorders, 275
Indiana Harbor Belt, 150
Indianapolis, Indiana, 148
Indication code, 109, 111-112
Inspection cars, 228-229
Interlocking system, 106, 107, 112
Intermediate cross-over, 115
Interstate Commerce Commission, 171

J

"J" engines, 59
J-1 Class 4-8-4 locomotives, 83-84
James Whitcomb Riley, the (New York Central), 198
Journal boxes, roller bearing, 213, 214, 216
Journal friction, 218
Journal, temperature control in, 25

K

K-2 brake equipment, 273
K-37 locomotives, 100
Kamela, Oregon, 227, 228
Kansas City, Missouri, 74, 136, 191
KBVH, radio station, 75
KBVI, radio station, 75
King Ranch, 272
Knickerbocker, the (New York Central), 198

L

La Grande, Oregon, 224, 227, 228
La Grange, Illinois, Electro-Motive shop at, 18-19, 94
Lake Charles, Louisiana, 139
Lake Erie & Western, the, 147
Lakefront Dock & Railroad Terminal, 201
Lake Shore Limited, the (New York Central), 198
Lake Shore, the (Twentieth Century Limited), 29, 33
La Pasada Hotel, Winslow, 47
Lark, the (Southern Pacific), 169, 222
Las Vegas, Nevada, 63, 224
Las Vegas, New Mexico, 47, 278, 280
Lawshe, Ohio, 178, 179
Lighting:
    on *Cincinnatian*, 128
    on *Powhatan Arrow*, 57, 58
    on Texas Eagles, 144-145
    on Twentieth Century Limited, 24, 25, 26
Line wires, and coded carrier control, 108-113
Linotyle, 4, 126
Little Falls, New York, 203, 204
Livestock dispatch service, on Union Pacific, 63
Locking, wheel, 40-41
Locomotive Development Center, 18
Loftis, J. D., 183-189
Lookout Lounge Observation Car (Twentieth Century Limited), 24, 26, 30, 33
Los Angeles, California, 64, 66, 169, 191
Los Angeles Union Stock Yard, 235
Louisiana & Arkansas, the, 139
"Louisiana Eagle," the (Missouri Pacific-Texas & Pacific), 137, 138, 140
Louisville and Nashville Railroad, 158
Louisville, Kentucky, 269
Lowry, C. B., 280
Lubricants, roller bearing, 215-217
Lund, Utah, 225, 226
Lynchburg, Virginia, 290

M

M-300, completion of, 19
Mail, handling of, on Santa Fe, 46-54
Mail cars:
    Missouri Pacific *Eagles*, 143
    Santa Fe *Chief*, 49
    Santa Fe *El Capitan*, 48, 49
    Santa Fe *Super Chief*, 47, 48
    Santa Fe *Texas Chief*, 47
    Twentieth Century Limited, 34
Marietta and Cincinnati Railroad, 259
Mastering Momentum, a book, 220
Matoon, Illinois, 200
Maumee Bay, docks at, 201
MDT reefers, 198
Memphis, Tennessee, 137, 157, 248
Merchant Despatch Transportation Corporation, 198
Mercier, A. T., 173
Metzman, Gustav, 200, 209
Michigan Central, the, 199
Mickey Mouse Theater, 265
Middle Division (Santa Fe), 114
Mikado Type locomotives, 100
Milwaukee Railroad, 97, 99, 211
Minchin, George, 287
Mississippi River Bridge, 276
Missouri Pacific, the (*see also* Missouri Pacific-Texas & Pacific lines):
    air-brake instruction car of, 272-275
    shipment of perishables by, 270-271

301

Missouri Pacific-Texas & Pacific lines:
"Colorado Eagle," the, 137, 138, 146
combined operations of, 136, 272
"Delta Eagle," the, 137
Diesel power on, 140
line revisions of, 140
"Louisiana Eagle," the, 137, 138, 140
"Missouri River Eagle," the, 136-137, 146
new equipment on, 136-146
"South Texas Eagle," the, 138, 139
"Sunflower," the, 138
"Sunshine Special," the, 138, 139
"Texas Eagles," the, 137, 138, 146
"Valley Eagle," the, 137-138, 146
"West Texas Eagle," the, 138, 139
"Missouri River Eagle," the (Missouri Pacific-Texas & Pacific), 136-137
Mohawk 4-8-2 type engine, 23
Mohawk River, 204, 206
Mohawk Valley, 203, 205
Morley, Colorado, 15
Moss Island, New York, 204-206
Motor car indicators, C.T.C., 119-120, 228-229
Motorola radio apparatus, 75
Mt. Clare shops (Baltimore & Ohio), 124
Mt. Zion, Ohio:
doubling operation at, 178-179
Norfolk and Western sidings at, 177-179
Mountain-Type passenger engines, 100
Murray Manufacturing Company, 165

N

Names, car, significance of, 29-30
Nampo, Idaho, 64, 232
Nashville & Chattanooga Railroad, 155-156
(see also Nashville, Chattanooga & St. Louis Railway)
Nashville Banner, a periodical, 167
Nashville, Chattanooga & St. Louis Railway:
alignment improvements on, 157
bridge improvements and replacements on, 159-160
car ferry of, 162-163
City of Memphis, the, 162
C.T.C. on, 158, 161
Diesels on, 167
educational program of, 166
five-year program of, 157
grade improvements on, 157
history of, 155-156
improvements on line of, 157-160
industrial development by, 164-165
plant and rolling stock improvements on, 160-162
shops of, 163-164
traffic department of, 164
Nashville Corporation, 165
Nashville, Tennessee, 155, 160, 162, 163
Nathan mechanical lubricator, 134
Needles, California, 18, 47, 278
Neff, P. J., 146, 272
New England States, the (New York Central), 197
Newton, Kansas, 278, 279
New York Central, the:
and Baltimore & Ohio, 201
Diesels on, 197, 198, 200-201
dock facilities of, 201
Freight Train Timetable of, 199
freight yards of, 201
instruction program of, 208-209
Merchant Despatch Transportation Corporation, 198

Moss Island, operation at, 203-205
new trains on, 197-198
personnel of, 206-208
postwar program of, 32, 196-209
public relations of, 206-208
refrigeration on, 198
safety program of, 202-203
shops of, 200
suburban service of, 199
travel aids of, 197
tugs of, 201, 202
Twentieth Century Limited, 21-35
"Water Level Route, The," 30
New York Central Main Line, the, 199
New York, Chicago & St. Louis Railroad
(see Nickel Plate Road, the)
Niagara 4-8-4 type engine, 23
Niagara Frontier food terminal, 152
Niagara-type steam locomotives, 197
Nickel Plate Road, the:
Bellevue yard of, 150
communications equipment of, 153-154
creation of, 147
freight operation on, 149-150
modernization program of, 152-153
motive power on, 151
operating statistics of, 148, 149-150
traffic department of, 152
traffic on, 147-148
No. 20 switch turn-out assemblies, 116
Noon Daylights, the (Southern Pacific), 169
Norfolk and Western, the:
area served by, 294
Cavalier, the, 175
coded track circuit control system on, 112
C.T.C. on, 174-182, 295
Elkhorn Tunnel project of, 288-289
hopper cars of, 291
improvements on line of, 55-56, 288-289, 295
Industrial and Agricultural Department of, 295
Motive Power Building of, 292
new equipment on, 57-59
pier facilities of, 292-293
postwar projects of, 55, 288-296
Powhatan Arrow, the, 55, 56-60, 175, 182
Roanoke shops of, 291, 292
safety record of, 59-60
siding capacities of, 177
Norfolk, Virginia, 112, 290
North Platte, Nebraska, Union Pacific yard at:
capacity of, 75
communications network at, 74-75
construction of, 63, 64
teletype system at, 74-75
traffic handled by, 74
Northern Ohio food terminal, 152
Northern Pacific, the, 211

O

Oakland, California, 169, 191
O'Connel, David F., 269
Official Railway Guide, 147
Ogden, Utah, 63, 64, 66
O'Grady, Tommy, 207
Ohio and Mississippi Railroad, 259
Ohio State Limited, the (New York Central), 197
Ohio Valley, 258
Olympian, the (Milwaukee), 211
Omaha, Nebraska, 66, 76, 136, 227
Operation recorder, Diesel (see Diesel operation recorder)

"Operating Statistics of Large Steam Railways," a periodical, 148
Oriental Limited, the:
  consist of, 91
  history of, 90
  new equipment on, 90-91, 237, 240
Osborn, Cy, 16-17, 18
Outside swing hanger suspension, 28-29
Overland Route, the, 168
"Overnight" merchandise trains (Southern Pacific), 173

P

Pacemaker, the (New York Central), 197, 198, 199
Pacemaker Freight Service, 198
Pacific Fruit Express, the (Southern Pacific-Union Pacific), 74, 170, 171
Pacific type engine, 23
Paducah & Illinois Railroad, 165-166
Panama Limited, the (Illinois Central), 222
Panhandle Division (Santa Fe), 114
Patapsco River, 84
Peconic Bay, the, (Twentieth Century Limited), 30
Pecos Division (Santa Fe), 114
Peekskill Bay, the (Twentieth Century Limited), 30
Pennsylvania, the, 131
Peoria, Illinois, 94, 147, 150, 244
Peoria Rocket, the (Rock Island), 244
Pere Marquette District (Chesapeake & Ohio), 264-265
Pere Marquette Railway Company, 264-265
Pere Marquettes, the (Chesapeake & Ohio), 264-266
Perishables, shipment of, by Missouri Pacific, 270-271
Perkins, W. C., 73
"Picture" windows, 87
Pier "N," Norfolk, 292-293
Pioneer Limited, the (Milwaukee), 211
Pittsburgh and Lake Erie, the, 80, 199
Pittsburgh and West Virginia, the, 80
Plains Division (Santa Fe), 114-115, 119, 121, 226
Plymetal, 145
Pneumatic brake, 37-38, 39, 40, 42 (see also "HSC" Electro-Pneumatic brake)
Pocahontas, the (Norfolk and Western), 59
Pocatello, Idaho, Union Pacific yard at:
  construction of, 67-68
  crest at, 68-69
  C.T.C. installation at, 226
  facilities at, 67-73
  inspection station at, 69-70
  lighting of, 73
  pneumatic tubes at, 72-73
  radio intercommunication in, 70-71
  traffic handled by, 66
Point Pleasant, West Virginia, 257-258
Polar code, 106-107
Pony Express, 48
Port Covington Terminal, facilities at, 84-85
Portland, Oregon, 66, 90, 239
Portsmouth-Cincinnati line (Norfolk and Western):
  C.T.C. on, 174-175
  passenger trains on, 181-182
  route of, 176
Portsmouth, Ohio, 175, 176, 181, 289
Potomac Valley, 83
Power ballasters, 202

Powhatan Arrow, the (Norfolk and Western), 55-60, 175
Prestwood, 145
Puget Sounders, Morning and Afternoon (Great Northern), 239, 240
Pullman-Standard Manufacturing Company, 28, 32, 33, 87, 144, 246
Pulses, coded track circuit, 104, 105, 106

Q

"Q.D." trains, 253
Quincy, Illinois, 50

R

Racon speakers, 75
Radio, FM, 201
Radio-telephone:
  first commercial call on, 11, 260
  on Empire Builder, 89
  on Twentieth Century Limited, 24, 26
  operation of, 11-12
Rail-auto plan, 197
Rail motor car, first, 19
Railroading from the Rear End, a book, 114
Railroads at War, a book, 225
Railway Express Agency, 54
Railway Mail Service, 48-54 passim, 143
Railway Post Office, 49-54 passim
Rainbow Canyon, 225
Raton Pass, New Mexico, 15, 192, 276, 278
Raton Summit, 278
Reading, the, 80
Rebels, the (Gulf, Mobile and Ohio), 222
Recorders:
  Diesel operation (see Diesel operation recorder)
  impact, 275
Red River, 97
Red River Limited, the (Great Northern), 237, 239, 240
Reed, John, 260-261
Reed-Bullwinkle Bill, 234
Reeves variable-speed drive unit, 278
Reiss, Winold, 88
Refrigeration, 57, 198
Relays:
  code-following, 104, 105, 107-108
  track-circuit detector, 104
Remote control signaling, 106, 107
Repeater, coded carrier, 111
Rio Grande Valley, 270, 271-272
Road and switch locomotives, Diesel, 13
Rock Island Lines, the:
  and Southern Pacific, 169
  Armourdale yard of, 102
  automatic block signal installation by, 97-98
  car service on, 247-248
  Chicago shops of, 247-248
  Choctaw Rocket, the, 245
  Corn Belt Rocket, the, 245, 246, 247
  C.T.C. installation by, 98
  Des Moines Rocket, the, 244
  Diesels on, 245, 246, 248-249
  electronics experiments by, 98-99
  engine houses of, 100
  freight service of, 248-249
  Golden State, the, 246
  history of, 93-94
  improvement campaign of, 95-102
  laboratory of, 100-101
  Peoria Rocket, the, 244
  performance of (1947), 250

radio communications on, 99, 102
rehabilitation of, 93-102
repair facilities of, 247-248, 249
Rocket fleet of, 94, 102, 222, 244-247
Rocky Mountain Rocket, the, 244-245, 247
shops of, 100
Texas Rocket, the, 245
Twin Star Rocket, the, 245, 246-247
Zephyr Rocket, the, 245
Rocket fleet (Rock Island), 94, 102, 222, 244-247
earnings of, 245, 246
performance of (1947), 250
"Rocket Freights" (Rock Island), 102, 248-249
Rocky Mountain Rocket, the (Rock Island), 244-245, 247
Rogers, E. P., 231
Roller bearings:
advantages of, 212-213, 218-222
development of, 210-212
hump yard operation of, 218-219
installation cost of, 223
manufacture of, 217
on freight cars, 212, 213, 215, 218-220, 222-223
on passenger cars, 211, 219-220
on steam locomotives, 211
servicing of, 215-217
tapered, 213
Timken, 2, 144, 146, 211, 214, 234, 235
trains using, 222
types of roller bearing application, 213-215
Royal Blue, the (Baltimore & Ohio), 11, 260
"RPO," 49-54
RPO cars:
development of, 51
first, 49, 50-51
modern, 51
on Santa Fe *Fast Mail and Express*, 52
RPO clerks, training of, 52-53
Rueping, Max, 280
Rueping process, 280-281
Russell, Charles M., 86, 88

S

Safety glass, 6
Safety programs:
New York Central, 202-203
Union Pacific, 63
St. Joseph, Missouri, 50
St. Louis, Brownsville & Mexico, the, 145, 146
St. Louis, Missouri, 136, 139, 147, 150
St. Paul, Minnesota, 89, 239
Salt Lake City, Utah, 66, 76, 226
"Sampson of the Cimarron," 95
San Antonio, Texas, 138
San Bernardino, California, 191
Sandberg, C. H., 282
San Diego, California, 191
Sanding, automatic, 39
Sandusky Bay, the (Twentieth Century Limited), 30
Sandusky, Ohio, 147
Santa Fe, New Mexico, 47, 279
Santa Fe Railroad:
Barstow shops of, 15
Canadian-Waynoka District of, 115
Canyon Diablo bridge on, 282-287
C.T.C. on, 114-122
Diesel instruction car of, 193-195
Diesel operation on, 15-16, 190-195
handling of mail by, 48-54
hotels of, 46-47

maintenance problems of, 276
motor car indicators on, 119-120
Operating Department of, 191
physical plant of, 276-280
Plains Division of, 114-115, 119, 121
routes of, 277-279
Super Chief, the, 190
trains of, 46-48
treatment of ties by, 280-281
yards of, 281
Santa Fe Trail, 46-54
Sardinia, Ohio, 175, 181
Savannah, Georgia, 155
Schaffgotsch, Count Felix, 231
"Scotchlite," 240-241
Scout, the (Santa Fe), 114, 116
SD-6 compressor governor, 274
Seattle, Washington, 66, 89, 238, 239
Secretarial service, Twentieth Century Limited, 26, 35
Sedalia, Missouri, 273
Seitz, Ambrose, 77
"Self-lapping" brake valve, 39, 40, 134
Seligman, Arizona, 18
"Sentinel Service" (Baltimore & Ohio), 251-257
"Series and Parallel Circuits," a film, 194
Serpentine seating arrangement, 9, 25
Shasta Daylight, the (Southern Pacific), 169, 170
Shasta Route, 169, 170
Shreveport, Louisiana, 139
Sidings, long, 180
Signals (*see also* Coded track circuits):
automatic block, 103, 105, 106, 107, 228
cab, 105, 107
motor car, 119-120
wayside, 105, 107
Signal systems, 103-104, 105, 106
Signaling:
automatic block, 105, 106, 174, 181
coded track circuit, 103-108 *passim*
C.T.C., 112
three-block, four-indication, 112
two-block, four-indication, 112
Sillcox, Lewis K., 220
Silvis, Illinois, 100, 249
6-ET brake equipment, 273, 274
Skykomish, Washington, 237, 239
Sleepers:
on *Chief*, 48
on Empire Builder, 87
on *Powhatan Arrow*, 59
on "Texas Eagles," 143-144
on Twentieth Century Limited, 25, 30, 48
on Union Pacific, 64
"Sleepy Hollow" chairs, 8, 9, 126
Slide-detector fences, 228
Sliding wheels, prevention of, 10, 40-41
Smith, R. H., 296
"South Texas Eagle," the (Missouri Pacific-Texas & Pacific), 138
Southern Pacific, the:
and the Santa Fe, 279
Cascade, the, 169, 170
City of San Francisco, the, 168, 169
Diesels on, 168-170, 171
Freight Department of, 172
freight handling by, 171-173
Freight Protection and Station Service Department of, 171-172
Golden State, the, 169, 170
Lark, the, 169
new equipment on, 168-171
Operating Department of, 172
Pacific Fruit Express, the, 170, 171
Shasta Daylight, the, 169, 170
Sunset Limited, the, 169, 170

Southwestern Line, the (New York Central), 198
Speed recorders, 151-152, 184, 186
Spokane, Portland & Seattle Railway, 90, 240
Spokane, Washington, 66, 90
"Sportsman," the (Chesapeake & Ohio), 269
Standardized cars, mass production of, 33
Standardized locomotives, mass production of, 18-19
Stand-by equipment, C.T.C., 110-111
Steady-energy track circuits:
  compared with coded track circuits, 104-105, 106, 107, 108
  line wires on, 113
  maximum operable length of, 108
  operation of, 103, 105, 107
  shunting sensitivity of, 107
Steam boilers, Diesel, 14
Steam turbine-electric locomotive, Chesapeake & Ohio's, 130-135 (see also "500," Chesapeake & Ohio's)
Steam turbines:
  on the Chesapeake & Ohio, 130-135
  on the Pennsylvania, 131
"Sterilseats," 266
Stock Special, the (Union Pacific), 234
Stoddard, A. E., 61
Summit, West Virginia, 81
"Sunflower," the (Missouri Pacific-Texas & Pacific), 138
Sunset Limited, the (Southern Pacific), 169, 170
"Sunshine Special," the (Missouri Pacific-Texas & Pacific), 138, 139
Sun Valley, Idaho, 226, 230-231
Sun Valley Lodge, 231
Super Chief, the (Santa Fe), 16, 46, 47, 48, 49, 190, 192
Superior, Wisconsin, 240, 242
Susanna, West Virginia, 289
Suspension, outside swing hammer, 28-29
Sway, steam locomotive, 28
Sweet Grass, Montana, 239
Switch engines, Diesel, 16, 191

T

Tallaluah, Louisiana, 137
Tamping hammers, 202
Tapered roller bearings, 213
Teletype, and "Sentinel Service," 251-252, 255
Tennessee Valley Authority, 159
Ten-wheel type engine, 23
Terminal Railroad Association, 258
Texas & Pacific, the (see Missouri Pacific-Texas & Pacific lines)
Texas Chief, the (Santa Fe), 47, 191
"Texas Eagles," the (Missouri Pacific-Texas & Pacific), 137, 138
Texas Rocket, the (Rock Island), 245
Texico, New Mexico, 114, 121, 279
Thompson, John Edgar, 156
Thunder Bay, the (Twentieth Century Limited), 32
Ties, treatment of, 280-281
Tight-lock couplings, 25, 145
Time code, 106-107
Time code control systems, 109
Timken Company, 214
Timken roller bearings, 2, 144, 146, 211, 234, 235
Tip Top-Gads Hill project, 140-141
Toledo, Ohio, 147, 201

Toledo, St. Louis & Western, the, 147
"Tommies of the Central," 207
Topeka, Kansas, 279
Track-circuit detector relay, 104
Track circuits:
  steady energy, 103-104, 106
  coded (see Coded track circuits)
Traction motors, 184, 185, 186, 189, 237
"Traffic Manual of Sentinel Service," 254
Train-detecting systems, 104-105
"Train of Tomorrow," 13
Train-radio-telephone (see Radio-telephone)
Transcontinental service, Diesel, 190-192
Transmitter code, 104
Travel-load plan, 197
Travel-service bureau, 197
Trucks, four-wheel, 14
Truman Bridge, Kansas City, 97
Tucson, Arizona, 169
Tugboats:
  Baltimore & Ohio, 260
  Nashville, Chattanooga & St. Louis, 163
  New York Central, 201
Tulsa, Oklahoma, 191
Tuohy, Walter J., 269
Turbines, steam:
  Chesapeake & Ohio, 130-135
  Pennsylvania, 131
Twentieth Century Club car, 24, 26, 29-30
Twentieth Century Limited, the (New York Central):
  appointments of, 24-28
  as mail train, 34
  building of, 31-34
  decorative scheme of, 25-28
  dictaphone service on, 34-35
  first, 21-22, 23
  history of, 21-23
  names of cars of, 29-30
  passenger revenue of, 22,23
  personnel on, 30-31, 206, 207
  postwar equipment of, 23-24
  production cost of, 23
  roller bearings on, 222
  train consist of, 24
24-RL brake equipment, 42, 134
Twin-Cushion Draft Gears, 234
Twin Falls, Idaho, 232
Twin Star Rocket, the (Rock Island), 245, 246-247
Two-cycle Diesel engine, 19, 194
2-8-4 steam locomotives, 151
2-10-0 Decapod type locomotives, 80
2-10-14 locomotives, 118

U

UC brakes, 273, 274
Uintah Mountains, 76
Union Pacific, the:
  area served by, 61
  Aspen Tunnel of, 76-77
  "B" cars of, 229-230
  California Division of, 224-225, 235
  Cedar City Branch, 225
  City of San Francisco, the, 168
  C.T.C. on, 224-229
  development of, 61, 235
  development of Sun Valley by, 231
  Electro-Motive Diesel power on, 14, 235
  equipment of, 65
  Hog Special, the, 235
  Idaho Division of, 226, 234
  income of, 65
  inspection cars of, 229-230

non-railroad activities of, 64-65
North Platte yard of, 63, 64, 74-77
Pacific Fruit Express, the, 170
Pocatello yard of, 62-63, 64, 65-73
postwar program of, 61-64, 232-233
roller bearing installation on, 214-215,
    221-222
Stock Special, the, 234-235
stock trains of, 234-235
Utah Division of, 234
war activity of, 65
Union Pacific Trail, 61
Union Switch and Signal Company, 43,
    69, 119, 224, 281
    centralized traffic control, 108-113
    coded carrier control, 108-113
    coded track circuits, 103-108
U. S. Post Office Department, 49, 50, 54
U. S. Postal Service, 34
U. S. Railway Postal Service clerks, 31
Utica and Schenectady Railroad, 203

V

"Valley Eagle," the (Missouri Pacific-
    Texas & Pacific), 137-138
Valve Pilot Corporation, 183, 184
Vancouver, B.C., 239
Vanderbilt University, 166
Van Eaton, G. R., 73
Van Ness, R. A., 282
Van Sweringens, the, 148
Vapor anti-freeze protection, 145
Vapor zone system of steam heat, 145
Vista dome car, 16-17
Volmer, W. G., 272

W

Wall Street Journal, the, 64
Walsh, Tommy, 207
Ward mail-catcher, 51
Wasatch Mountains, 63, 76
Wassell Organization, 268
"Water Level Route, The," 30
Waughmat Twin-Cushion draft gear, 145
Waynoka, Oklahoma, 114, 121, 122
Weehawken, New Jersey, 201
Wenatchee, Washington, 237, 238, 239

"West Texas Eagle," the (Missouri Pa-
    cific-Texas & Pacific), 138, 139
West Wayne yard (Nickel Plate), 150
Western Electric paging speakers, 75
Western Maryland, the:
    coal movement on, 82-83
    earnings of, 79
    freight trains on, 80
    loads handled by, 79
    motive power of, 79-80
    mountain operations of, 81-83
    operations of, 78, 81-83
    passenger traffic on, 79
    personnel of, 85
    pilots on, 83
    Port Covington Terminal of, 84-85
    shops of, 85
Western Pacific, the, 17
Westinghouse Air Brake Company, 36,
    41, 42, 43, 145
Westinghouse Brake (see "HSC" Elec-
    tro-Pneumatic brake)
Westinghouse traction motors, 133
"Wheel and Axle Manual," the, 217
Wheland Company, 165
White, Lynn L., 154
White, Roy B., 125, 257, 258, 259
White Sulphur Springs, 263-264
Willard, Ohio, 260, 261-262
Willard yard (Baltimore & Ohio), 260,
    261-262
Williams, Eugene S., 85
Winnipeg Limited, the (Great Northern),
    239
Winston-Salem, North Carolina, 289
WM-1's, WM-2's, WM-3's, WM-4's, on the
    Western Maryland, 80
Wolverine, the (New York Central), 198

Y

Y6 locomotives, 291
Yellowstone National Park, 226, 232
Yermo, California, 224, 225, 234

Z

Zephyr Rocket, the (Rock Island-Burling-
    ton), 245
Zion National Park, 226